EYES ON THE UNIVERSE

A HISTORY OF THE TELESCOPE

EYES ON THE UNIVERSE

A History of the Telescope

Isaac Asimov

Illustrated with Drawings and Photographs

HOUGHTON MIFFLIN COMPANY BOSTON *1975*

A portion of this book has appeared
in *Science Digest*.

Library of Congress Cataloging in Publication Data

Asimov, Isaac, 1920–
   Eyes on the universe.
   Includes index.
   L. Telescope — History. I. Title.
QB88.A76   522'.2'09   75-15830
ISBN 0-395-20716-9

Printed in the United States of America

v 10 9 8 7 6 5 4 3 2 1

To Marcia and Austin,
with love

Contents

(Photos follow page 132.)

EYES ON THE UNIVERSE

A HISTORY OF THE TELESCOPE

1. Before the Telescope

Early Astronomy

In the first chapter of the Bible, the creation of the heavenly bodies is described: "And God made the two great lights, the greater light to rule the day, and the lesser light to rule the night; he made the stars also" (Genesis 1:16).

This reflects the astronomical progress of early mankind. First, human beings became aware of the greater light, the sun; then, of the lesser light, the moon. The stars came afterward — perhaps long afterward.

The alternation of day and night is a clear fact to any dimly intelligent being, and it must be obvious from the start that this depends on the presence or absence of the sun in the sky. Clouds that obscure the sun dim the day, and a total eclipse of the sun darkens the world to a dim twilight.

Less immediately overriding is the alternation of the seasons, but this, too, is of immense importance to man, and this, too, can be related to the sun. The exact point on the horizon at which the sun rises moves back and forth with the seasons, and the height to which the noonday sun rises moves up and down against the vault of the sky.

Uniquely beautiful is the moon, which may shine dimly by day but is particularly noticeable at night against the black of the sky. The moon goes through a cycle of phases, waxing and waning twelve times and a little over in the course of a single cycle of seasons.

The quality of light by night (important in a pretechnological society) depends on the phase of the moon, and the twenty-nine-to-thirty-day cycle of the phases offers a handy way of measuring time.

Primitive calendars are almost always based on the cycle of phases of the moon, and these may antedate civilization by thousands of years.

And "he made the stars also."

For an indefinite period after the sun and moon had become of clear importance to mankind, the stars may have existed merely as an interesting pattern of points of light in the night-sky for those who had the leisure to look.

The first thing that may have become obvious to the observer was that the stars retained a fixed pattern night after night. They all moved in the course of the night, but they retained that fixed pattern as they did so.

It was natural to interpret this as indicating the sky to be a solid bowl set over the Earth (or, as astronomical thought grew more sophisticated, a solid sphere enclosing a spherical Earth) on which the stars were fixed (hence "fixed stars") like luminous nailheads.

The sun and the moon, although they were also in the sky, could not be fixed to the solid vault of the sky. This was very obvious in connection with the moon, since from night to night its position against the stars changed radically — visibly so, even in the course of a single night.

The sun shifts, too, though its case is less obvious. When the sun is in the sky the stars are not visible, dimmed by the sun's overwhelming blaze. The night-sky, however, contains the stars in the other half of the sky and the pattern of that visible half shifts from night to night.

It eventually became clear that the visible pattern of stars makes a complete turn in a little over 365 days, and this can be interpreted as indicating that the sun makes a complete circle against the background of the stars in that length of time. The 365-day cycle of the sun matches the seasons and even before 2500 B.C., the Egyptians were using a calendar based on this cycle.

A crucial turning point in the history of astronomy came when it was observed that the sun and the moon were not the only objects that changed position relative to the stars. Five of the brighter stars did the same. They wandered over the face of the sky and, from the Greek word for "wanderer," we call them "planets." (The term originally included the sun and moon, too, since they also shift position.) The starlike planets we know as Mercury, Venus, Mars, Jupiter, and Saturn.

Whereas the sun and the moon mark out a circular path about the sky, moving always in the same direction at more or less the same speed, the starlike planets have complicated paths indeed. They move now rapidly, now slowly; and on occasion they even turn and move in the direction opposite to that of their usual motion.

The complicated pattern of planetary movement was a challenge to those who studied the stars. There was no question that the sun and moon influenced the Earth and mankind by their positions in terms of the light and heat they provided. The other planets might be important, too, and if so their positions and motions ought to be studied. Could a system be imposed on them? Could the future position of the planets be predicted?

If the sun and moon are included as planets, then the working out of planetary motion was the first great problem of astronomy, and it was the complexities of the motion of the starlike planets that first turned astronomy into the subtle study it is.

We do not know who first discovered the planets, but it would seem that the first people we know of to study planetary positions systematically were the Sumerians. They lived along the lower courses of the Tigris and Euphrates rivers (in what is now Iraq) and shortly after 3000 B.C. were the first people to have developed a system of writing and to have kept historical records.

The stars form recognizable patterns which all can detect and learn to recognize easily enough. The Sumerians may have been the first, however, to divide the sky systematically into star groupings which we now call "constellations." They may possibly have done so as early as 4000 B.C.

In particular, they marked out the sky along the path followed by the sun, moon, and planets and divided that circumscribing belt of the sky into twelve constellations. This is the group we call the "zodiac" today.

The sun, moving through all twelve of the constellations of the zodiac in 365 days, remains in each one of the constellations roughly 30 days, which happens to be about the time in which the moon moves through all twelve. In other words, the sun remains in each constellation for one month — a neat arrangement. The moon remains in each constellation for two and a half days, but the positions of the remaining planets are not so easily stated.

It isn't sufficiently precise to say that this planet is in this constellation at one time and in that constellation at another. To work out the details of planetary motion, we need a more or less accurate measurement of the position of a planet relative to some nearby fixed star.

But how to make that measurement? There is no way to hold up a yardstick or a tape measure to the sky. Instead one can only look first at one object and then at another and try to measure the angle through which the eyes have to turn.

The Sumerians set up a system for angular measure that has been retained by astronomers ever since. They divided a circle into 360 equal parts, each of which we now call a "degree" and symbolize as °. To trace the complete circuit of a circle is to move through 360°.

It would seem that the figure 360 was chosen at least partly so that the sun could move 1° against the pattern of the stars each day. To make that movement per day exactly 1°, it would have been preferable to choose the number 365. All primitive people, however, had difficulty in handling fractions, so that a number that can be divided equally in a number of ways simplifies computations greatly. The number 360 can be divided equally by no less than 22 smaller integers.

Each degree is divided further into 60 equal smaller divisions we now call "minutes" ('), and each minute into 60 equal smaller divisions we now call "seconds" (").

Our method of dividing the time of a day also traces back to the Sumerians and to their predilection for numbers with many equal divisors: 12, 60, and 360. Both the day and the night are divided into 60 minutes, each minute into 60 seconds.

To differentiate the minutes and seconds of angular measure from the minutes and seconds of time, we can call the former "minutes of arc" and "seconds of arc."

It is easy, of course, to define divisions of the circle (or of the day) and make divisions of those divisions, and divisions of those smaller divisions. But can those fine divisions be measured?

In actual fact, the ability to do so was sharply limited. Throughout ancient times, it remained difficult to measure accurately an angular distance in the sky of even a degree, let alone such fractions of a degree as minutes and seconds of arc. In the same way, it was difficult to measure accurately a period of time as short as an hour, let alone such fractions of an hour as minutes and seconds.

To study the motion of the planets, we must know the position of the planets on a number of different occasions and the amount of time that has elapsed between successive occasions. We must therefore measure both angles and time, and if we cannot do either accurately, we are left with only a crude approximation of planetary movement.

Greek Astronomy

The Greeks borrowed the astronomical observations of the Sumerians and of those peoples who succeeded them in the area which the Greeks called Babylonia. The Greeks were not satisfied with observations only but tried to build up a logically deduced structure of the universe, beginning with what seemed to them to be self-evident.

To them it seemed that the star-studded sky was a large sphere enclosing a spherical Earth which was located at the center. The Greeks concluded the Earth was a sphere partly as the result of certain clear lines of evidence — such as the shape of the shadow of the Earth on the moon at the time of a lunar eclipse — and partly through the firm conviction that the sphere was the simplest and most beautifully symmetric solid and that the universe must be built simply, beautifully, and symmetrically.

Since the sun, moon, and planets moved independently of the star-studded sky, they must be set into a series of nested spheres, each perfectly transparent, and each of which moved independently. Since the sphere of the starry sky revolved about the Earth in a majestically steady motion with a period of twenty-four hours, it followed that the other spheres must also revolve in a majestically steady motion. (Besides, constant motion is simpler and more beautiful than changing motion.)

As a matter of fact, however, the planets did not move in a steady motion and that was apparent even to the primitive measuring capacity of the Greeks. Some of the planets did not even always move in the same direction.

5

This did not cause the Greek philosophers to alter their view of the universe. To modern scientists, observations come first and theories must fit those observations or be thrown out (though sometimes with considerable reluctance). The Greeks, however, felt reasoning powers to be superior to sense impression and, having reasoned out the beautiful, the simple, and the necessary, they then found it necessary to interpret the observations in such a way as to make them fit the theory. This is called "saving the appearances."

The Greek astronomers therefore modified their view of the heavenly spheres by adding more and more to them. All the spheres moved in perfect circles at a constant velocity. The motion of a particular planet, however, depended on the constant circular motion of several spheres moving in different fashions and intricately interconnected, so that the total motion summed up to an irregular effect.

The final scheme drawn up by Claudius Ptolemy, an astronomer living in Egypt, in the second century A.D., was enormously complicated, but mathematical computations based on it could indeed predict the changing positions of the planets fairly well. At least, it could predict them to within the broad limits allowed by the very crude instruments of astronomical measurement of the time.

Had there been devices that allowed measurements to be made to the nearest minutes of arc, it would have been seen that the whole structure built by the Greeks simply would not do. The Ptolemaic system, with the Earth at the center within a nested series of complexly interrelated spheres, yielded only a poor approximation of planetary motions, but since poor appoximations were all that could be measured in any case, the system was accepted.

This is not to say that the Greeks could not achieve startling results even with their crude systems of measurement. About 240 B.C., the Greek geographer Eratosthenes (276–195 B.C.) attempted to measure the circumference of the Earth. He was working in Alexandria, Egypt, where on June 21 (the day on which the noonday sun is farthest north), the noonday sun was only 7° from the zenith. This Eratosthenes could calculate from the length of the shadow of a stick of known height held vertical at noon of that day.

Eratosthenes was told that in the city of Syene (the modern Aswan) the sun was exactly overhead at noon on June 21. The 7° difference he attributed to the curvature of the Earth and decided that the total circumference was 360/7 times the north-south distance from Alexandria to Syene. This gave him a figure of about 40,000 kilometers (25,000 miles) for the Earth's circumference and 13,000 kilometers (8000 miles) for its diameter.

These figures we now know to be correct, but the Greek astronomers disputed it, and Ptolemy adopted a lower figure. Eratosthenes wasn't confirmed conclusively until the first circumnavigation of the Earth in 1522, over seventeen centuries later.

The Greek Hipparchus (who flourished from 147 to 126 B.C.) was the greatest of all the ancient astronomers. It was he who worked out most of the details later incorporated into Ptolemy's system of the universe.

In 129 B.C., there was a total eclipse of the sun at the Hellespont. At Alexandria, Egypt, the sun was only four-fifths obscured. This meant that the moon was seen in a slightly different position against the sun from those two places on Earth. This shift in position of a nearer object against a farther one, when the two are viewed from different places, is called "parallax." From the size of the parallax, one can determine distance, for the smaller the parallax the greater the distance according to a rule which can can be worked out by trigonometry — something Hipparchus himself developed.

From this, and also by observing the size of the Earth's shadow as compared with that of the moon on the occasion of a lunar eclipse, Hipparchus worked out the distance of the moon as equal to about thirty times the diameter of the Earth. This comes to about 390,000 kilometers (240,000 miles) if Eratosthenes' value for the diameter of Earth is used, and this, too, is correct.

That, however, is as far as astronomers could go with the kind of instruments the Greeks possessed, or that were developed throughout ancient and medieval times. The moon, which, of all the visible heavenly bodies, is nearest to Earth, is the only one with a parallax large enough to measure reasonably accurately under those circumstances.

It would have been possible to get the relative distances of the sun and the moon from Earth, if certain small angles could have been measured at the time when the moon was an exact semicircle of light. About 270 B.C., an attempt was made to do just this by a Greek astronomer named Aristarchus. He missed the measurement

7

rather badly and concluded that the sun is about 20 times as far away from the Earth as the moon is. (The actual figure is 400 times.) As to the remaining planets, and the fixed stars, nothing could be done.

Nevertheless, considering what the Greeks had to work with, their achievement was a great one. The moon, 240,000 miles away, had to be an object over a quarter of the diameter of the Earth to appear as large as it did. The sun, even if it were only twenty times as far away as the moon, would have to be considerably larger than the Earth. It was the first glimpse of a universe that was enormously larger than the planet we live on.

From Hipparchus on, the ancient and medieval astronomers made use of graduated instruments. There would be a fixed vertical or horizontal post (or both) and a movable rod that could be adjusted until the eye at one end could just see a star peeping over the rim of the other end. The angle formed by the movable rod with the fixed one could be read directly from the graduated arc along which it moved. In this way, the angular distance of the star from the horizon or from the zenith could be measured.

Instruments of this sort could be used to locate the different stars relative to one another so that a star map could be prepared. Indeed, Hipparchus was the first to prepare such a map.

The instruments used by the Greeks and by the astronomers of the Middle Ages became quite intricate and were in many cases beautifully designed, but in the end, it always became a matter of sighting by eye and it is the delicacy with which the eye can measure a position along the sighting rod that limits the accuracy.

One way of increasing the accuracy of such instruments is to make them larger. If you adjust a long hinged rod by a small amount when holding the end away from the hinge, you alter the angle far less than when you adjust a shorter rod by the same amount. On the other hand, making the instruments larger also makes them unwieldy.

There is a limit, and that limit seems to have been reached in early modern times — in Denmark.

Sun at the Center

In 1580, the Danish astronomer Tycho Brahe (1546–1601) established an astronomical laboratory on an island in the sea between Denmark and Sweden. It was the first real astronomical observatory in history and Tycho spared no effort to build the best and largest observing instruments he could. He sighted along a rod seven feet long, for instance.

It is not surprising, then, that Tycho observed the positions of heavenly bodies more accurately than anyone ever had before. Ptolemy had never been able to measure the separation of two stars with an accuracy of better than plus-or-minus 6 minutes of arc, but Tycho could measure it plus-or-minus 1 minute of arc. It is very likely that Tycho made the best measurements possible with the kind of instruments that existed before 1600.

Using his large and meticulously manufactured instruments, Tycho followed the movements of the planets and, in particular, recorded a long and careful series of observations of the planet Mars. These observations came at a time when a new astronomical theory had in recent decades convulsed the intellectual world and threatened to utterly change man's view of his own place in nature.

The Polish astronomer Nicholas Copernicus (1473–1543) had written a book (published on the day of his death) which showed how to calculate planetary positions in the sky on the assumption that it was the sun that was the center of the universe and not the Earth. Instead of imagining concentric spheres about the Earth as Hipparchus and Ptolemy had, Copernicus imagined them around the sun. And the third sphere outward from the sun contained the Earth, with the faithful moon still circling it.

It meant the Earth was moving through space.

This seemed, of course, to go against the plain indication of one's senses that the Earth was motionless. It was hard to believe that something as enormous and heavy as the Earth could be flying through the air without anyone's being aware of the fact.

And what was there in favor of the new Copernican system? Only that the changing position of the planets could be calculated more easily (though no more accurately) by imagining the sun at the center than by supposing the Earth at the center.

It is not surprising that Copernicus's theory met with stout resistance. People were not prepared to deny the revered knowledge of the Greeks, the apparent word of the Bible, and the evidence of their own senses, and to believe that the Earth moved about the sun — merely in order to lighten the burden for some lazy mathematicians.

For the better part of a century, those who supported the Copernican view had an uphill battle. Tycho himself did not support the notion that the sun was the center of the planetary system. He tried to work out a compromise system in which all the planets moved about the sun while the sun, with its load of attendant planets, moved about the Earth.

Tycho's compromise theory also made it easier for astronomers to calculate planetary positions, and it avoided making the Earth move. It seemed to combine the best features of both theories and Tycho hoped that his observations of Mars might be able to demonstrate that his compromise was actually the best when it came to planetary calculations.

In 1597, Tycho broke with the new Danish king and left for Prague. There he took on as his assistant the German astronomer Johann Kepler (1571–1630). When Tycho died in 1601, Kepler inherited the invaluable data that the older man had collected over the years, including, particularly, his careful observations of the changing positions of Mars.

Kepler, however, accepted the Copernican view and tried to fit the observed positions of Mars into a path about the sun without reference to the sun's motion about the Earth. Searching for something better than the complicated combinations of circles that both Ptolemy and Copernicus (and Tycho, too) had used, he found that the observations fit very well indeed if he supposed Mars to be following an elliptical path about the sun, with the sun at one of the foci of the ellipse.

An ellipse can most easily be described as a flattened circle, with two foci, one at either side of the center. The ellipse in which Mars moved was not very flattened and if it were drawn to scale it would look pretty much like a circle at first glance. The sun would not be at the center but a little to one side of the center, at one of the foci.

In 1609 Kepler published a book describing the planetary system in these terms. All the planets, including the Earth, traveled about the sun in elliptical orbits. The moon traveled about the Earth (as she did in every system), but also in an elliptical orbit. It is this system of Kepler's that is still accepted today.

Let's summarize then. Systematic astronomical observations have been continuing from the time of the Sumerians till the moment at which I am writing this book for possibly as long as 6000 years. By 1609 as much as fifty-six centuries of observation had taken place, about 93 percent of the entire period. During all that time the instrument of observation had been the unaided human eye. Instruments might have served to determine, more or less accurately, the direction in which the eye was looking, but the eye could at no time see more than it could see.

In these fifty-six centuries of observation by the unaided eye, there had been notable accomplishments. The dimensions of the Earth-moon system were accurately determined and the correct model of the planetary system — the sun at the center and the planets moving about it in elliptical orbits — had been worked out.

It may well have been impossible to go any further than that by eye alone, impossible even to prove that Kepler's theory was correct. At the time Kepler published his book, his system was justified only by the fact that it yielded planetary positions with greater accuracy and in more elegant mathematical fashion.

This wasn't enough to persuade many astronomers, and certainly not enough to persuade the general public. To almost all people, the stars and planets were just luminous dots in the sky, the sun and moon were small lights in the sky, and the Earth itself was flat.

Nothing astronomers could have said, no mathematical demonstration, no lofty arguments could possibly have persuaded people otherwise. And then something happened ——

In the very year 1609, in which Kepler published his account of elliptical orbits, an instrument was invented which almost at once altered man's view of the universe and opened his eyes to visions to which, otherwise, he might have remained forever blind.

Light and Lenses

Let's begin with light. It is the common experience of mankind that light travels in straight lines. Any observation of a shadow cast by the sun, or by an artificial light for that matter, will demonstrate that.

Light can also be reflected. From a smooth surface, such as an unruffled sheet of water, you can see objects above the water repeated in reverse below the water. Most particularly, you can see yourself. Metals are very efficient at reflecting light, and a polished sheet of bronze or silver, for instance, will do much better than the surface of water and will never be ruffled by waves either.

Water will transmit light as well as reflect it, and this is also true of glass, which is basically a sodium-calcium silicate, formed by melting sand (silicon dioxide) with soda ash (sodium carbonate) and limestone (calcium carbonate). As long ago as 3500 B.C. the Egyptians were making glass, though throughout ancient times glass remained rare and was imperfectly transparent.

Light travels in a straight line through some medium (air, water, glass) provided that medium possesses properties that are constant from point to point. If light passes through air, successive parts of which are different in temperature, it will travel in a curved path. The curve is usually gentle and gradual so that we are not generally aware of it.

When the temperature change from point to point in the air is large, however, as it sometimes is in desert areas or near the surface of a highway in the sun, light travels in a marked curve and can give rise to mirages. Our eyes, trained to the belief that light travels in straight lines, sees objects in the sky that really are at ground level, or are greeted with other distortions of reality.

This change from the ordinarily straight-line travel on the part of light (something called "refraction") affects astronomical observation.

Refraction is least when light is traveling in a line that is perpendicular to the boundary of changing conditions. Light from a star directly overhead penetrates the atmosphere in a vertical line while all the boundaries between regions of different temperature are horizontal and the starlight is not refracted.

When a star is not at the zenith (directly overhead), its light strikes the Earth's atmosphere obliquely and the effect is to curve the light slightly toward the perpendicular. The eye, following the final direction of the starlight outward in a straight line, sees the star nearer the zenith than it really is. This effect is quite small until one approaches the horizon, when the obliqueness of entry into the atmosphere is so great that the shift toward the zenith is large enough to observe easily with the unaided eye.

When the sun is nearly at the horizon, for instance, its bottom portion is shifted upward by refraction noticeably more than the top portion is, since the bottom portion is closer to the horizon and the extent of refraction is increasing sharply. The result is that the setting sun seems squashed and flattened at the bottom when it is about to set. In fact, the whole sun is shifted upward so that at the apparent instant of sunset the sun may actually be entirely below the true horizon. The exact amount of the shift will also vary from day to day.

As astronomers attempted to measure the position of heavenly objects more and more accurately, it became more and more important for them to work out the rules of refraction and make allowance for it. (This is a general rule for all observations, scientific and otherwise. The more accurate you try to be, the more carefully you must allow for possible sources of error.) The first to point this out in connection with refraction was an Arabic physicist, Alhazen (965–1038).

The refraction of light traveling through a single medium with changing properties is gentle. It can be sharp indeed, and impossible to overlook, when light passes from one medium into another. This must have been noticed even in earliest times, for when a stick is partly submerged in water, it seems to be sharply bent at the interface, that is, at the surface separating the two media. Yet if the stick is pulled out of the water, there is no break visible. The bend is not in the stick but in the light.

Suppose light, traveling through air, strikes a curved surface of glass. The light rays striking the center of the curved surface pass perpendicularly through, so that they remain unrefracted and continue to travel in a straight line.

Light striking at a distance from the center enters the glass obliquely and (provided the curve is convex so that it bulges toward the light source) is refracted in such a way as to bend toward the center. The farther from the center of the glass surface the light strikes, the more sharply it is refracted.

The result is that all the light striking the curved glass is so bent as to be concentrated at or near a point called the focus, located on the other side of the lens.

Imagine the eye placed between the lens and the focus. All the light rays are bent toward it and the eye follows them out past the glass as though those rays were moving in straight lines. The object giving rise to those rays seems to be extended through space for more than it really is. The object is magnified. Every portion of it is magnified.

Long before anyone had any notion how light behaved on entering a curved transparent object, the magnifying effect must have been noticed. A raindrop or dewdrop resting on a leaf will show the vein pattern of that leaf in magnified form. A transparent gem polished into a smooth curve will act as a magnifier. A glass globe containing water will act as one, too.

If sunlight passes through a water-filled glass globe, its rays, which would ordinarily be spread over a sizable area, will all be concentrated on the focus. Anything at the focus will absorb so much sunlight as to grow hot; it may even burst into flame.

The Greek scientist Archimedes (287–212 B.C.) was supposed to have used such "burning glasses" to set fire to the ships of a Roman fleet that were laying siege to his town of Syracuse in Sicily. The story seems rather unlikely, but it was quoted by the Roman philosopher Seneca (4 B.C.–65 A.D.) and became part of the folklore of history. Alhazen, too, wrote about the magnifying effects of glass spheres.

Glass was a rare substance, however, and to make a whole sphere of it was a difficult job and, after all, unnecessary. Imagine a small piece of a sphere sliced off. On one side there would be a spherical segment, convex and bulging outward; the other side would be a flat, or plane, surface. It would be a "plano-convex" piece of glass.

You might even imagine a piece of glass that was symmetrical, a convex surface on both sides meeting in a line all around the edge. You can imagine it best, perhaps, as two plano-convex pieces of glass placed together flat side to flat side. The result is a "biconvex" piece of glass.

The biconvex piece of glass has the shape of a lentil seed, and it came to be called by the Latin version of that name. It was a "lens." Strictly speaking, only the biconvex piece of glass has a right to the name, but its use has spread to all kinds of transparent objects with smoothly curved surfaces. You can speak of a "plano-convex lens," for instance, even though there are no lentil seeds with a plano-convex shape.

Crude lenses have been unearthed in Crete and in Asia Minor, and some may date as far back as 2000 B.C. Alhazen's writing on light and refraction mentioned lenses and his books began to be translated into Latin about 1170. They served to stimulate thought and experiment in a Europe that was beginning to grow interested in science.

The first systematic studies of lenses in Europe were made by the English scholar Robert Grosseteste (1175–1253) and his pupil, Roger Bacon (1220–1292). Neither knew what was happening to light, but they could observe the magnification. Bacon used lenses to magnify letters on a page and to aid himself in reading. He suggested the wearing of lenses to aid vision, and about 1300 spectacles came into use in Italy.

The first spectacles were made of biconvex lenses, which enlarged objects and which were particularly useful to old people who are often far-sighted.

It is also possible to have a "biconcave" lense, one in which the glass is thick at the edge of the lens all around and in which the curve on each side bellies inward, so that the glass is thinner as one moves inward from the edge and is thinnest at the center. With such a lens, light is bent away from the center and the effect is just the opposite of a biconvex lens. Objects viewed through it seem smaller.

It may seem that such a lens is useless. What is the good in seeing things smaller? The fact is, however, that biconcave lenses are useful in correcting near-sightedness, and spectacles for that purpose began to be used about 1450.

Spectacles-making became an important industry in early modern times, particularly in the Netherlands, where men grew skilled in the manufacture of lenses.

Thus, rather than making lenses either biconvex or biconcave, men could make them convex on one side and concave on the other, so that the resulting "concavo-convex lens" is thinner and more delicate than either the biconcave or the biconvex lenses. If the curves are so chosen that the center of the concavo-convex lens is thinner than the edges, such a lens will correct near-sightedness; if the center is thicker than the edges it will correct far-sightedness.

The shop of a Dutch spectacles-maker, with lenses of every variety lying about, is just an invitation to the playing of games, for no one has ever had lenses available to him without at once beginning to peer through them at various objects. A magnification effect is most interesting and it is only natural to attempt to make the magnification as great as possible.

Two English mathematicians, Leonard Digges (c. 1510–c. 1571) and John Dee (1527–1608), even experimented with combinations of lenses in an attempt to increase the magnifying effect but reported no successes.

When the discovery came, according to the most-often-repeated version of the story, it came by accident.

Hans Lippershey (c. 1570–c. 1619) was a spectacles-maker in the city of Middelburg, in the Dutch province of Zeeland, about eighty miles southwest of Amsterdam. What is supposed to have happened is that an apprentice of his, idling away his time in the absence of his master, amused himself by looking at the world through the lenses that had been left in his care. Eventually, he took two lenses and held them both before his eyes, one nearby and one far off, and found, to his astonishment, that a distant weathervane appeared to be much larger and closer.

With considerable excitement, he showed this to Lippershey when that man returned to the shop. It may be that the apprentice was not beaten for wasting time, for Lippershey seems to have caught the significance of the finding at once.

Lippershey realized that one could not expect to stand about holding two lenses in appropriate positions, one in each hand. He therefore devised a metal tube into which the two lenses could be fitted in the proper place and he had what he called (in Dutch) a "looker," something one could look through.

It came to be called, more pretentiously, an "optic tube" or "optic glass" or "perspective glass." In the first book of *Paradise Lost,* published in 1667, John Milton still refers to such a device as an optic glass. In 1612, however, a Greek mathematician, Ioannes Dimisiani, who was secretary to an Italian cardinal, suggested the word "telescope" from Greek words meaning "to see at a distance." By about 1650 this word began to gain ground and eventually drove out all others. We can say, then, that Lippershey had invented the first telescope.

But did he? Once the instrument became famous, other Dutchmen lay claim to having been first in the field. This is very possible, for given a supply of lenses, anyone could invent it by accident. One with a particularly good case is another optician of Middelburg, a neighbor of Lippershey's named Zacharias Janssen (1580–c. 1638). He claimed to have constructed a telescope in 1604 and it is possible he may have; Lippershey may have borrowed the idea and made up the story of his apprentice to cover the theft.

Nevertheless, Lippershey deserves credit whether he originated the telescope in the strict sense of the word or not. All his competitors for the honor did nothing with their telescopes, as far as we know, except indulge in viewing for their own amusement. Lippershey made the world conscious of the instrument by offering it to the Dutch government as a war weapon.

At that time, the Netherlands had been fighting a bitter war of independence against Spain for forty years, and all that was keeping the small nation alive against the superior military power of Spain was the Dutch navy. An instrument that would allow ships of the Dutch fleet to see the approach of an enemy long before that enemy could be aware of the Dutch would place the Netherlands in a strong position.

Maurice of Nassau, the capable man who was then Stadholder of the Dutch Republic, was interested in science and saw the importance of the device at once. He paid Lippershey 900 florins and ordered him to produce for the government telescopes of a binocular variety, ones that could be looked through with both eyes at once.

Maurice tried to keep the telescope a secret, but that was impossible; the device was too simple. The mere rumor that such a thing existed meant that any ingenious man could duplicate it at once. Telescopes were offered to Henry IV of France before 1608 was over, but King Henry, while amused, was not interested.

The secret war weapon, then, was no secret — but the Dutch did not lose too much. In 1609, a truce with Spain was worked out and the Dutch were never in real danger (from Spain, at least) thereafter. The telescope could go its way, then, with not even the sketchiest attempt to keep it secret — and it did.

2. The Sky Transformed

Galileo

In Italy at that time, there was living Galileo Galilei (1564–1642), who is usually known by his first name, as Tycho Brahe had been.

Galileo had studied the motion of falling bodies and had shown that the Greek views on the matter, as exemplified by those of the philosopher Aristotle (384–322 B.C.), were quite wrong. Galileo's findings represent the beginning of modern physics, and his brilliance, combined with his masterful sarcasm at the expense of his less brilliant adversaries, made him many enemies.

Galileo favored the Copernican view of the planetary system, but he was cautious about expressing this belief. The scholarly establishment, backed by the power of the Church, was strongly pro-Aristotle and pro-Ptolemy, and Galileo was uncomfortably aware of the difficulties he was already having over his challenge to Aristotle. He didn't wish to challenge Ptolemy as well.

In 1592, he left Pisa, where he had been teaching, to take up a post as professor of mathematics in Padua. Padua was in Venetian territory and Venice was not very concerned with religious orthodoxy. In Padua, Galileo was relatively safe and could run the risk of investigating the heavens.

In May 1609 Galileo, then forty-five years old, was visiting Venice. There he heard a tale of a Dutchman who had invented a telescope by placing two lenses in a tube. Galileo thought about it, went back to Padua, and in one day (according to the story he himself told) had devised a telescope of his own.

He made use of a plano-convex lens and a plano-concave lens fitted into opposite ends of a lead tube, 4.2 centimeters (1.6 inches) in diameter. The plano-concave lens was the one near his eye when Galileo looked through it; it was the "eyepiece." The plano-convex lens was the one nearer the object being looked at; it was the "objective."

Galileo did not know what it was that the lenses did to the light passing through them, but he knew that when he looked through his telescope, distant objects appeared three times larger in diameter.

Galileo's first thought, like that of Lippershey, was to use the device as a military weapon at sea. He brought his telescope to Venice and the portly leaders of the state puffed their way up staircases to the top of a tower so that they might take turns looking through the telescope in order to see distant ships that could on no account be made out with the unaided eye.

As a result, Galileo was given academic tenure and his salary was doubled.

Back in Padua, Galileo carefully ground new and larger lenses and built still better telescopes, including, eventually, one that was 4.4 centimeters (1¾ inches) in diameter, 1.2 meters (4 feet) long, and capable of magnifying objects to thirty-three times their diameter. The ability of a telescope to see detail has a theoretical upper limit which depends on the diameter of the telescope lens. Thus, Galileo's telescope could not have performed better than a modern binocular with a lens 44 millimeters in diameter. At best it would then fall short of modern 7 x 50 (magnification 70, lens diameter 50 millimeters) binoculars.

But even this was a dramatic step forward and so there came a great and crucial event that utterly changed man's view of the universe and of himself, for Galileo turned his telescope on the sky and looked at the moon. To see the importance of what Galileo saw when he did so, let's consider what had been thought of the moon before that day ——

*

The Greek philosophers noted that whereas on Earth objects fell downward, in the sky, they moved in grand circles. On Earth, objects changed and decayed and grew; in the sky, all was unchanging. On Earth, objects were generally dark, with no light of their own; in the sky, objects were all luminous.

With all this in mind, Aristotle concluded that objects in the sky were made of a substance fundamentally different from the substances making up Earthly objects. The substance making up the objects in the sky he called "aether" from a Greek word meaning "glowing." It was luminous and unchanging. Change was a property of Earth alone.

Of all the heavenly bodies, it was the moon alone that presented difficulties in connection with this Aristotelian view. For one thing it changed shape and that in itself violates the assumption of nonchange.

The Aristotelian view can be rescued when it is pointed out that the changing shape of the moon is not a true and actual change of shape. The moon remains circular in outline at all times, and the apparent change arises only because only part of it is luminous and this part changes progressively in time. This is most noticeable at the time of the crescent moon, when the rest of the body can sometimes be made out very dimly, as though it were shining with a faint, ruddy glow.

The luminous portion of the moon always faces the sun and the nature of the phases can easily be explained by supposing that the half of the moon that faces the sun reflects sunlight. We see the reflecting hemisphere of the moon at different angles depending on the relative positions of Earth, moon, and sun.

Even by Aristotle's time, then, it appeared that the moon, like the Earth, was *not* a self-luminous body. It was a dark body and shone only by reflecting sunlight. The unchanging aspect of Aristotle's aether was rescued only by sacrificing its luminous nature.

Worse yet, from the Aristotelian view, the moon possessed visible smudges, shadowy markings which were most visible at the time of the full moon, and which seemed always the same. This was the only visible flaw in the blank perfection of the heavenly bodies.

Nevertheless, right down to Galileo's time, the general scholarly view tended to minimize or even to ignore these uncomfortable facts about the moon and to cling to the Aristotelian view of the un-Earthly perfection of all the heavenly bodies. At most, there was a tendency to suppose that effluvia from the Earth's imperfections might stain the moon which, after all, was known to be the heavenly body closest to Earth, and which was therefore most exposed to Earth's imperfections.

But then Galileo looked at the moon and saw it magnified. That meant he saw details that no amount of staring with the unaided eye could have made visible.

He saw a rough surface; he saw mountains and craters; he saw that the smudges visible to the unaided eye were in reality stretches of relatively smooth surface which he called "seas." In short, the telescope showed the moon to be another Earth, a world as uneven and imperfect as our own.

New Worlds

The very first observations of the heavens with the first crude telescope used for the purpose showed something that could not have been discovered in any other way. It at once destroyed one of the assumptions of Greek science which had been reverently accepted over a space of nearly 2000 years.

Of course, it was possible to argue against Galileo's finding, and much of the intellectual establishment of the time did so. One could, after all, take up the Greek attitude that sense impressions were notoriously subject to illusion and that the only safe guide was the reasoning powers of the thoughtful mind arguing from self-evident axioms. For that reason, a number of Galileo's contemporaries refused to look through telescopes for themselves, insisting that anything seen that contradicted Aristotle was an artifact of the instrument itself.

It was also possible to extend the argument that the moon was subject to the effluvia of Earth's imperfection and say that even if it were imperfect and Earthlike, the remaining, more distant heavenly bodies were perfect and unchanging. It was even possible to argue in desperation, as one contemporary did, that the moon was actually a perfect sphere of perfect substance but that one could look through the perfect transparency of the substance to see an illusion of mountains, craters, and seas beneath.

Despite all this, it was clear that from the very first use of the telescope that the situation had changed. The Copernicans had hitherto been on the defensive, forever trying to explain how it was that the solid, motionless Earth could really be moving. Now it was the

Ptolemaists who were on the defensive, forever trying to explain away what Galileo and then others clearly saw through their telescopes.

There was the question, for instance, about the dim, ruddy glow that made the main body of the moon just barely visible at the time when one edge was sunlit into a crescent shape. Galileo saw this glow more clearly in his telescope and argued that it was the result of "Earthshine." The Earth, he pointed out, hung in the moon's sky, as the moon did in Earth's; and the Earth, illuminated by the sun, went through similar phases. At the time of the crescent moon, the side of the moon facing us was exposed to "full-Earth" and was bathed in our reflected light, which, it, in turn, reflected once more to us.

Not only was the moon a dark body and only luminous by reflection, but the Earth, equally dark, shone like the moon by reflected sunlight. The difference between the Earth and the heavenly bodies (the moon, at least) was decreased still further.

The telescope in no way proved that Copernicus was right and that the Earth moved around the sun. It did, however, make the idea seem steadily less ridiculous and more natural. If the moon and Earth were so much alike and if the moon moved through the heavens, why should not the Earth do likewise?

It would have been bad enough for the traditionalists if Galileo had studied only the moon, but he did not. Systematically, he turned his telescopes on this object and that.

He observed the stars and found that they remained stars in the telescope. They seemed brighter, but did not magnify into visible discs.

This was important in itself. One of the objections to the Copernican theory had been the point that if the Earth moved in space, the stars would seem to shift position in the course of the year. At least the nearer ones would shift with reference to the farther ones in a "stellar parallax." This didn't happen, as the Ptolemaists pointed out triumphantly, and that was a clear indication that the Earth was motionless.

The Copernicans could only retort, rather lamely (but, as it eventually appeared, correctly), that the stars *did* shift position with the Earth's motion, but that they were so far away that the shift was too small to be detected. The fact that the stars remained mere points of light in Galileo's telescope was, however, a point in favor of their great distance — and of the Copernican theory.

But the stars *were* brighter when seen through the telescope. The telescopic objective, far larger than the eye itself, caught more light and concentrated it all into the eye. What, then, if there were stars that were so dim that they could not be seen by the eye. The greater light-gathering power of the telescope would make them visible, would it not?

It did. Galileo saw many stars through the telescope that were not visible to the unaided eye at all. When he looked at the Pleiades, a star cluster made up of only six or seven stars as far as the unaided eye was concerned, he saw forty stars. When he looked at the Milky Way, he saw that band of luminous fog become an innumerable host of stars.

Hipparchus had been the first to divide the stars on the basis of their apparent brightness. The brightest stars were described as of the "1st magnitude." Dimmer stars were of the 2nd, 3rd, 4th, and 5th magnitude, while those which could just barely be seen under the best conditions were of the 6th magnitude. Through the telescope, then, Galileo saw stars of magnitudes higher than the 6th.

The presence of these innumerable additional stars that no one had ever seen before served two purposes.

First, it sharply illustrated the limits of knowledge of the Greek astronomers. To be sure, some of them, notably Democritus (c. 460–c. 370 B.C.), had speculated that the Milky Way was made up of a vast cloud of stars too dim to be seen individually. Aristotle, however, had thought the Milky Way was a luminous manifestation of the atmosphere. Most later thinkers went along with Aristotle.

Even granted, then, that some had suspected the true nature of the Milky Way, it remained only a suspicion, and the dispute between Democritus and Aristotle could never have been settled by the unaided eye. The telescope, however, settled the matter at once. Galileo's study of the Milky Way reinforced the feeling that the Greek astronomers did not know all there was to know about the universe and that the system they built up simply could not be accepted blindly.

Second, Galileo's vision of new stars was the first indication that the universe was much vaster and more complex than any ancient had dreamed — or could possibly have dreamed.

Galileo next turned his telescope on the planets and found that, unlike the stars, they appeared as tiny circles of light in his telescope. They seemed small moonlike objects. From this, it was tempting to conclude that they were bodies like the moon (and presumably like the Earth), which appeared to be mere dots of light simply because of their enormous distance from Earth. The mere fact that they could be magnified into discs made it appear, however, that they were much closer than the stars, concerning whose nature one could not yet draw conclusions.

The moon was known to be roughly 3500 kilometers (2100 miles) in diameter and it was therefore a body of respectable size. It might be that the other planets were also large bodies, perhaps larger than the moon, perhaps even larger than the Earth. The actual size of the planets could not be determined, however, until their distances were known, and to determine their distances was beyond the power of Galileo, even with his telescope.

From the moment, though, that Galileo saw the planets as discs, the notion of the "plurality of worlds" left the realm of speculation and entered that of fact.

In earlier times, it had been assumed that the universe consisted largely of the Earth and that the sky was only a canopy hanging over the Earth or surrounding it. The heavenly bodies were only markings on that canopy or objects swinging along just below it.

With such a view of Earth-is-all-there-is, it was quite easy to suppose that the universe was created for mankind, that human beings were the only living things of importance, that their role in such a small man-centered universe might be a temporary one leading to their reappearance after death in a much larger and better universe.

To be sure there were speculations about a man in the moon to account for its markings and there were writers who, even in ancient times, wrote of trips to the moon and beyond, and of living creatures there encountered. All this, however, was legend and fiction, and serious thinkers ignored it.

A German archbishop, Nicholas of Cusa (1401–1464), had, a century and a half before the telescope was invented, suggested the stars were other suns, possibly in infinite numbers. Each of them, he thought, might have in its neighborhood other worlds inhabited by other intelligent creatures. Yet this, too, was merely speculation which was greeted at most with an indulgent smile, and was, for the most part, ignored.

But when Galileo looked at the planets and saw them as discs, that was the beginning of *seeing* other worlds, rather than merely thinking of them. To be sure, people continued to view themselves as part of a small man-centered universe and have done so down to this very day — but only with increasing difficulty. For increasing numbers of people, the universe has become a vast collection of worlds in which mankind itself has shrunk to less than a speck.

This smallness of Man may depress some people, but mankind cannot be magnified by creating a small universe that doesn't exist. Indeed, insofar as he creates an illusion for himself, he is further decreased. Then, too, when we think of the incredibly vast universe and realize that, beginning with Galileo's telescope, we worked it all out from our station on less-than-a-dustspeck, we can feel an enormous pride. Man may be a pygmy but his observing and thinking mind is a giant. Mind is, indeed, a magnificent object, far greater than the mere physical matter of the stars, and we have no cause to be abashed by the mere size of all the nonmind about us.

Planetary Detail

On January 7, 1610, Galileo made perhaps his most crucial discovery. He was using his best telescope that night and when he looked at Jupiter, he discovered three sparks of light in the vicinity of its yellowish disc. All three were in pretty much a straight line.

Night after night he watched them. Their positions shifted back and forth, night after night. Always they remained in more or less a straight line and always they remained near Jupiter. On January 13 he observed a fourth.

What he saw, he was quite certain, were four small bodies moving steadily about Jupiter in the same fashion that the moon moved about the Earth. When Kepler heard of this he called the new bodies "satellites" from a Latin term for those who constantly attached themselves to some rich or powerful man in the hope of gaining favors.

These four bodies, still lumped together as "the Galilean satellites" today, were visible proof that not all heavenly bodies revolved about the Earth. Here were four that clearly revolved about Jupiter — and four bodies that were completely unknown to the ancients, unknowable altogether to anyone without a telescope. (Actually, the Galilean satellites are bright enough to be seen without a telescope if Jupiter were not there, but the always present blaze of the planet drowns them out unless the eye is helped.)

The Galilean satellites were the first new bodies to be discovered within the planetary system in all recorded history. In March 1610 Galileo published his tale of the satellites and of his other discoveries in a small pamphlet called "Siderius Nuncius" ("Messenger from the Stars") and shook the intellectual world.

The furor thus created was enormous, especially over the new satellites. Some of the traditionalists denied everything and simply would not look through the telescope. Some consented to look through telescopes but insisted they saw nothing. Nor need we suppose that those who saw nothing were lying. Early telescopes were crude; the lenses were imperfectly ground and were made out of poor glass. Furthermore, telescopes were usually held by hand and the small tremors that resulted made it difficult to focus the eye.

Yet independent confirmation was not delayed. Others were already using telescopes. A German astronomer, Simon Marius (1570–1624), obtained a Dutch telescope and announced that with it he saw the satellites of Jupiter. He claimed, in fact, to have seen them before Galileo did, but this Galileo hotly disputed. Most people side with Galileo in this, but if Marius did not see the satellites earlier than Galileo, he certainly saw them not long after.

It was Marius, by the way, who gave the satellites the names that are now accepted. Galileo called them "the Medicean stars" in order to flatter a princely patron, but Marius went back to the ancient myths that had given the names to the planets themselves. Taking the satellites outward from Jupiter, Marius called them Io, Europa, Ganymede, and Callisto, the names representing four mythical individuals with whom Jupiter (Zeus) had formed amorous attachments.

Galileo's discoveries brought him enough fame to secure him a well-paying sinecure at Florence (whose ruler he had flattered with his name for the satellites). There he did not have to spend time lecturing and could devote himself to research. However, the fact that he thus removed himself from the protection of the tolerant Venetian Republic was an unwise move.

He continued to use his telescope. In July 1610 he turned it on Saturn. It appeared to be a tiny globe like Jupiter, but on either side there seemed to be smaller globes, as though Saturn were a triple body.

Saturn was the most distant of the then known planets and therefore the hardest to observe. Galileo did his best to make out what those subsidiary bodies were but could not. Indeed, as he returned to observations of Saturn, those bodies on either side grew steadily less noticeable and by 1612 they had disappeared altogether. In the Greek myths, Saturn (Kronos) was the father of Jupiter (Zeus) and all the other gods and goddesses and had swallowed them at birth in an unsuccessful attempt to keep them from supplanting him. "Does Saturn still swallow his children?" growled Galileo bitterly.

It was a most upsetting experience for him. It was the first time that Galileo had observed anything which could really be considered a hallucination. How could something first be there and then not there? Was he really observing objects that were created by the lenses and did not exist in reality?

The Saturn experience seemed to cast doubt on all his work and, in annoyance, he refused ever to look at Saturn again. Others who did use telescopes to look at Saturn saw those subsidiary bodies return, but it was forty more years before the mystery was solved.

Galileo's disappointment with Saturn was made up for in another direction. Looking at Venus, on August 10, he observed that it showed phases. Studying it over a period of months he noticed that it went through a succession of phases just as the moon did.

This showed that Venus, like the moon, was a dark body that shone only by light reflected from the sun. What was true of both the moon and Venus was logically true of the remaining planets as well. All were, like the Earth, dark bodies that shone only by reflected sunlight, so that once again the difference between the Earth and the other planets was reduced.

Furthermore, the pattern of phases could not be made to fit with the Ptolemaic scheme. If Venus retained the relative position to the sun it would have to have by Ptolemy's view, it would, if it were a dark body, remain always in the crescent phase. The fact that it could be seen to take on all phases in succession, from crescent to full, and back to crescent again, could easily be made to fit the fact that it revolved about the sun.

This was supported by the observed fact that Venus did not remain very nearly the same size through all its phases as the moon did. Instead it was much smaller when it was more than half full than when it was less than half full. This was what was to be expected by the Copernican view since when more than half full, it would be traveling toward the far side of the sun away from us.

Combine all this with the fact that Venus's position in the sky with respect to the sun was very much like those of the Galilean satellites with respect to Jupiter. All the observed facts then spoke very strongly of Venus moving around the sun; and if this were true of Venus, why not of the other planets as well? It was another giant stroke in favor of Copernicus.

Then, toward the end of 1610, Galileo began to observe the sun itself, probably at times when it was near the horizon or its light was markedly cut down by mist. (Even so, these observations probably contributed to his later blindness.)

By the middle of 1611, Galileo was ready to announce that there were dark spots on the sun.

These sunspots had been seen before. Indeed, there were times when the sun, near the horizon or shining through fog and dim enough to look at directly, showed a spot large enough to be seen with the unaided eye. This happened on very rare occasions and could be attributed to something other than the sun itself. Galileo, however, saw many of them at all times and could watch them come and go.

Of all the heavenly bodies, the sun itself had to be considered the most clearly and obviously perfect, since it seemed to the unaided eye (when that eye could look at it at all) to be a perfect circle of perfect unchanging light. Indeed, there were not wanting those who saw the sun as a symbol of the divine. To suppose that there could be spots upon it seemed more directly sacrilegious, therefore, than any of Galileo's other discoveries.

A German astronomer, Christoph Scheiner (1579–1650), who had independently discovered sunspots, tried to explain them away by supposing them to be opaque objects circling near the sun.

This did not stand up, however. Galileo saw them move steadily across the face of the sun, slowly when still at the western edge but moving steadily faster as they approached the center of the visible face, then slowly again as they approached the eastern edge. At both edges, the sunspots were foreshortened. This was all exactly what was to be expected if the spots were actually on the sun's surface, if they were part of the sun and if the sun rotated on its axis once in about twenty-five days and carried the spots with it. Galileo announced his discovery, setting forth exactly this view of the sun.

This was the first clear observational evidence for the rotation of any heavenly body, of a body, moreover, which even the Greek astronomers had noted must be larger in size than the Earth. The concept of the Earth's rotation, insisted on by the Copernican theory, became easier to accept.

It was, in a way, the final straw. There had been fascination over Galileo's remarkable discoveries among the scholars in Italy, even those high in the councils of the Church. Yet these men could not help but see that the cumulative effects of his work — the imperfections of the sun and the moon, the new bodies both within the planetary system and among the stars, the rotation of the sun and the revolution of the four satellites about Jupiter, the phases of Venus — all served to reinforce the Copernican theory. It made the older model of the universe, advanced by the Greeks and accepted by the Church, increasingly untenable.

There was bound to be a counterattack, therefore, and it came against the only vulnerable object — Galileo himself. For a long time Galileo had prudently hidden his Copernican views, but as his own discoveries made it increasingly impossible to deny Copernicus, Galileo became more open.

Finally, in 1632, he published a book that was clearly Copernican under the mask of presenting the two competing theories impartially. Indeed, Galileo's skill at sarcasm served to poke irritating fun at those who supported the Greek-and-Church theories. Pope Urban VIII (1568–1644), once a friend and supporter of Galileo's, was persuaded to believe that some of the jibes were aimed at him personally — and that meant trouble for the astronomer.

In the evening of his life, Galileo was brought up before the Inquisition on a charge of heresy and, under the threat of torture but not its actual use, was forced to recant his Copernican beliefs — at least in words.

It did no good, of course. Galileo might recant, but his discoveries would not, and however much Copernicanism might be condemned by men, it was clearly supported by the universe. In this, as in every battle between man's opinion and nature's laws, it is the laws that must win.

The Greek view of an Earth-centered universe was dead after 2000 years in which it had reigned unquestioned. Three years of discoveries with the earliest telescopes, by one man, had been sufficient to kill it.

Silencing that one man was of no use for another reason. The use of the telescope was spreading rapidly and other men were peering at the heavens through lenses.

On December 15, 1612, Simon Marius, the namer of Jupiter's satellites, noted in his telescope a star in the constellation of Andromeda which did not appear like a dot of light at all. It was instead a small piece of blurred luminous fog "like a candle flame seen through the horn window of a lantern." This came to be called the "Andromeda nebula" (from the Latin word for "cloud").

Actually, the Andromeda nebula can just barely be made out as a very dim spot of light with the unaided eye, but Marius, in showing it to be a luminous cloud, had unearthed an entire new class of objects that were to provide dramatic chapters in the history of man's exploration of the universe in the centuries to come.

Another luminous cloud was detected by the Swiss astronomer Johann Baptist Cysat. The middle star in the group of three called the "sword of Orion" in the constellation of that name turned out to be such a cloud and it is now called the Orion nebula. (Cysat was also the first to observe a comet by telescope, though he discovered nothing of importance in doing so.)

And yet the man who, after Galileo, did most to forward the use of telescopes never looked through one.

Kepler

The telescope aroused enormous interest in the science of "optics," that is, the manner in which light travels through transparent media.

The telescope was invented and used at a time when scientists knew very little about optics and when nothing had yet been done beyond Alhazen's bare beginnings. There was still argument, for instance, as to whether light originated in the object viewed or in the eye. And Galileo, remember, knew merely that the telescope worked, and not why it worked.

In 1610, however, Kepler, who had worked out elliptical orbits the year before, received a telescope from a friend. He knew of Galileo's discoveries and had been in correspondence with him (though the friendship had been broken off, perhaps because Kepler had been too pressing in urging Galileo to become an open Copernican).

Kepler was perfectly aware of the importance of the instrument, but he had bad eyes and had great difficulty seeing anything sharply, with or without a telescope. He knew he could never become a telescope-observer and this made him more anxious to work out in theory an instrument he could not use in practice.

Kepler was the first to describe the way light passed through a convex lens to meet in a point. He was also aware of the fact that in actual fact rays of light met only approximately in a point in the case of lenses actually in use. Failure to meet in an exact point meant there was a certain fuzziness of the expanded image which spoiled the "seeing." Such failure due to the failure of light rays to meet perfectly at a focus is called "aberration."

One thing that made it difficult to see objects sharply through the early telescopes was a rim of color about a luminous object such as a star or planet. Nothing could remove this "chromatic aberration" and no one could account for it. Kepler couldn't either. The problem had to wait half a century for another and even greater man to explain it.

Kepler did, however, find one cause for aberration in the shape of the lens itself. In grinding a lens, the easiest shape to form is one that is a section of a spherical surface. This requires equal grinding at all points and that is clearly a natural thing to do. Light passing through a convex lens with either one or both sides ground into a spherical section does *not* bring light to an exact focus as Kepler pointed out. This is called "spherical aberration."

As it happens, the eye itself does not produce spherical aberration (at least in bright light when the pupil is vèry small) and when Kepler studied the lens of the eye, he found that its surfaces were *not* spherical sections. He was the first to suggest that a more complicated surface was required.

Suggesting this, and actually doing something about it, however, were two different things. It is easy to say that something other than a spherical section is needed but very hard to grind something other than a spherical section. For over a century after Kepler, therefore, spherical sections continued to be employed and methods other than changing the shape of the lens were used in efforts to minimize spherical aberration. Even to this day the problem is not fully solved and spherical surfaces are used in the vast majority of lenses.

Kepler studied the lens system of the "Galilean telescope" with its convex objective and concave eyepiece, in the light of his own newly developed principles of optics and explained how it produced a magnified image.

Kepler suggested that the telescope be lengthened so that the light rays passing through the objective have a chance to come to a focus. In fact, he suggested that they be allowed to pass through the focus and begin to diverge again. The eyepiece could then be placed on the other side of the focus from the objective; and the eyepiece could be made convex rather than concave.

This is one complication. If light rays pass through a focus, they would cross as they do so. Beyond the focus, the light rays which had been on top would be on bottom and vice versa. The whole arrangement of light rays would be reversed so that through a Keplerian telescope, an image would seem upside-down, whereas in a Galilean telescope, where the eyepiece comes before the light reaches the focus, the image remains right-side-up.

This new telescope proved to have important practical advantages. It can have a wide field-of-view. Because a cross hair (as in a rifle sight) could be placed right at the image formed by the objective, it would become possible to use the telescope to measure the position of a star. Galilean telescopes are practical up to magnifications of only two to three times, as in the "opera glass" binoculars, still in use, fashioned like those that Maurice of Nassau had asked of Lippershey. But for Earthly viewing at higher magnification and for astronomy, Kepler's form is almost always used.

Even with a Keplerian telescope, it is possible to have a right-side-up image if a couple of additional lenses are added to reinvert the inverted image. This was first suggested by a Bohemian astronomer, Anton Maria Schyrle, in 1645. This device is used today in such Earthbound devices as the telescopic gunsight and the engineer's transit.

Additional lenses absorb a portion of the light passing through and four lenses absorb twice as much light as two lenses do. They therefore dim the image, and while this does not matter in the brightly lit objects on Earth, it matters a great deal where the dim objects in the sky are concerned.

Since the heavenly objects don't have a "right-side-up" and since all make just as much sense in one direction as in another, astronomers ever since the time of Kepler have made no effort to reinvert the image but have saved light by allowing it to remain upside-down. That is why reproductions of the moon as seen through the telescope always show south to be on top in a reversal of the convention of Earthly maps.

Scheiner may have used a Keplerian telescope in 1630 but it was not till Schyrle wrote of it that astronomers generally grew aware of it.

The first to use a Keplerian telescope regularly for planetary observations was an Italian astronomer, Franciscus Fontana (c. 1600–?). With such a telescope, in a series of observations beginning after 1640, he was able to see belts across Jupiter and to observe vague markings on Mars.

It was now Jupiter and Mars that proved not to be shining globes of perfectly featureless light. Like the Earth and moon, they were imperfect.

And where a generation before, Galileo had barely been able to make out the four satellites of Jupiter, the Italian astronomer Giovanni Battista Riccioli (1598–1671) could actually see the shadows they cast upon the illuminated face of the planet. The fact that

Jupiter was dark in places where the satellites cut off the sunlight showed that Jupiter, like Earth, the moon, and Venus, was a dark body shining only by reflected light.

All this additional evidence was scarcely needed any longer to prove Aristotle wrong and to suggest that Ptolemy was, too, and that Copernicus was right. Riccioli himself was an example of one who refused to accept the Copernican view even a century after Copernicus's book and a third of a century after Galileo's first views through the telescope, but that didn't matter.

The Aristotelian-Ptolemaic view of the universe was dead. After 1650, only a few diehard traditionalists remained and they could be ignored. Astronomers had become Copernican.

And the Galilean telescope which had accomplished the revolution was also dead. It was the Keplerian telescope that now undertook additional tasks.

Almost as though to symbolize all this, Tycho's instruments, the greatest that had existed in the pretelescopic age, passed away. Now useless, they had been allowed to gather dust in storage and, during the first years of the Thirty Years' War (which lasted from 1618 to 1648), they were burned, as a by-product of the senseless violence of war, and vanished forever.

3. Measuring the Heavens

The Long Telescopes

Kepler's discovery of spherical aberration was placed on a firm mathematical foundation by the Dutch mathematician Willebrord Snellius (1591–1626).

Light going obliquely from one transparent medium into another, say from air into glass, will strike the glass at some angle to the perpendicular. In entering the glass the path of the light is bent toward the perpendicular so that it makes a different and smaller angle to the perpendicular.

As the angle to the perpendicular in the air ("angle of incidence") gets larger, so does the angle to the perpendicular in the glass ("angle of refraction"). It seems natural to suppose that the ratio of the two angles remains the same, that as the angle of incidence is doubled, so is the angle of refraction.

Snellius discovered that it was not the ratio of the angles themselves that remained constant, but the ratio of the sines of those angles instead. (Sines are a property of angles that are of importance in trigonometry. They can be calculated readily enough and their values for any angle can be looked up in a table.)

Snellius's discovery, a key finding in the science of optics, was made in 1621 but went largely unnoticed until it was publicized by the French mathematician René Descartes (1596–1650) in 1638. (Descartes used the finding without adequately mentioning the source so that for a time it was thought that Descartes was the discoverer of the principle of constant ratio of the sines.)

If it were true that the angles to the perpendicular in air and in glass maintained a constant ratio no matter what their size, then a lens with a surface that was a spherical section would bring light to a sharp focus. It was because the ratio of the sines was constant, and not of the angles themselves, that spherical aberration existed.

As it happens, though, for small angles, the sines vary almost exactly as the angles themselves do. Therefore light striking near the center of a spherical-section lens and making only a small angle with the perpendicular will come very nearly to a perfect focus. If an astronomer so designs his telescope that only the central section of his objective is used, spherical aberration is very nearly abolished and so (as it happens) is the image blur caused by chromatic aberration, though not to the same degree.

Galileo had realized this by sheer guess-and-try but now less brilliant astronomers knew what was necessary to do and increasingly finer work was accomplished with telescopes even though the spherical surfaces on the lenses was retained.

The Polish astronomer Johannes Hevelius (1611–1687) studied the moon patiently for four years and in 1647 published a book, *Selenographia,* in which he reproduced the pictures he had drawn of the moon's surface. Galileo, in his earliest telescopic studies of the moon, had sketched some of its features as seen in his imperfect instrument, but Hevelius was the first to draw a map of the moon good enough to be recognized as such by modern astronomers.

He pictured the seas and mountain ranges and gave them names copied from those of the Earth. Some of these we still use today so that the moon, like the Earth, has its Alps and Apennines, and even a Pacific Ocean ("Mare Serenitatus").

He also named individual craters, but these names did not survive. Instead Riccioli (who had first noted the shadows of Jupiter's satellites) published a book called *New Almagest* in 1651, in which he introduced the system of using the names of dead astronomers and other men of science for the craters. He was an admirer of Tycho's and gave his name to the most prominent crater of all.

Hevelius was willing to use the telescope for his studies of the moon and the planets, but since it did not magnify the images of the stars but only brightened them, he did not care to struggle with the difficulties of the instrument in its early days for the sake of those stars.

Instead, he observed the positions of those stars visible to the

37

unaided eye in Tycho's fashion and prepared a catalogue of the precise position of 1564 stars. This was the last important bit of work done in astronomy without a telescope.

Again, Riccioli went beyond Hevelius in a fashion and showed that the telescope could do more with respect to the stars than merely detect dim ones that could not be seen by the unaided eye. In 1650, he noted, by telescope, that one of the stars of the Big Dipper was, in actual fact, two closely placed stars that could be seen separately by telescope but not by the unaided eye. It was the first important stellar discovery after Galileo's initial discovery that there were more stars than met the unaided eye.

Consider, now, that in order to minimize the aberrations, one had to use lenses that curved only very gently, so that light struck them everywhere at only a small angle. Such gently curving lenses bend light only slightly and it takes a long distance for those slightly bent rays of light to come to a focus.

Since the eyepiece in a Keplerian telescope must be put at the other side of the focus, the distance between objective and eyepiece became very long. The first century of the Keplerian telescope became an age of very long, skinny, flimsy instruments.

Thus, while Galileo's telescopes were 1.2 meters (4 feet) long or less, Hevelius was making his observations of the moon with telescopes that were up to 3.6 meters (12 feet) long — and which could magnify up to fifty times.

Hevelius's success encouraged astronomers to enter into a race for larger and better instruments — a race that has continued ever since. Telescopes became large, clumsy instruments that had to be designed and built with every thought and act aimed at delicacy of precision.

Until then, scientific instruments had been ornamented and decorated into things of art as well as science but now this became impossible. There was neither time nor energy left for that sort of thing. The telescope introduced an era in which scientific instruments became utterly functional and where such beauty as existed consisted of that which was inseparable from an object designed to fulfill some task with maximum efficiency and delicacy.

The age of really long telescopes opened with the work of the Dutch astronomer Christian Huygens (1629–1695). He and his brother ground lenses as a hobby and he came to realize that lenses with only a slight curvature gave the best images, but this did mean that the telescopes had to be very long. He worked out a superior system of grinding them and in this he had the help of the Dutch-Jewish philosopher Benedict Spinoza (1632–1677), who was a skilled lens-grinder by profession.

In 1655, Christian Huygens produced his first important effort, a telescope which had an objective a little over 5 centimeters (2 inches) in diameter. It was about 3.6 meters (12 feet) long and could magnify up to fifty times. To test it, he turned it on Saturn, the most distant of the planets then known; and he had high hopes as he did so.

Saturn had presented a puzzle to Galileo, and to those who had followed him, too. Astronomer after astronomer had looked at Saturn and had reported that it seemed to have handles like those of a teacup, one on each side. Even Hevelius saw the handles. The trouble was that nobody could make out their nature clearly.

Huygens was confident that with his new telescope he would solve the problem, but he didn't. To his disappointment, all he saw was Saturn as a simple globe. There was no sign of handles anywhere.

On March 25, 1655, however, he did see a small starlike object in the vicinity of the planet and began to watch it. For several months, he followed it as it shifted from one side of Saturn to the other and in 1656 he announced the discovery of a satellite of Saturn which circled the planet in sixteen days. Eventually, it was given the name of Titan, since Saturn (Kronos) had, in the Greek myths, ruled over a group of gods who were called Titans.

Huygens also studied the Orion nebula and found stars within its fogginess. Whatever the nebula might be, it seemed to glow by the light of those included stars.

Huygens continued to build better telescopes with larger lenses, ones that were, inevitably, longer and longer till, eventually, he had one that was 37 meters (123 feet) long. With each improved telescope, he returned to the observation of Saturn and finally managed to detect the handles, together with a shadow which they cast on Saturn itself. From the existence of that shadow, he knew that the handles didn't exist on the sides of the planet alone but must be something that encircled the planet.

It was only in 1659 that Huygens was ready to announce to the world that Saturn was surrounded by a thin flat ring that nowhere touched the planet.

Apparently, as Saturn circles the sun every twenty-nine years, these rings were seen at various angles. At 14.5 year intervals, they are seen edge-on and are so thin that they seem to disappear. Galileo had first viewed them when they were being seen more and more edge-on and finally lost them. Huygens had begun watching Saturn when the rings were nearly edge-on and had to wait for them to tip somewhat before he could see them well enough to realize what they were.

The success of Huygens inspired Hevelius to build long telescopes of his own and by 1673 he had constructed one that was 46 meters (150 feet) long. Such a long telescope proved to be a white elephant. A metal tube that long would have been too heavy to manipulate so Hevelius used lengths of wood to keep the lenses in place.

Even so, the telescope could only be used by suspending it from a mast ninety feet high and by raising it and lowering it with ropes worked by numerous assistants. Even small breezes shook the telescope and, more than that, the wood warped and the ropes changed in length with changes in humidity. Looking through such a telescope was a symphony of constant adjustment and it could hardly ever be used.

As for Huygens, he eventually avoided the difficulty introduced by the weight of something even as light as wood in his longest telescopes by dispensing altogether with tubes. He had an objective mounted in a short metal tube and attached to a high pole where it could be manipulated from the ground. The eyepiece was in another small tube resting on a wooden support. Between the two was a length of cord which, when taut, aligned the lenses properly.

Such an "aerial telescope" had its difficulties, too. Adjusting the two lenses so that one could look through both was a delicate matter and stray light found its way into the lenses entirely too easily, tending to wash out the image.

Nevertheless, out of sheer lack of anything better, the long telescopes remained the chief tools for studying the heavens for decades. As late as 1722, the English astronomer James Bradley (1693–1762) was making use of a telescope 65 meters (212 feet) long.

Throughout the period, astronomers dreamed of still longer telescopes. The Frenchman Adrien Auzout (1622–1691) speculated on the possibility of a 305-meter (1000-foot) telescope which, he thought, would make it possible to observe animals on the moon, if any were there.

Such a telescope was never built, of course. The state of the art at the time would not allow it and if it had been built, it would certainly not have performed as well as the sanguine Auzout hoped.

The fact was that the long telescopes had reached their limits with the opening of the eighteenth century. The astronomers of the time did not know it, but it is the diameter of the lens, not its length of focus, which determines how much useful magnification is possible. But shorter telescopes would have to wait for technological advances. And yet before those limits were reached, interesting findings continued to be made with the long telescopes.

Perhaps the most skillful observer of this era was the Italian astronomer Giovanni Domenico Cassini (1625–1712). Once he obtained long telescopes of sufficient power, he concentrated on the most distant known planets, Jupiter and Saturn. He noted a roundish spot on Jupiter's surface in 1664 and in 1672 published a drawing of Jupiter in which the spot was shown for the first time. The English scientist Robert Hooke (1635–1703) also referred to the spot in 1664 and for years it was called "Hooke's Spot," though it is now referred to as the "Great Red Spot."

The Italian astronomer Francesco Maria Grimaldi (1618–1663) had noted, toward the end of his life, that Saturn was *not* perfectly round but had an elliptical shape. This meant that the planet was not a sphere, but an ellipsoid, flattened at opposite ends. Cassini confirmed this and noted that it was also true of Jupiter.

This was a most interesting discovery. The sun, moon, Mercury, Venus, Mars (even the Earth itself judging from the shadow it cast on the moon) were perfectly round, as nearly as astronomers could determine in the seventeenth century, and therefore perfectly spherical in three dimensions. Omitting the irregularly shaped comets, which lacked sharp edges in any case, Jupiter and Saturn were the first heavenly bodies found to have shapes other than spherical — in this case, ellipsoidal.

This was a clear visual demonstration that the circle was not the inevitable shape of all things heavenly, as the Greeks, and even Copernicus, had thought. It made Kepler's theory of elliptical orbits all the more plausible, though, to be sure, there were few who by that time felt that this needed further confirmation. One of those few, oddly enough, was Cassini himself, who was the last astronomer of note to retain reservations concerning Kepler's ellipses.

In 1669, Cassini's successes secured for him an invitation to Paris and he spent the remainder of his life in France. There he studied Saturn with successively longer telescopes and finally with one that was 41.5 meters (136 feet) long. With them, he discovered four more satellites to add to Huygens' discovery of Titan. These were all named after Titans and Titanesses who had been ruled by Saturn (Kronos) in the Greek myths. Iapetus was discovered in October 1671, Rhea in December 1672, and Tethys and Dione in March 1684.

The total number of new bodies discovered in the solar system (as we can now fairly call it since there was no longer any question that the sun — sol to the Romans — was the center of the planetary bodies) by means of the telescope was now nine; four satellites of Jupiter and five of Saturn.

Cassini also extended Huygens' work in connection with Saturn's ring. In 1675, he discovered that the ring was actually two rings separated by a dark gap. That gap is called "Cassini's division" to this day.

Cassini's greatest discoveries, however, involved not the telescope alone but additional devices which, added to the telescope, greatly multiplied its powers.

The Clock

During the first half century of telescopic observation, the instrument was used almost entirely qualitatively. That is, it was used in order to see things that could be seen only in lesser detail without it, or even not at all. The telescope could see mountains on the moon, spots on the sun, phases of Venus, new satellites, and new stars, but all this (important though it was) could be described in words alone. Numbers were not needed.

And yet numbers would certainly be useful in astronomy if only to measure the passage of time. The sun, moon, planets, and stars all rose and set at particular times that changed in more or less regular fashion. The sun, moon, and planets moved against the background of the stars at particular (and, particularly in the case of the planets, changing) rates.

Much could have been learned about the movements of the heavenly bodies if there had been some way to measure the passage of time accurately, but that was a problem that had not really been solved even by the mid-1600s.

What was needed to measure time was some periodic phenomenon of great regularity but the only ones known in pretelescopic days were the movements of the heavenly bodies themselves. The rotation of the Earth and the movements of the moon and sun against the stars made it possible to mark off days, months, seasons, and years, but for periods shorter than a day the simple counting off of astronomical periods was insufficient.

One method of refining time measurements was to follow the changing length and position of the shadow cast by a rod stuck in the ground as the sun moved from eastern horizon to western. Such "shadow clocks" or "sundials" were first used in Egypt as long ago as 3500 B.C. Constructed with sufficient delicacy, they weren't bad and could be made to allow for the changing height of the sun with the progress of the seasons. Nevertheless, they were useless at night and on cloudy days and could at best only give the time to a sizable fraction of an hour.

Other methods sought to make use of some steadily progressive event that did not involve the heavenly bodies at all — the burning of a candle, the sifting of sand through an orifice, the dripping of water through a hole. These methods were used in ancient and medieval Europe and had the virtue of working indoors and by night as well as by day but, even at best, they were no more accurate than sundials.

In the 1300s, mechanical clocks were first devised. In these a weight was slowly dragged downward by the pull of gravity and, as this happened, the weight served to turn a hand around a circular dial marked off into twelve equal parts in such a fashion that the hand made two complete turns per day. Such devices were originally used to signal the times for the ringing of a bell that would call the monks in a monastery to their prayers. (The word "clock" is related to the French word for "bell.")

And yet mechanical clocks were not the answer either. They, too, could be relied on for nothing better than a large fraction of an hour.

Galileo had, in his experiments with falling bodies, been forced to rely on counting the water-drips through a hole or on counting the beats of his own pulse. The rate of water-drips, however, depended on the quantity of water in the container, and the rate of the pulse-beat depended on the level of excitement of the experimenter (and was bound to go up when it looked as though an experiment might succeed — or unexpectedly fail).

Galileo hoped that the advent of the telescope might make it possible to return to a reliance on the regularity of the movements of heavenly bodies — those new heavenly bodies that he himself had discovered, the four satellites of Jupiter.

Each of the four had a different pattern of revolution and, in combination, they could set up a complicated pattern that might suffice to split time accurately into very small units. The pattern was *too* complicated, however, and the technology of the period could not set up a table of times when each satellite might be expected to move behind Jupiter and be eclipsed with sufficient accuracy to allow such a table to serve as the basis for measuring time on Earth.

What was needed was a short-period phenomenon on Earth, something that could be handled, adjusted, transported, and coddled by human beings and that was more regular than anything known before Galileo's time. Actually, Galileo had discovered just such a phenomenon.

In 1581, when he was only seventeen years old and was studying medicine at the University of Pisa, he attended services at the cathedral and found himself watching a swinging chandelier. It seemed to him that it swung back and forth in the same period, whether the changing air currents forced it through a wide arc or a narrow one. Instead of listening to the sermon, he began to check the matter against his pulsebeat and when he got home, he experimented.

He set up pendulums of the same length and set them swinging through different arcs and found that they kept together pretty well.

By trying pendulums of different lengths, he found that a short pendulum swung more rapidly than a longer one. Clearly, by adopting a pendulum of the proper length, you could beat off time-intervals of any duration you wished.

Rather than count the beats, however, it would be better to have the pendulum connected to gears in such a way as to turn the hands of a clock by a fixed tiny amount with each beat. In order to keep the pendulum from quickly losing its energy as it does so, slowly falling weights restore that energy.

Galileo did not apply the pendulum beat in this way. The first to do so was Huygens in 1656. His greatest difficulty lay in the fact that the pendulum does not have a period that is completely independent of the length of the swing. Long swings take a *little* longer than short swings. His first solution was to arrange to have the pendulum beat through a very small swing, since the smaller the swing, the less the deviation from equal periods as the length of the swing varies slightly.

Huygens showed the trouble to be that a pendulum bob marks out a segment of a circle as it swings. If, somehow, the bob could be made to follow a curve known to mathematicians as a "cycloid" then its period would not vary at all with the length of swing.

By 1659, Huygens solved the problem by not allowing the pendulum to swing freely. Instead, the top of the cord moved against a curved stop, so that less and less of the cord was truly free to swing as the bob moved outward. The stop curved in such a way on either side of the cord that the bob swung in a cycloidal arc.

In 1670, an English clockmaker, William Clement, introduced the use of a long pendulum that beat in a one-second rhythm and was more regular than the short-pendulum clocks first used by Huygens. The whole was enclosed in a case to keep out the disturbing influence of air currents, and the "grandfather's clock" was the result.

The result of all this was that from 1656 on, there existed a reliable method of measuring units of time as small as minutes and seconds. For the first time, it made sense to have two hands on a clock face, the hour hand and the minute hand — and eventually even a second hand.

The pendulum clock was, by its very nature, a large and rather clumsy instrument, and the question arose as to whether a periodic movement involving an object not as long as a pendulum could be made use of. Suppose a pendulum were made of a highly elastic material that was bent into a loose spiral. This spiral (a "hairspring") would take up very little room and could be made to pulse in and out with great regularity. Just as a pendulum could be powered by a falling weight, a hairspring could be powered by a slowly opening larger "mainspring."

The spring-powered clock is a "watch," and both clocks and watches were periodically wound. In the clock, the fallen weight is lifted again by the mechanical turning of a key; in the watch, the loosened mainspring is tightened again by turning a knob.

The new timepieces were at once snapped up by astronomical observatories as methods of measuring time. Two of the first astronomers to take advantage of the instruments were the Frenchman Jean Picard (1620–1682), who headed the Paris Observatory, and Cassini, whom he brought to Paris.

In 1676, the observatory at Greenwich, England, was using two clocks with pendulums 4 meters (13 feet) long, with two-second beats. At the other extreme, the Scottish astronomer James Gregory (1638–1675) was using a pendulum with a third-of-a-second beat as early as 1673.

The new clocks showed that the regular motions of the heavenly bodies were not necessarily very regular. The pendulums and springs kept more accurate time. It was shown, for instance, that the interval between successive periods in which the sun passed over the meridian to indicate noon was not invariable. It changed slightly in the course of the year.

This was not because Earth's rate of rotation changed. It was because certain complications were introduced by the fact that Earth's orbit about the sun was elliptical rather than circular and that the Earth's axis was tipped 23.5° from the perpendicular to the plane of its revolution.

It became necessary to imagine a "mean sun," an imaginary body that reached the meridian at exactly twenty-four-hour intervals. The real sun lagged behind at some times of the year and raced ahead at others, being as much as a quarter-hour behind in February and a quarter-hour ahead in November.

The use of clocks made possible other discoveries. Cassini, for instance, noted certain spots and irregularities in the belts of Jupiter and watched them move more progressively from one side of the planet to the other and then appear, after a lapse of time, at the first side again. It was clear that Jupiter was rotating on its axis and by observing enough of these passages and keeping track with his clock, he decided, in 1665, that Jupiter rotated with a period of nine hours and fifty-six minutes.

This was the first accurate measurement of the revolution period of any heavenly body, except for the slow turn of the sun itself, and its mere existence made the rotation of the Earth a more likely possibility if anyone still had doubts about the matter.

Furthermore, from the direction of the movement of the spots, Cassini could see that the axis of the rotation was the short axis of Jupiter's ellipsoidal globe. Its equator stretched across the long axis. Jupiter, therefore, had an "equatorial bulge." Presumably, this was true of Saturn, too, though its greater distance precluded the study of small markings on its surface and the determination of the exact period of its rotation was not carried through for another century and a quarter.

The importance of the matter of precise timing showed up in a particularly startling fashion in connection with the revolution of the four satellites of Jupiter about that planet. Given a good clock, it was possible to measure the exact periods of revolution of each and to predict the times at which each satellite would be lost to sight as it passed behind Jupiter.

Cassini had made these observations and calculations with precision, but the table he prepared did not serve for successful predictions. At those times when Earth, in its orbit about the sun, was moving closer to Jupiter, the time of eclipses of the satellites by Jupiter came progressively earlier. When Earth moved around its orbit and began moving away from Jupiter again, the time of eclipse came progressively later. It all averaged out properly, but the variations first this way, then that, were puzzling.

In 1675, a Danish astronomer, Olaus Roemer (1644–1710), took up the matter and wondered if these deviations in time took place because it took time for light to travel. When Earth and Jupiter were on the same side of the sun, and as close to each other as possible, the eclipses were seen by the light that traveled from Jupiter to

Earth at the near point in the latter's orbit. When Earth and Jupiter were on the opposite sides of the sun, then the eclipses were seen by the light that traveled from Jupiter to the near point of Earth's orbit and then across the full width of Earth's orbit *in addition,* to where Earth was located on the other side.

Roemer decided, on the basis of his analysis, that it took light twenty-two minutes to cross the full width of the Earth's orbit. If the width of the Earth's orbit were known, the speed of light could then be calculated.

As it happened, Roemer was fortunate, since a few years before he had made his analysis of the situation the full width of the Earth's orbit had been determined with reasonable correctness for the first time in history as the result of the development of a device much simpler than the clock, but scarcely less important.

The Micrometer

For half a century after Galileo had introduced the telescope to astronomy, it was used chiefly as a device with which to look at objects. There was no way in which it could be used to determine the position of the objects it looked at with reference to other objects in the sky.

Let's consider this matter of position. Objects located on the surface of any sphere can be located by making two measurements, appropriately chosen. On the surface of the Earth, for instance, we can make use of latitude and longitude. The former is the angular distance north or south of the equator. The latter is the angular distance east or west of an arbitrarily chosen reference line passing through London.

This same system could be transferred to the sky (the "celestial sphere"). If we imagine Earth's axis extended to the sky, north and south, it would intersect the celestial sphere in a "north celestial pole" and a "south celestial pole." Halfway between the two celestial poles is an imaginary line circling the sky, called the "celestial equator."

Every star is located at a certain angular distance north or south of the celestial equator and this celestial latitude is known as the "declination" of that star.

It would then be possible to pick out some arbitrary north-south line passing through some star and then measure the angular distance east or west of that to work out the celestial longitude of any star. Astronomers, however, choose the alternative of letting the Earth make the angular measurement for them.

The Earth turns evenly on its axis, west-to-east, and as a result we see the sky move evenly in an east-to-west direction. The sky makes a complete turn of 360° in a day; therefore it moves 15° in an hour, 15' in a minute, and 15" in a second.

If we measure the times at which particular stars cross the "meridian" (that is, the imaginary north-south line in the sky which passes through the "zenith," which is the point immediately above our heads), then we have a set of times, one for each star. The time at which a particular star crosses the meridian is its "right ascension." If we know the right ascension of two different stars, we can tell from the difference in times the difference in celestial longitudes.

By measuring the declination and right ascension of each star, we can pinpoint the relative positions of the stars and draw a map of the sky.

Such maps had been drawn (or prepared as listings of the two figures for each star) since ancient times and were, of course, based on the determinations of star positions by the unaided eye. The best star map, before the day of the telescope, had been worked out by Tycho. He measured declination by sighting along a straight rod attached to a segment of a circle marked off accurately in degrees and fractions of a degree. To get the right ascension without a decent clock, he had to measure the angular distance between stars and then calculate the equivalent of the right ascension by trigonometry.

Given the primitive nature of his instruments, Tycho did a splendid job, as did Hevelius after him, and for many decades the telescope did not help astronomers to do better.

In 1638, however, the English astronomer William Gascoigne (1612–1644) first made use of a "micrometer" (from Greek words meaning "small-measurement"). Gascoigne's micrometer consisted of a pair of thin pieces of metal with finely ground edges facing each other. These were placed in the telescope at the focus of the objective. In such a position, they could be seen sharply against the images of the heavenly bodies.

The two pieces of metal could be made to approach each other, or recede from each other, by the turning of a screw of very fine pitch. One complete turn of the screw would advance or withdraw the edges by a very small amount, and the size of this could be calculated from the known and measureable amount of advance or withdrawal produced by many turns of the screw. Furthermore, the screw was marked off into a hundred equal parts so that one could calculate the advance or withdrawal of the edges resulting from the hundredth part of a single turn of the screw.

When, therefore, Gascoigne moved the edges of his micrometer so that they just touched the opposite sides of a planet, the angular width of that planet could be accurately measured, provided the magnifying power of the telescope was also known. Similarly, by placing each edge at a different star, the angular distance between two close stars could be measured with an accuracy far beyond that possible by any work with the unaided eye.

As it happened, Gascoigne did not publicize this invention but spoke of it only to a few close friends. Then he himself died at the Battle of Marston Moor in the course of the English Civil War and his friends did not long survive him. His discovery was, for a time, forgotten.

In 1658, Huygens independently worked out a device for measuring small angular distances that was inferior to the Gascoigne micrometer and it wasn't till 1666 that an advance was made. In that year, Auzout independently devised a micrometer very like Gascoigne's, except that in place of metal edges, fine hairs were used. The English scientist Robert Hooke worked out a similar device at about the same time and, also at about that time, Gascoigne's discovery became known.

Micrometers using fine threads (spider-web strands sometimes) are called "filar micrometers" from a Latin word for "thread." Often one thread is stationary and the other movable.

The first to apply the micrometer to professional astronomy on a large scale was Picard, who had also been the first to make use of a pendulum clock. He used the micrometer in 1667 in connection with his effort to make very accurate triangulation measurements in the neighborhood of Paris. This was an attempt to see how much the angles of large triangles deviated from what they would be if the Earth were flat. From the amount of the deviation, one could determine the degree of curvature of the Earth and therefore its diameter.

Picard accomplished this task with unprecedented accuracy, and a value of the Earth's diameter, very close to that accepted at present, was worked out.

The English scientist Isaac Newton (1642–1727) had earlier tried to work out a law of universal gravitation, and had done so with marvelous insight. When he checked the moon, however, to see if it were moving in such a way as to agree with his theory, he found that it was not and was forced to scrap his theory.

The reason for the apparent misbehavior of the moon was that Newton, in making his calculations, used a figure for the radius of the Earth that was substantially too small. For this reason his calculations seemed to show that the moon ought to be moving at a speed other than it was.

Eventually, when Newton returned to his theory, he made use of Picard's value for Earth's diameter (together with the methods of calculus, which Newton had invented in the meantime) and found that his predictions agreed with the facts after all. It is possible, then, to tie in the law of universal gravitation (certainly one of the crucial discoveries in the history of science) to the workings of the delicate micrometer. (The micrometer had less grand, and sometimes less admirable, uses closer to home, where the unimaginative might value it more. As late as 1890, the use of telescopic sights using the principle of the micrometer led to a revolution in naval gunnery.)

If a micrometer marks the meridian, a clock can be used to measure the exact time a star passes ("transits") the meridian. Picard used a clock for this purpose, counting its loud ticks in order to pin down the exact second of transit.

It was Picard's notion to devise a special telescope very firmly mounted on a perfectly horizontal pivot in such a way that it could only move up and down so as to focus on the line of the meridian, north and south. By measuring the angle of pivot, such a telescope could focus at some point on the meridian that is at a particular celestial latitude. Then, when a star located at that celestial latitude moves into sight and crosses the appropriate thread of the micrometer, both declination and right ascension are at once measured. Such an instrument is called a "transit instrument."

Picard did not live to see the instrument in operation but Roemer, who had worked with Picard, built one in 1684 in Copenhagen. Instead of having the lenses contained in a cylindrical tube, he placed each in a cone arranged in such a way as to have the wide openings of the two cones sealed together. This was a more rigid arrangement than a cylinder would have been and increased the precision with which the focus would remain on the meridian.

Planetary Distance

The clock enabled mankind to move beyond the Greeks for the first time in the plumbing of astronomical distances.

The Greeks, by the use of parallax, had worked out the distance of the moon as thirty times Earth's diameter, or 380,000 kilometers (240,000 miles). They could not, however, determine the parallax of any of the more distant heavenly bodies, since the parallax grew smaller with distance; and for anything more distant than the moon, the parallax is too small to measure with the unaided eye. The best Greek guess on the distance of the sun, based on faulty unaided-eye measurements of angles, was 8,000,000 kilometers (5,000,000 miles) and up to Cassini's time no better estimate could be made.

To be sure, when Kepler had worked out his elliptical orbits in 1609, he was able to construct a model of the solar system that was quite accurate. This meant that if the distance of any planet from Earth could be worked out at any accurately known time, then all the other planetary distances could be worked out for any time by making use of the proportions in the model. In particular, the distance to the sun could be calculated.

The distance of the sun was the key value as far as the solar system was concerned. Since all the planets, including the Earth, were constantly moving in their orbits, the distance of any planet from the Earth, or from any other planet, is constantly changing by substantial amounts. On the other hand, the sun is at the center of the solar system with the Earth moving about it in nearly a circular orbit so that the distance of the sun from the Earth changes only slightly with time.

In order to measure the tiny parallax of a planet, the distance between it and some convenient nearby star should be measured from two different places on Earth at precisely the same time. For this, one must have a telescope equipped with a micrometer at each place, and a clock as well.

The distances of objects beyond the moon became a reasonable goal for astronomers only in the second half of the 1600s and even then it wasn't easy.

To expect the parallax of the sun to be measured directly was unreasonable. The sun is an extended body with no visible stars nearby to serve as references, and its brilliance made it hard to observe anyway. What was wanted were some other bodies of the solar system that were more nearly points of light, and therefore easier to observe, and with nearby stars against which to measure shifts in position. (Stars are so distant that their parallaxes are virtually zero and they can be considered as stationary.)

There are three large bodies in the solar system that can, at times, be closer to Earth than the sun is. They are Venus, which is at times only 27 percent the distance of the sun, if we go by Kepler's model; Mars, which is at times only 38 percent the distance of the sun; and Mercury, which is at times only 54 percent the distance of the sun.

Of these three, Venus and Mercury are at their closest when they are more or less in line with the sun as seen from the Earth and they are then very difficult to deal with. Mars, on the other hand, is at its closest when it is high in the midnight sky and then it is particularly easy to observe.

It was clear, then, that the best chance of determining the dimensions of the solar system was to measure the parallax of Mars when that planet was at its closest.

The parallax of any given object is increased if the distance between the two points from which it was observed is increased. Consequently, it would pay astronomers to engage in a long trip for the purpose of measuring the parallax of anything as distant as Mars.

In 1670, Picard and his assistant, Cassini, heading the Paris Observatory, which was then the most advanced in the world, were anxious to determine the parallax of Mars and were prepared to make one set of observations from home base. They therefore arranged to send a fellow-astronomer, Jean Richer (1630–1696), across the Atlantic Ocean to the town of Cayenne, which was 6500 kilometers (4000 miles) from Paris along the Earth's surface, or about 6000 kilometers (3700 miles) measured in a straight line through the substance of the Earth itself. (Cayenne is located in what is now French Guiana on the northern shore of South America and even in the 1670s it was claimed by France and held against the competing claims of Great Britain and the Netherlands.)

Richer remained in Cayenne from 1671 to 1673, and in that time he made two significant observations.

One of them involved the pendulum clock he brought with him. When he made measurements of transits, he found that his results were slightly different from what they should have been as calculated for Paris. The transit always took place a little too soon. It wasn't reasonable to suppose that the sky moved differently in Cayenne than in Paris, so the most logical conclusion was that the pendulum beat more slowly in Cayenne than it would beat in Paris.

Why should that be? The rate at which a pendulum beats varies, all other things being constant, with the strength of the gravitational pull. If the pull were weaker than normal, the pendulum would beat more slowly than normal. If the Earth were not perfectly spherical and if Cayenne were slightly more distant from the center of the Earth than Paris was, and if the strength of the gravitational pull was weaker as the distance from the center of the Earth increased, then, indeed, the pendulum beat should be slower in Cayenne than in Paris and the changed transit times would be accounted for.

In the 1670s the fact of universal gravitation was not yet understood. In 1687, however, Newton published the book in which the law of universal gravitation was worked out. Gravitation *did* decrease as the distance from the center of the Earth increased and according to a relationship that made it possible to calculate the extent of the change easily and precisely.

Newton's theory also explained that a rotating body produced a centrifugal effect that partially countered the pull of gravity. This effect increased from a minimum at the poles to a maximum at the equator, so that surface gravity steadily decreased as one approached the equator. The effect was for the planet to bulge outward, the maximum extent of the bulge being at the equator. It was the rapid motion of Jupiter's surface as that planet rotated on its axis that accounts for Jupiter's marked equatorial bulge, and the same explanation was eventually shown to hold for Saturn and its even more marked equatorial bulge.

Richer's observation of the pendulum beat in Cayenne was a good indication that the Earth, too, had an equatorial bulge, even though one that was far smaller than those of Jupiter and Saturn.

There was considerable dispute over this, since some astronomers (notably Cassini himself) were reluctant to accept Newton's theory and maintained that the Earth did not possess an equatorial bulge. It was not till the 1740s that careful measurements of the Earth's curvature in the far north and in equatorial regions, by two French expeditions, settled the matter and showed that Richer's observation jibed with Newton's theory and that the Earth did have an equatorial bulge.

But whatever the explanation, Richer allowed for the anomalous pendulum beat and made careful measurements of the position of Mars with reference to nearby stars by comparing transits at a time when Mars was at very nearly its closest approach to Earth. At the same time, Cassini was making measurements of the position of Mars with reference to nearby stars from the observatory in Paris.

When Richer returned to Paris in 1673 with his observations, Cassini set to work calculating the parallax and, from that, the distance of Mars at the time of the observation. Once that was determined, other distances of the solar system, most particularly the distance of the sun from the Earth, would automatically be known.

From Cassini's calculations, it appeared that the sun was at the unexpectedly great distance of 140 million kilometers (87 million miles) from Earth. Actually, this was not quite right, being about 10 million kilometers (6 million miles) short of the real value. Nevertheless, as the very first estimate of the dimensions of the solar system in the telescopic age, it was reasonably accurate.

For the first time, mankind got a glimpse of the true dimensions of the solar system. Saturn, which was then the farthest known planet, is 9.5 times as far from the sun as Earth is. The overall width of Saturn's orbit had to be in excess of 2600 million kilometers (1600 million miles). Where the Greeks had spoken of orbital widths in the millions of kilometers, the astronomers of the last quarter of the seventeenth century found themselves speaking in the billions of kilometers.

Knowledge of the distance of the various members of the solar system gained by the clock meant that the size of those bodies could be determined by micrometer. The angular size of each body could be translated into actual size when the distance was known.

It turned out that Venus was about the size of the Earth, while Mars and Mercury were distinctly smaller than Earth (though larger than the moon). Jupiter and Saturn, however, turned out to be giant planets. Saturn's globe is about nine times as wide as that of Earth, while Jupiter (well-named for the king of the gods) was eleven times as wide as the Earth. As for the sun, it was over 1,300,000 kilometers (850,000 miles) across — over a hundred times the diameter of the Earth.

Cassini's revolutionary measurement put Earth in its place — from its proud one-time position as the center and almost the whole of the universe, it had become, physically at least, an undistinguished member of the solar system.

Cassini's measurement also put startling life into another measurement soon to be made. Roemer had concluded at just about the time Cassini was producing his result that light crossed Earth's orbit in twenty-two minutes. To cross the vast extent of that width, as calculated by Cassini, light would have to be traveling at about 227,000 kilometers (140,000 miles) per second. As it happened, this was about 25 percent below the correct figure, but it was excellent for a first attempt and high enough to astonish the scientific world.

But if the clock and micrometer brought a new and grander vision of the universe to mankind and a smaller and more humble position for ourselves and our world, it also made possible an important application of astronomy to the everyday affairs of the world.

Since the beginning of the great explorations of the Earth by European navigators in the 1400s, European ships had been crawling over all the vast oceans of the planet. They had explored the coasts of the continents, established empires, carried immigrants abroad, and had brought back the spoils of trade. All this could have been done more efficiently if the ships could somehow work out their position at sea accurately at all times instead of having to more or less blunder along.

The ship's latitude could be determined by noting the position of the highest point reached by the sun on any particular day and this could be done, easily enough, by the use of appropriate sighting instruments. The determination of longitude was, however, a much more difficult problem.

Since the time at which a star crossed the meridian differed with the longitudinal position of the observer on Earth (supposing a clock to be set always to the local time of a fixed spot on the planet), then longitude could be determined by measuring the hour angle of prominent stars of known right ascension. For this, though, a clock was needed that could keep accurate time over extended voyages. A pendulum clock wouldn't do, for it would be thrown out at once by the rolling and pitching of a ship.

Great Britain dominated world trade and, in 1713, she offered a series of prizes that mounted to 20,000 pounds for an adequate "chronometer" that would keep rigidly good time on the unstable deck of a ship, one that could always tell London time so that the right ascension as it was measured could be compared with what it should be. The prize was finally won by a series of clocks built by an English instrument-maker, John Harrison (1693–1776).

In this way, for those who find little to admire in a better understanding of the universe and want instead something that can be measured in money, the instruments and techniques of astronomy contributed to the efficiency of sea voyages, to the ease of trade, and to the prosperity of a number of nations, particularly Great Britain, of course.

4. Seeing by Reflection

Color

Throughout the seventeenth century, as telescopes grew steadily longer and more difficult to handle, astronomers rather desperately sought ways of shortening the telescopes while still obtaining good images.

Hooke had the ingenious notion of using mirrors. By placing them properly within a tube, the slowly converging rays of light could be reflected back and forth. They would be bent repeatedly, like a folding ruler, and made to fit into a tube only a fifth as long as would be required for the unbent convergence. There was nothing wrong with the theory but the state of the art in those days could not produce mirrors good enough to do the job adequately.

The other alternative was to remove the aberrations that plagued lenses. If that could be done, sharply curved lenses with short focal lengths could be used and telescopes could magnify highly and still be comparatively short.

In the case of spherical aberration, the way out was known. The lenses had to be ground into a nonspherical surface, a paraboloid that grew less curved as the rim was approached. The difficulty, there, rested in the mechanics of grinding. In 1666, for instance, the young Isaac Newton tried his hand at grinding surfaces that were not spherical, but he was not successful.

But correcting the spherical aberration would not by itself have solved the problem. It was chromatic aberration, the rings of color which surround the telescopic image, which was the culprit. Here, no one knew the cause so there wasn't even a hope of improving technical capacity in a known direction to remove the problem.

It occurred to Newton to study the problem by refracting light through a surface less complicated than the steady curve of a lens. He could refract light through flat glass surfaces provided he did not use a piece of glass with two parallel flat surfaces, since in that case, the second surface would undo the work of the first and leave the light unrefracted. He could, however, use a triangular piece of glass (a "prism") so that light would pass through two of the non-parallel surfaces.

Newton obtained a prism and worked in a darkened room, with a shutter drawn and a hole in the shutter. This meant that a circular beam of sunlight entered the room through the hole; and, if undisturbed, it would move through the air in a straight line and fall on the opposite wall as an elliptical blob of white light.

He then placed the prism in the path of the light so that the light was refracted and fell on a different spot on the wall. When that happened the ellipse lengthened considerably and the light was no longer white. It now showed a progression of colors. There was red nearest the point where the unrefracted spot of light would have been on the wall, so that the red portion was least refracted. Then, in order of increasing refraction, there came orange, yellow, green, blue, and violet.*

This had been observed before and, as a matter of fact, the succession of colors (called a "spectrum" from the Latin word for "ghost," since it was an insubstantial thing) was precisely that in a rainbow. This is not surprising since the rainbow is produced by the refraction of light through tiny raindrops in the air after a shower. Those who observed a spectrum before Newton were convinced, however, that white light was fundamentally pure — that is, that it contained nothing but white light — and that the colors were produced by the prism, or by the atmosphere in the case of the rainbow.

Newton, however, passed a restricted part of the light, consisting of one color only, through a second prism. That portion of the spectrum was further lengthened, but no new colors appeared. Furthermore, he let the beam of light that had passed through the prism and had been divided into colors fall upon a second prism

* It is customary to list indigo as a color lying between blue and violet, but it has never seemed to me that indigo is worth the dignity of being considered a separate color. To my eyes it seems merely deep blue.

held upside-down compared to the first. This drew the colors back together again and produced white light.

Newton maintained, therefore, that white light was actually a mixture of light of different colors. Each color of light was refracted by a characteristic amount so that on passing through a prism white light was sorted out into its various colors. Even the separate colors as you moved along its length in a spectrum seemed to exist in smoothly varying shades so that there were no sharp dividing lines between the colors. The various colors produced out of white light would, if combined again, become white once more.

This view of light, as put forward by Newton, was strongly combatted by others, but it was correct, as far as it went, and was eventually accepted.

The array of colors produced in the spectrum was not an inherent property of the light but was the effect of that kind of light on the retina of the eye. After all, some people are totally colorblind, but the colored light doesn't disappear for them, only the color does. Thus, colorblindness is of no use in combatting chromatic aberration. The colored rings of light would no longer be colored, but there would still be a blur of light and this would still interfere with seeing a sharp image.

In Newton's time, colorblindness had not yet been studied and was little known, but that did not prevent Newton from seeing that chromatic aberration was an inevitable consequence of spectrum-formation by light refraction through lenses.

If each color passing through the lens was refracted to a different extent, then red, being refracted least, would come to a focus farthest from the lens. Orange, yellow, green, blue, and violet would come to a focus at points successively closer to the lens. If the lenses were arranged in such a way that the red end of the spectrum would focus well, the rest of the colors would be past their focus and would form a bluish rim about the image. If the lenses were arranged to focus the violet end of the spectrum, the rest of the colors would not yet have come to focus and would form an orangey ring about the image. No amount of focusing anywhere in the spectrum could get rid of colored rings altogether.

Newton's instinct for correctness failed him here. Performing inadequate experiments, he decided that light passing through glass was always refracted in the same way and that there would never be any way of modifying lenses to correct chromatic aberration. He cast about, therefore, for some way of achieving the purpose of a telescope without the use of lenses.

Mirrors

Actually, lenses are not indispensable. Mirrors are lenses inside out, so to speak, and it was known from ancient times that curved mirrors could do the sort of thing curved lenses do. A properly shaped mirror could focus light, just as a properly shaped lens could. Parallel rays of light would converge if they were refracted through a transparent convex lens, or if they were reflected from the surface of a concave mirror.

Of course, glass transmits far more light than it reflects, so that glass alone cannot be used effectively as a reflecting device in telescopes. Nor was it possible in the seventeenth century to place a metal film on a glass mirror in order to make it an astronomically effective reflecting device.

Instead, one had to turn to substances that had served mankind as mirrors before glass ever became effective for that purpose — the various metals.

A mirror, like a lens, is most easily ground into a curve that is the section of a sphere, and a spherical mirror doesn't bring light to a true focus any more than a spherical lens does. The use of mirrors does not, therefore, necessarily correct spherical aberration and, in the beginning, did not. Mirrors, however, reflect all the colors of light in precisely the same way and a spectrum cannot be produced merely by the reflection of light from a mirror. A telescope, using a mirror in place of a lens, would therefore be free of chromatic aberration, an important step forward.

Newton was convinced that this would solve the chief problem, leaving spherical aberration behind as, in comparison, only a minor trouble. He set about, therefore, to construct a telescope that worked by reflection of light rather than by refraction.

He was not really first in the field. Telescopes using mirrors ("reflecting telescopes" or "reflectors") had been suggested in a purely theoretical way by several people around the mid-1600s, but the notion did introduce a complication that couldn't help but make reflectors more complicated than the ordinary "refractors."

When light passes through a lens, or system of lenses, in a refractor, it moves from one end of the telescope tube through the lenses to the other. The object to be viewed is at one end of the tube and the eye of the viewer is at the other, and this introduces no problem; it is a perfectly natural situation.

If a mirror is used, light enters at one end of the tube, strikes the mirror, and bounces back through the same end. The viewer leaning over that end to see the image blocks the entry of the light.

The first person to attempt to deal with this problem in practice and actually to try to build a reflecting telescope was James Gregory. In 1663, he advanced a scheme which made use of two mirrors, a primary and a secondary, used in the following manner:

Light entered the telescope tube from one end and struck the primary mirror at the other end and was reflected. This primary mirror, however, had a hole in its center, which cut down the total amount of light trapped and focused but did not interfere with the focusing of such light as was reflected by the rim of the mirror that existed.

The reflected light rays converged to a focus and began to diverge again. Before diverging very far they struck the secondary mirror in the center of the tube, one that was so positioned as to block the light entering the telescope from reaching and passing through the hole in the primary. The secondary mirror was also concave and the light rays reflected from it, and after this second reflection, the light did converge into the hole in the primary. This produced an image, as was the objective, and the light then passed through an eyepiece to produce a magnified image.

Thanks to the presence of two mirrors and a hole in one of them, light entered the telescope at one end and could be seen by the viewer at the other end.

Gregory, however, aimed too high. He wanted to eliminate spherical aberration as well as chromatic aberration. He was mathematician enough to know that he needed a paraboloid surface for the primary mirror. He also wanted an ellipsoidal surface for the secondary mirror.

The trouble was that there was no optician capable of grinding such surfaces accurately, so that Gregory could not get mirrors that did him any good at all and never managed to build a working reflector. There was nothing wrong with the theory, however, and "Gregorian telescopes" built since his time have worked perfectly.

Newton's aim with respect to a reflector was much more modest than Gregory's. Having failed to grind some appropriate nonspherical surface, he decided to be content with a spherical surface and endure the aberration that resulted.

He experimented with various metal alloys to find one which was useful as a "speculum metal" (from a Latin word for "mirror"). It seemed that bronze would be the most useful base, for it was not too expensive, nor too easily corroded, and it took a high polish. Its color was objectionable, however, since ordinary bronze, an alloy of copper and tin, is quite yellow and would lend a yellow tinge to the images. Newton therefore increased the tin content and added a bit of arsenic, too, to make the alloy white in color and capable of taking a still better polish. In the end, his speculum metal was copper, tin, and arsenic in the proportion of 6 to 2 to 1 respectively.

Newton constructed a primary mirror out of this metal, polishing it painstakingly himself and making it into a concave section of a sphere. The mirror was about 2.5 centimeters (1 inch) across. The light it reflected did not strike another concave mirror after passing through focus as in the Gregorian system. Instead, it struck a small flat mirror (easy to grind) before reaching focus. This flat mirror was placed at a 45° angle to the primary mirror.

The light that, converging, struck the flat secondary mirror, was reflected at an angle of 90° and, still converging, was sent out through an eyepiece in the side of the tube near that opening into which light enters in the first place. The secondary mirror, as in the case of the Gregorian reflector, blocked some light from reaching the central portion of the primary mirror.

The telescope, which Newton made with his own hands in 1668, was the first working reflector ever made. It was about 15 centimeters (6 inches) long, but though tiny compared to the string-bean refractors in use, it yielded a magnification of forty times and did the work of refractors that were a meter or two long. Remembering that it is really the diameter of the aperture that counts, we should not be too surprised about that.

Newton had made this first instrument for himself and did not publicize it much. Once word of his researches on light spectra spread, however, people wanted to see the reflector, concerning which rumors were also being bruited about. Newton therefore made a second one with a primary mirror 5 centimeters (2 inches) across and on January 11, 1672, presented it to the Royal Society. Along with this telescope (which still exists) he presented formal reports on his work on light.

Others were in the field, too, and in 1672 a Frenchman, N. Cassegrain (concerning whom almost nothing is known except for what is about to be described), advanced still a third design for a reflector.

In the "Cassegrain reflector," light is first reflected by a primary mirror with a hole and is then reflected from a secondary back through the hole in the primary to an eyepiece. In this respect, it is like the Gregorian.

The difference lies in this — that the reflected light reaches the secondary before it reaches focus (as in the "Newtonian reflector"). Furthermore, the secondary mirror was neither concave as in the Gregorian design nor flat as in the Newtonian. It was convex so that the light reflected from it diverged somewhat, lowering the magnifying power of the telescope. The advantage gained from this loss in magnification was that the process of first converging the light and then slightly diverging it tended to cancel out the spherical aberration. This permits the telescope to be quite short for its focal length. The optical principle though, with mirrors, is very similar to that used to make modern short telephoto lenses.

A Cassegrain reflector could be further modified by incorporating the Newtonian notion of a flat mirror at 45°, which would intercept the light rays as they returned from the convex secondary and send them out through an eyepiece in the side. This side eyepiece in the Cassegrain reflector is near the rear of the telescope rather than near the front as in the Newtonian reflector, and this rear position is the more convenient as the telescope grows larger. Most Cassegrain telescopes have a hole in the primary mirror to let the light through, as with the Gregorian telescope.

The 1670s, then, saw the reflector become a workable device, something that could be used to observe celestial objects without enormous lengthening. Because a reflecting telescope could be made small and compact, yet provide respectable magnifications, it was of particular interest to amateurs, and attained a popularity which persists to this day.

It had flaws, however, that prevented it, for a while, from serving the purposes of the professionals.

For one thing it was difficult to get metal mirrors to reflect as much light as a good lens of the same diameter would transmit. Newton's mirrors reflected only 16 percent of the light that fell on it. This meant that size for size, the image produced by a reflector was dimmer than that of a refractor.

Secondly, though speculum metal did not tarnish easily, it did tarnish after a time and even a slight tarnish cut down reflection all the way. This meant that reflector mirrors were forever having to be repolished whereas refractor lenses could get by with nothing more than an occasional dusting.

Finally, it was easy to use micrometers in connection with refractors and difficult with reflectors, so that astronomers who wished to make accurate measurements in the heavens were condemned to use the long refractors even after the compact reflectors were in the field. Bradley was using his 65-meter (212-feet) refractor half a century after the reflector had been invented.

Yet these long early refractors, for all their inconvenience, continued to make important discoveries and, indeed, managed to advance man's knowledge beyond the solar system and out to the stars.

The Unfixed Stars

During the first seven decades after the invention of the telescope, almost all the discoveries it had made possible were within the boundaries of the solar system. Telescopic observation had done very little with the stars except to discover new ones too dim to be seen by the unaided eye, plus a few objects such as the Andromeda nebula that looked different than ordinary stars.

Yet determining the positions of the stars had been one useful activity of the pretelescopic astronomers. Numbers defining the positions of the stars (as, for instance, the declination and right ascension) could be listed and this was the equivalent of a star map, for, using those numbers, the stars could be marked off on a sphere.

Even as late as the 1670s, the best star maps were those of Tycho and of Hevelius, who prepared them by observing with the unaided eye and included in them just a little over a thousand stars. The accuracy of the numbers obtained was only within 1 minute of arc (or 60 seconds of arc) and that, probably, was the limit the unaided eye could attain.

Once the filar micrometer was invented and put to use, it seemed logical to redetermine the numbers and make more accurate star maps.

In 1676, the English astronomer Edmund Halley (1656–1742) set about performing such a task, and chose to do so, moreover, in a part of the sky that had been neglected by astronomers because, for one thing, it was invisible from any point in Europe at any time of the year.

Halley traveled to the island of St. Helena in the South Atlantic (where a century and a half later, Napoleon was to spend his final wretched years). It was 16° south of the Equator, and from St. Helena all the stars in the southern half of the celestial sphere were visible at night at one time or another in the course of the year, including those regions in the neighborhood of the south celestial sphere which were never visible from Europe.

Of course, these southern stars had been seen constantly not only by the native peoples of Australia and the southern sections of South America and Africa but also by various European explorers. Halley, however, was the first to bring advanced astronomical instruments south of the Equator. He had a large telescope 7.3 meters (24 feet) long, together with micrometers and clocks.

Halley spent two years in St. Helena, enduring miserable weather for an astronomer, who needs clear skies, but ended up recording the precise position of 341 stars in the southern heavens. It was the first telescopic star map, though a restricted one.

Meanwhile, in 1675 the English astronomer John Flamsteed (1646–1719) was appointed first astronomer royal by Charles II and he was instructed to set up an observatory in Greenwich, which was then a suburb of London. He was given no money with which to make this possible, but with utter dedication, he begged, borrowed, and built, ending up with two small telescopes, nothing like the much more advanced instruments being used by the astronomers in the Paris Observatory.

Flamsteed was a meticulous man, however, and a dedicated workman who devoted himself to measuring the position of the stars, one by one, steadily and regularly, making use of a clock and a micrometer for the purpose. He also laboriously went through all the calculations necessary to reduce his observations to some single standard that would produce a star map.

He delayed publishing the star map since he was forever attempting to gain more and still more precise data. Finally, it was published in 1712 by Halley without Flamsteed's authorization — to the latter's fury. An authorized version of Flamsteed's star map finally appeared in three volumes, posthumously, in 1725.

Flamsteed's star map was the first large one of the telescopic age. It had 3000 stars in it, with its numerical measurements accurate to within 10 seconds of arc. Nothing like it could have been done without a telescope.

This accurate star-mapping by Halley and Flamsteed did more than merely prepare number tables. It led, indirectly, to a simple observation that utterly changed man's view of the stars and of the universe as a whole.

In the Greek view of the universe, the stars were fixed to the outermost celestial sphere. The starry canopy of the sky enclosed the Earth together with the spheres of the various planets that circled Earth.

This view was modified, but not seriously altered, as a result of the great changes in the view of the planetary system that began with Copernicus. Copernicus still viewed the starry sky as a canopy enclosing the sun and the various planets that circled it. So did Kepler.

The dimensions of the solar system turned out to be far larger than anyone had thought once Cassini had worked out the parallax of Mars. Nevertheless, although this moved the starry canopy outward, it did not abolish it. Even as the 1700s opened, there was no reason to think of the stars as anything but decorative effects on a distant solid sphere. Nicholas of Cusa, to be sure, had, two and a half centuries earlier, suggested the stars were suns distributed through infinite space, but few seemed willing to take seriously so science-fictionish a notion.

There did exist some reason to attempt to determine the distance of the starry sphere. When Copernicus had advanced his theory that the Earth was revolving in a large orbit about the sun, traditionalists objected on the ground that this should produce a parallactic displacement in the stars. The stellar sphere should appear to shift as the Earth swung about from one side of the sun to the other and this should show itself in an apparent shift of position of the stars.

The Copernicans argued, however, that the stellar sphere was so far away that the parallax was too small to measure, that compared with the size of the stellar sphere, the entire circle of Earth's orbit was merely a dot.

This may have seemed a lame excuse at first since few could possibly be willing to accept a universe so huge as to make the planetary spheres (whether centered about the Earth or about the sun) to be insignificant in comparison.

As telescopic observations made the Copernican theory seem steadily less bizarre and more necessary, the distance of the starry sphere simply had to be accepted as enormous in view of the absence of parallax. This acceptance limited the interest in even trying to determine the stellar parallax. The vast distances put the measurements beyond the scope of the telescopes of the day and there was, after all, still much to be done in the solar system itself.

With the growth of systematic telescopic studies of stellar position by men like Halley and Flamsteed, something was bound to arise that would break this indifference. That something came in 1718, when Halley made an observation that finally changed the attitude of astronomers toward the stars.

In that year, Halley reported that the positions of at least three prominent bright stars — Sirius, Arcturus, and Aldebaran — were far removed from the positions reported by the ancient Greeks. The difference was as high as 30 minutes of arc in one case.

Even though the Greeks had to work with the unaided eye, they couldn't have made mistakes so large. Nor could it be a slip of a pen, since several Greek astronomers, working independently, had all reported the same positions with which Halley now quarreled.

The positions for those stars in Tycho's map, which was considerably more accurate than those prepared by the Greeks, agreed much more closely with Halley's findings, and even so, Sirius had shifted slightly in the century and a half since Tycho's time.

Nor was it a general movement of the stars, since most of the stars that Halley checked had not changed their positions significantly since Tycho's time, or even since Greek times.

Halley felt himself forced to conclude that the stars were not fixed after all, but that they had a "proper motion" of their own. If all of them moved at more or less the same speed, then the apparent shift in position with time would be greater for those close to us than for those far from us. It followed, then, that Sirius, Arcturus, and Aldebaran were closer to us than were most of the stars in the sky, and this possibility was made more likely since all three were among the brightest stars in the sky and one would expect relatively close stars to be brighter than relatively distant ones.

From Halley's time on, it was clear that mankind was dealing with "unfixed" stars after all.

Halley's observation, tending to show that the stars were at different distances and that some were sufficiently close to Earth to allow their motions to become large enough to be noticed after the passage of years, made the customary notion of the solid, starry sphere difficult to retain. Nicholas of Cusa's suggestion that the stars were suns distributed through infinite place suddenly seemed less bizarre.

The universe of stars was raised to a new level of complexity and fascination in this way, and the notion of measuring the parallax of at least the closest stars instantly gained greater interest among astronomers.

It seemed to Halley that the probable size of the parallax of the nearer stars could be reasonably estimated if Nicholas of Cusa's suggestion were followed.

Consider Sirius, which, as the brightest star in the sky, might be the closest, or at the very least one of the closest. Suppose it were indeed a body like our sun. How far away from us would the sun have to be, Halley asked himself, to shine with only the brightness that Sirius does?

Halley made the calculation and found that Sirius must be something like 120,000 times as far from us as the sun is. At that distance its parallax, resulting from the vast change in Earth's position as it moved around the sun, would carry Sirius only about 1 second of arc or so from its average position during the year.

This could not possibly be detected with the telescopes of the early 1700s, but on the other hand, who could be sure that Sirius was as bright as the sun? It might be considerably less bright * than the sun and, therefore, be considerably closer than Halley judged. In that case, the parallax might be large enough to detect — and with that the search for stellar parallax began.

One man who attempted to detect the possibly very slight shifts in star positions that would be involved in parallax was an Irish astronomer, Samuel Molyneux (1689–1728). His notion was to erect a telescope and fix it in a practically vertical position.

Any stars visible in that telescope would be shining directly downward and would be only minimally affected by light refraction. Any change in the position of such stars, Molyneux argued, would then much more likely be the result of parallax and much less likely be the result of atmospheric interference.

In 1725, he constructed a long telescope in his own estate at Kew, a suburb of London. It was 7.3 meters (24 feet) long and 9.4 centimeters (3¾ inches) in diameter. He erected it up the chimney shaft in such a way that the star Gamma Draconis swam into view as it crossed the meridian nearly at the zenith. The telescope was so fixed that all through the year it would be pointed at the same spot and the position of the star as it crossed the hairlines, as well as the time of crossing, could be measured with great accuracy.

Working with him was a younger astronomer, James Bradley. When Molyneux dropped out because his political activity in the Admiralty took too much of his time, Bradley continued alone. Bradley began a series of observations on December 14, 1725, and by December 28, he noticed that Gamma Draconis was cutting across the hairlines a little to the south of its original position.

Day after day, month after month, that star was followed while it remained in the night sky. It continued to move south, and then

---

* Actually, Sirius is considerably brighter than the sun and is actually over 500,000 times as far away as the sun, but, of course, there was no way of knowing that at the time.

north. It made an oscillation that was 40 seconds of arc across in the course of a year. It looked like parallax but it *wasn't* parallax because if it had been caused by the motion of the Earth about the sun, it would have been farthest south in December, whereas it was actually farthest south in March.

Bradley set up a smaller telescope in 1727 and found similar oscillations. He could not account for this out-of-phase movement until 1728. In that year, he noted, in the course of a pleasure sail on the Thames River, that the pennant on top of the mast changed direction according to the relative motion of ship and wind and not according to the direction of the wind alone.

That set him to thinking — suppose you are in a rainstorm with all the raindrops falling vertically downward because there is no wind. If you have an umbrella, you then hold it directly over your head and remain dry. If you are walking, however, you will walk into some raindrops that have just cleared the umbrella, if you continue to hold the umbrella directly over your head. You must angle the umbrella a little in the direction you are walking if you want to remain dry.

The faster you walk, or the slower the raindrops fall, the farther forward you must tilt your umbrella to avoid walking into the raindrops. The exact angle through which you must tilt your umbrella depends upon the ratio of the two velocities, that of the raindrops and that of yourself.

The situation is similar in astronomy. Light is falling on the Earth from some star in some direction and at some velocity. Meanwhile, the Earth is moving around the sun at another velocity. The telescope, like the umbrella, must be tilted a little in the direction the Earth is moving to catch the light squarely on the telescope lens. This tilt Bradley referred to as "the aberration of light."

Because light is traveling very much faster than the Earth is moving in its orbit, the velocity ratio is such that the telescope must be tilted only very slightly indeed.

The tilt was measured by Bradley's observations and, from that, the ratio of the speed of light to the speed of Earth in its orbit could be calculated. Bradley decided that the speed of light was such that light would cross the full width of Earth's orbit in sixteen minutes and twenty-six seconds.

This is very nearly correct, but allowing that the size of the Earth's orbit was at that time believed to be a little smaller than it really is, Bradley's figure comes out to be about 283,000 kilometers (176,000 miles) per second. This second determination of the speed of light is much closer to the true value than Roemer's first determination was.

Bradley did not detect stellar parallax, which was clearly a much smaller displacement than that of the aberration of light, and which seemed to be beyond the capacity of his telescope. However, his discovery accomplished two things.

In the first place, the aberration of light would not exist if the Earth were not moving. It was therefore as good a piece of evidence for the fact that the Earth was moving about the sun as parallax would have been.

Secondly, with aberration discovered, the displacements due to it could be taken into account. (So could another small, regular shift of the stars, called "nutation," which was also discovered by Bradley.) Once these displacements were indeed allowed for, the still smaller shifts caused by parallax would be detected — provided telescopes and auxiliary devices continued to be improved.

Such improvements were indeed taking place.

No Color

In 1721, the English mathematician John Hadley (1682–1744) produced the first reflecting telescope that could hope to compete with the refractors then in use and that was of professional value in the astronomy of the time.

Hadley worked more meticulously on grinding his mirror than anyone before him. He produced a Gregorian reflector that was 15 centimeters (6 inches) in diameter, which showed rather little in the way of spherical aberration.

Hadley did not try to grind out a paraboloid surface on a purely geometrical basis. Instead, he worked it out by trial and error, letting the actual condition of the surface guide him to the next step in grinding without knowing the actual geometric nature of the surface.

He devised an optical test (the first man to do so) by which he could judge the precision with which the mirror brought light to a focus. Hadley placed an illuminated pinhole at the focus of the mirror and studied the manner in which light was then reflected from the different portions of the metal surface. If the surface actually brought all the parallel rays falling upon it to an exact focus, then, in reverse, an illuminated dot at the focus ought to strike all parts of the surface and be reflected in parallel rays. The surface ought to light up evenly.

Where the even illumination was marred the surface was not bringing rays of light to the focus and further grinding was indicated. It took a keen and practiced eye to judge the nature of the imperfections that showed up, but Hadley managed and eventually ended with a Gregorian reflector 15 centimeters (6 inches) in diameter that produced very little spherical aberration.

Hadley's reflector, first revealed to the Royal Society in January 1721, turned out to work almost as well as a large refractor which belonged to the Society and whose lenses had been ground by Huygens. The refractor lens was a little wider than Hadley's mirror so that it collected more light and produced somewhat brighter images, but that refractor was 37.5 meters (123 feet) long while Hadley's reflector was only 1.8 meters (6 feet) long.

The advantage in maneuverability of such a short telescope far outweighed any inferiority in brightness of image. Furthermore, a short telescope could have its length easily enclosed in metal so that there need be no concern for scattered light. Hadley's telescope could be used in twilight, for instance, where an aerial telescope could not.

The work on reflectors was carried on by a Scottish instrument-maker, James Short (1710–1768), who was encouraged and patronized by the Scottish mathematician Colin Maclaurin (1698–1746). Short was even more painstaking in the grinding and polishing of metal mirrors than Hadley had been and was the first to develop the techniques required to grind paraboloid surfaces with reasonable ease and true precision. That cut down the labor required to make the final adjustments by optical testing.

In 1740 Short went into the business of manufacturing reflectors in a virtually wholesale manner, producing the Gregorian variety for the most part. Many of his reflectors were small enough to be held in the hand. Others were unprecedentedly large for reflectors, reaching diameters of 45 centimeters (18 inches) and lengths of over 3.6 meters (12 feet). These large ones were very expensive and were usually sold to aristocratic amateurs who didn't do much serious work with them.

The work of Hadley and Short brought reflectors to such a pitch of practical worth that the only virtue left the clumsy refractors of the time was the ease with which they could be outfitted with micrometers. As soon as better methods for micrometrizing reflectors were developed, refractors would have been replaced — except that they, too, underwent improvements.

In order for refractors to become short and maneuverable without losing power of magnification, sharply curved paraboloid-surfaced lenses would have to be used. Spherical aberration would then be avoided but chromatic aberration (to which reflectors were immune) would still remain. The shortening of refractors depended, then, on the defeat of chromatic aberration. Only then could they hope to continue to compete with the up-and-coming reflectors.

To be sure, Newton had been of the opinion that nothing could defeat chromatic refraction since a spread of color was inherent in the refraction of white light. Such was the reputation of Newton in the wake of his working out of the law of universal gravitation in 1687 that few cared to doubt his word in anything.

Yet some did. The Scottish mathematician David Gregory (1661–1708), the nephew of the originator of the Gregorian reflector, pointed out that the eye possessed a lens, yet showed no chromatic aberration. Light was refracted not only through that lens but by the corneal surface and the various fluids in the eye. Gregory guessed that because there were different fluids in the eye, the chromatic refraction of some canceled the others. (Actually this is not entirely true since the optic of the eye has a great deal of chromatic aberration, but the idea suggested a useful direction.)

In fact, had Newton tried prisms made of different varieties of glass, he would have found that some stretched out the spectrum to a greater extent than others; in other words, each different kind of glass had a characteristic "dispersion" of its own. Differences in dispersion had indeed been reported after Newton had announced his experiments with prisms, but Newton had dismissed this overhastily, and where Newton led the way, others, just as overhastily, followed.

Suppose, then, you combine two different kinds of glass. You begin with a convex lens which makes light converge to a focus (which is what you want in a telescope) and a concave lens which makes light diverge. If the convex lens and concave lens were of equal power and were combined, the light passing through would converge in passing through one and diverge in passing through the other. The two effects would cancel and the light would pass through both, neither converging nor diverging

Suppose, though, that the concave lens were considerably less powerful than the convex. There would be considerably less divergence than convergence, and light passing through both would converge to a focus. It would not do so as sharply as it would if it passed through the convex lens alone, but it would do so.

Now suppose that the convex lens had a low dispersion and the concave lens a high dispersion for a given amount of convergence or divergence. The concave lens, although it would not be powerful enough to cancel out the convergence of light through the convex lens, would, in view of its high dispersion, nevertheless be powerful enough to cancel out the separation of colors.

This was in the mind of an English lawyer and mathematician who dabbled in optics, Chester Moor Hall (1703–1771). He, like David Gregory, respected the evidence of the lens of the eye and began to experiment with different kinds of glass.

He discovered that flint glass * had a considerably higher dispersion than crown glass (the ordinary glass used in windows). He therefore decided to make a convex lens out of crown glass and a concave lens out of flint glass, designed in such a way that the two would fit together to form a single biconvex lens that would converge light to a focus *without* an overall separation of color. It would be an "achromatic lens" (from Greek words meaning "no color").

This meant that the lenses could be made with more highly curved surfaces so that the achromatic lens would bring light to a focus

---

* Flint glass, which contained lead compounds, is a dense, durable, highly transparent glass. It was first formed in 1674 by the English glassmaker George Ravenscroft (1618–1681), and its use made Great Britain the leading glass-producer in the 1700s. It is not surprising, then, that achromatic lenses were first developed in Great Britain.

much more quickly than the very gently curving lenses of the long refractors could. An achromatic refractor could be made almost as short as a reflector without losing power.

Hall was anxious to have his scheme remain secret till he had the telescope in hand, so in 1733 he arranged to have one optical firm grind the convex lens of crown glass and another firm altogether grind the concave lens of flint glass. In this way, he hoped that neither would know what he was getting at.

Unfortunately, each optical firm, lacking the time to do the work, subcontracted the lens, and each sent the work to the same subcontractor, a man named George Bass.

Bass noted that both lenses were for Hall and that they were so designed that one could fit against the other to make an overall biconvex lens. Naturally, when he had completed the grinding, he fitted them together, looked through, and realized he had an achromatic lens.

Hall completed his instrument, which had an objective 6.5 centimeters (2.5 inches) in diameter and yet had a length of only 50 centimeters (20 inches), but his secret was out. What's more, since he was not really either an optician nor an astronomer, he did not effectively publicize his instrument and the ground was clear for someone more enterprising.

That someone was John Dollond (1706–1761), who *was* an optician and who heard about the achromatic lens from Bass. Dollond had earlier been firmly convinced that Newton was right and that chromatic aberration could not be removed, but now he made detailed experiments on refraction and dispersion by glass and water. He established the theoretical basis for achromatic lenses thoroughly. Then, in 1757 he constructed an achromatic lens of crown glass and flint glass.

An additional step was needed to correct the spherical aberration of the lens. The ratio of dispersion of the two glasses determines the required ratio of focusing points for the convex and concave lenses. Fortunately the spherical aberration from the negative lens tends to compensate for that of the positive lens. By changing the curve of the lenses but still maintaining the required ratio of focusing power, it was possible to bring the spherical aberration almost to zero. Thus, it was unnecessary in the end to solve the difficult problem of making nonspherical surfaces in lenses.

Dollond did not mention Hall's previous work in his own reports. The result is that despite Hall's twenty-year precedence, Dollond usually receives the credit for the achromatic lens.

This is not entirely without justice. Dollond did the painstaking theoretical work that offered solid backing for the concept of achromaticity. For another he patented the lens and, with his son, Peter (1730–1820), began the manufacture of achromatic refractors. In 1765 Peter introduced a triple lens combination: a concave lens, with a convex one on each side. Jesse Ramsden (1735–1800), a son-in-law of the elder Dollond, also manufactured achromatic refractors.

Achromatic refractors completely killed the long telescopes that had preceded and that had reigned for a century. From 1757 to the present day, astronomers have studied the light from objects in the sky with either reflectors or with achromatic refractors.

5. The Stars Succumb

The New Planet

The chief shortcoming of the achromatic refractor was that there was a sharp limit to the size of the lens that could be prepared. It was not known in Dollond's time how to cast large pieces of flint glass sufficiently free of defect to be of use in telescopes. For that reason, a 10-centimeter-wide (4-inch) lens was about all that could possibly be hoped for in the early days of the achromatic refractor.

The reflector did not suffer in this way, for it was easier to cast large pieces of metal than large pieces of glass. Then, too, while a glass lens had to be perfect throughout, a metal mirror needed only a perfectly glossy and well-shaped surface.

As a result it was clearly easier to think of large reflectors than of large refractors in the closing decades of the 1700s. And in this case we mean by "large" an increase primarily in the width of the mirror and telescope rather than length alone. To the age of the long refractor, there succeeded the age of the wide reflector.

The beginning of this age came about through the work of William Herschel (1738–1822).

Herschel was born in Hanover, a German region which was then under the rule of King George II of Great Britain. He emigrated to Great Britain in 1757 (to avoid being drafted into the Hanoverian army to fight the invading French) and there, first in Leeds, then in Bath, he made a living as a music teacher.

The study of musical sounds led him to mathematics, which in turn led him to optics, and that led him to an aching desire to observe the universe through telescopes. He could scarcely dream of buying a telescope in his straitened circumstances so he began by buying lenses that he then attempted to fit into old-fashioned long refractors for which he made the tubes himself.

That only whetted his appetite. He dreamed of observing not only the planets but the stars as well and he quickly saw that with long refractors he would quickly escalate himself into impossible lengths. He therefore shifted to reflectors and rented a Gregorian reflector that was 60 centimeters (24 inches) long. It wouldn't do either; he wanted longer and larger reflectors and found that none were available for renting. Nor could he afford to have one made for him.

There was nothing to do but grind his own mirrors and build his own telescopes in his spare time. He brought his sister, Caroline, from Hanover in 1772 and began to devote himself to the task of grinding, grinding, grinding. Herschel ground at his mirrors for hours at a time (sixteen hours running on one occasion according to Caroline) while she read to him and fed him.

He experimented with a variety of metal alloys and was the first astronomer to attempt to improve on Newton in this respect. He found that he had to increase the copper content, little by little, to improve the reflectivity. He eventually got his alloy to the point where it reflected 60 percent of the light that fell upon it, far better than was the case with earlier reflectors. In doing this, however, he reached the point where he was compromising the color of the white bronze and beginning to impart a yellow tinge to the image.

He learned how to grind the mirror in such a way as to produce a paraboloid shape efficiently, and finally, in 1774, he had the first telescope he had built himself. It was a Newtonian reflector with a 15-centimeter (6-inch) mirror that was 2.1 meters (7 feet) long and that produced a fortyfold magnification. With it he saw the Great nebula in Orion and clearly made out the rings of Saturn. It was not bad for an amateur.

It was Herschel's intention, however, having tasted this first success, to build larger and larger reflectors. As soon as the 15-centimeter (6-inch) reflector was shown to work, he began to prepare a mirror that was 22.5 centimeters (9 inches) in diameter that would fit into a 3-meter (10-foot) length of telescope. Then he produced a 45-centimeter (18-inch) mirror which he fitted into a telescope that was 6 meters (20 feet) long.

What made this possible and, indeed, what this made still more possible, was a discovery Herschel made in 1781 with his 15-centimeter (6-inch) reflector.

He had been using it to move systematically from one object in the sky to another. He prepared papers on the mountains on the moon, on sunspots, on variable stars (those that changed periodically in brightness), and on the Martian poles. He was the first to note that Mars's axis was tilted at about the same angle as Earth's was, so that Mars had an Earthlike arrangement of seasons except, of course, that the Martian seasons were generally colder than ours since Mars is farther from the sun than we are.

Then, on March 13, 1781, in the course of his systematic study, he came across an object that appeared to be a disc rather than a mere point of light.

The only objects that appear as discs rather than points are planets, satellites, or comets — that is, the larger members of the solar system. Since Herschel knew where all the planets were supposed to be, each with its train of any satellites it might have, he assumed at first he had discovered a new comet and announced it as such. If so, it was a minor discovery, for new comets were (and still are) constantly being discovered.

Further observations, however, showed that the disc had a sharp edge like a planet and not fuzzy boundaries like a comet. Furthermore, when enough observations had been made to calculate an orbit, Herschel (and others who were by now watching the reported object) found that orbit to be nearly circular, like that of a planet, and not very elongated, like that of a comet. What's more, from the slowness of its motion against the stars it had to be considerably farther from the sun than Saturn was — and at the time Saturn was the farthest known planet.

What it amounted to was that Herschel had discovered a new planet, over 2800 million kilometers (1700 million miles) from the Sun, or twice as far from the sun as Saturn was. At one stroke, he had increased the known width of the solar system (barring cometary orbits) four times. Until then, new stars, new satellites, and new comets had been discovered by means of the telescope, but never till then (172 years after the first use of the telescope in astronomy by Galileo) a new *planet*.

Actually, the newly discovered planet is just barely bright enough to be seen by the unaided eye so it had to have been seen innumerable times by casual scanners of the heavens. It was reported some twenty-two times by telescope before Herschel's time, the first time as long before as 1690. It was even included in the star catalogue prepared by Flamsteed a century earlier. He had noted it in the constellation Taurus and had recorded it as 34 Tauri. The combination of its dimness and its slow motion (because it was so far from the sun that the latter's gravitational pull upon it was weak) kept it from appearing to be a planet on the face of it. Nor did astronomers have any reason, before Herschel's time, to return to it again and again in order to note its motion.

It was Herschel's small, but excellent, instrument that clearly showed the new object to be a disc and therefore not a star. It was Herschel who followed it from night to night and recognized its planetary nature, so he deserves the credit as its discoverer.

Herschel tried to name the planet "Georgium Sidus" ("George's Star") in honor of George III, and some astronomers suggested it be named "Herschel" in honor of its discoverer. However, the mythological motif that governed the names of all the other astronomical objects won out. The German astronomer Johann Elert Bode (1747–1826) suggested it be named Uranus after the father of Saturn, as Saturn was the father of Jupiter and Jupiter of Mars, so that one went up the line of generations as one moved outward from Earth. The suggestion was adopted.

The discovery of Uranus made an enormous sensation. Herschel was at once elected to membership in the Royal Society and was awarded its most prestigious honor, the Copley Prize. He was made astronomer to the King at a salary of 300 guineas a year, so that he could abandon his musical career and devote himself to the life of a professional astronomer thereafter. (It also helped that he married a rich widow in 1788.)

The discovery also roused considerable interest among the general public. It was the kind of glamorous finding that could be easily understood by anyone and at no time since Galileo's initial discoveries had the telescope created such excitement.

It was years before the excitement of that moment faded. A quarter-century later when the English poet John Keats (1795–

1821), in his "On First Looking into Chapman's Homer," wished to find a way of expressing the extreme of joyous surprise, said, "Then felt I like some watcher of the skies / When a new planet swims into his ken."

Spurred on by his discovery and new fame, Herschel, in 1781, tried at once to manufacture a 9-meter-long (30-foot) telescope, but failed. To prepare the mirror he needed for that telescope he had to begin by casting a block of metal over 225 kilograms (500 pounds) in weight and found he could not handle that.

He raised his sights anyway. In 1786 he determined to construct a telescope that would have a mirror 122 centimeters (48 inches) across, one that would fit into a tube 12.2 meters (40 feet) long. King George III came through handsomely with 2000 pounds down and 2000 pounds promised toward the huge instrument. Up to forty laborers worked on different aspects of the project under Herschel's personal direction. The huge mirror was beyond even Herschel's formidable industry when it came to grinding, and he designed a mechanical device to do the job.

By the end of 1789, it was erected in the midst of a gigantic framework, looking like a giant cannon poking at the heavens. Once again, the age of monsters had arrived, fat ones this time. Herschel's new, and largest, telescope was large enough for him to crawl into in search of the place of focus.

The value of the large diameter was that in Herschel's hands, the telescope became an enormous light-gathering device. The light-gathering power of a mirror (or a lens) depends on its area and this in turn depends on the square of the diameter. A mirror 122 centimeters (48 inches) in diameter is twice as wide as a 61-centimeter (24-inch) mirror and has 2 × 2 or 4 times the light-gathering power. The larger mirror is eight times the diameter of a 15-centimeter (6-inch) mirror so that Herschel's 1789 pride had 8 × 8 or 64 times the light-gathering power of the little telescope with which he had discovered Uranus.

Although even the largest telescopes did not succeed in magnifying stars to the point where they were more than points of light, an increase in light-gathering power did make them brighter and made visible successively dimmer and dimmer stars.

Even a perfect paraboloidal mirror would not bring all the light of a star to an exact point image even though the star itself cannot be distinguished from a point. Since light consists of waves, a phenomenon called diffraction spreads the light in the image into a small blur.

In later years, it was shown how to calculate this blur, but the early telescope makers learned by trial and error that a well-made mirror of 100 centimeters (4 inches) diameter would just resolve or separate two stars separated in the sky by the second of arc. An eight-inch aperture would go to one-half second, a twelve-inch to one-third second, and so on.

Thus, a large telescope has more possible "resolving power" than a small one. In practice, the turbulence of the earth's atmosphere begins to limit the seeing for telescopes larger than a foot or two in diameter even when these are in ideal locations, such as a remote mountaintop. Telescopes larger than this may fail to give increased resolution, but they do gather more light and so let the astronomer see fainter or more distant objects.

In constructing his giant telescopes, Herschel departed from the Newtonian design by slanting the primary mirror so that it did not send the converging light exactly forward. The focus arrived near the lip of the front aperture and Herschel could lean over to look at the image. This was a "Herschelian reflector" or a "front-view reflector."

The advantage of the Herschelian reflector was that no second mirror was required — and that meant much less grinding. It did mean, however, that Herschel had to be high in the air to do his viewing (something also true of the Newtonian reflector when that was large enough). Exposure to cold winter nights and the danger of falling (the list of astronomers who have fallen off their telescopes is a fairly long one) kept astronomic observation from being an absolute pleasure.

Herschel found that his most useful instrument was the 61-centimeter (20-inch) reflector. With it, in 1787, he located two satellites of Uranus, his own planet. A considerable time after the discovery, these two satellites were named by Herschel's son, John Frederick William (1792–1871). The names the younger Herschel gave them were Titania and Oberon, after the queen and king of the fairies in William Shakespeare's *A Midsummer Night's Dream* rather than after characters in classical mythology.

Herschel's telescopes were the best ever built up to his time and each time he built a bigger and better telescope he used it, once more, to look at everything in the heavens. Each time he made new and startling discoveries.

The 122-centimeter (48-inch) telescope, the largest Herschel built, was no exception. On the first night it could be put to use he turned it to Saturn, his favorite viewing object, and at once discovered two new satellites of Saturn, which came to be known as Mimas and Enceladus, after two giants in Greek mythology. This brought the total known satellites of Saturn to seven.

Still the 122-centimeter (48-inch) reflector was a disappointment. It was too clumsy. It took Herschel and two assistants to move it and make records and the net result of its size was that too much time was spent on mechanics and not enough on seeing.

In addition to that, the large bronze mirrors required constant babying and that was especially true of the largest of them. Herschel's increased copper content had increased reflectivity and light-gathering power, but it had also increased the ease of corrosion. A large proportion of Herschel's time was spent in repolishing the mirror to restore its brightness.

To avoid the problem of tarnishing, it occurred to the French astronomer Alexis Marie de Rochon (1741–1817) to use a platinum alloy in place of a copper alloy for mirrors. The platinum alloy would not be as reflective as the copper alloy, but it would never tarnish. He intended to begin with a 20-centimeter (8-inch) Gregorian reflector some 1.8 meters (6 feet) long. One of the motives behind this, by the way, was to bring back to France the astronomical pre-eminence which she had held in Cassini's time but which now Herschel had brought to Great Britain.

About 100 pounds of platinum were finally shipped to France from Spain in 1793, but France was in turmoil at the time and an expensive telescope didn't look like a good idea. The platinum was diverted to the manufacture of standard weights for the new metric system — which was, on the whole, a better use for it. No platinum-alloy telescope mirror was ever built, but it was no loss, for such telescopes would not have been practical. Platinum is too heavy, too rare, too expensive.

The Galaxy

It was inevitable that with his excellent instruments in hand, Herschel would make his attempt to solve the problem that had been too much for Bradley and his long refractors. That was the measurement of stellar parallax.

Herschel did not plan to fix a telescope toward the zenith and try to measure slight deviations of a star relative to the Earth-base of observation as Bradley had done. Instead, he planned to follow a more flexible system which once Galileo had suggested.

The trick was to observe two stars that were very close to each other. It was logical to suppose that they weren't really very close to each other but simply happened to lie in very nearly the same direction from Earth. One of the two, the dimmer one almost certainly, would be so far away as to show virtually no parallax. It could therefore be considered as the stationary one. The brighter one of the pair might, on the other hand, be close enough to show a detectable parallax. This would show up as a small yearly shift with reference to the dim stationary star near which it was.

Herschel began to look for appropriate "double stars" for the purpose and at once began to find them. He found double stars that were so very close together that they would have been seen as a single point of light in any telescope in the world other than his own large, high-resolving instruments.

In fact, he found too many. If all the stars were individual stars, strewn randomly through space, then it is easy to calculate in how many cases there should be where two stars of more than a certain brightness would be so nearly in the same direction as to be within a certain distance of each other.

The chance is, for instance, only 1 in 300,000 that two stars of a certain brightness should be within 5 seconds of arc of each other and Herschel found many more cases of such neighborliness than could be expected from such odds. In 1784 he prepared a catalogue of 434 very closely spaced pairs of stars.

The conclusion was that the stars were not distributed randomly. The stars that seemed very closely spaced must be closely spaced in actuality in almost every case. In only a few exceptional cases could it be just the accident of same direction. These stars which are close together in reality are called "binary stars."

If Halley's discovery of the proper motion of stars initiated the era of stellar observation, Herschel's discovery of binary stars brought the era to full growth. Herschel, with his large telescopes, was the father of astronomy beyond the solar system.

Herschel carefully recorded the position of the fainter star in comparison with the brighter one in the case of each binary star he observed. To do so, he found the usual filar micrometer useless because the thinnest threads he used were too thick for the purpose. He set up a "lamp-micrometer" therefore. This consisted of two pinholes at a distance of ten feet through which light from a lamp showed. He watched the pinholes with his left eye and the telescope image with his right and adjusted the pinholes till they exactly matched the binary star.

Twenty years later, in 1804, he returned to his binaries and found that in three cases, including that of the bright star Castor, he found a perceptible change in the relative positions of the two components of the binary system. The motion was enough to make it seem to Herschel that the dimmer star was circling the brighter one in very much the same fashion that the Earth circles the sun.

When Newton's law of universal gravitation had been announced in 1687, it had been applied only to the solar system. That did not actually make it seem that the objective "universal" was bombastic, for it was honestly thought that the solar system was virtually the universe. Only the stars existed outside and since they seemed to be motionless except for the apparent motion inflicted upon the entire sky by the rotation of the Earth, the law of gravitation was irrelevant to them.

Once it came to be understood that the stars were bodies which *were* in motion, then it was fair to wonder whether Newton's law was truly universal or whether it was merely a local phenomenon of the solar system.

Herschel's observation was the first piece of direct evidence that Newton's law of universal gravitation really was universal, and steadily increasing knowledge in the century and three-quarters since has but confirmed it further.

In all these studies of binary stars, however, Herschel did not succeed in detecting or measuring stellar parallax. In that respect, the stars remained inviolate.

Herschel also used his magnificent instruments to study the cloudy patches in the sky called "nebulae," patches which earlier instruments had been able to detect but could do no more than that.

These had first been studied systematically by a French astronomer, Charles Messier (1730–1817), who was primarily a comet-detector and wanted to locate and mark these in order that they not be confused with comets in the future. For the purpose, he used two relatively small achromatic refractors, the larger of which was only 1.5 meters (5 feet) long. In 1784 he drew up a list of 109 of the nebulae, which he carefully located and which have ever since been known as M1, M2, and so on, according to their position on his list.

Beginning in 1786, Herschel turned his much greater telescopes on these objects and on many similar ones that Messier did not record. By 1802, he had compiled a three-volume catalogue listing a total of 2500 of them.

Herschel found that some objects that looked like mere patches of light in smaller telescopes seemed to be vast crowds of stars when seen with his. He was the first therefore to detect "star clusters." Some nebulae he could not resolve into stars. They remained hazy patches of light even in his telescopes and for a while he wondered if they might be very enormous collections of stars so distant they could not be resolved. (He abandoned this notion after a while, but the problem was to come up again in time.)

In the Milky Way, he found the reverse of the luminous patches. He found dark, starless patches surrounded by the blaze of numerous stars. He thought that he just happened to be looking in a direction in which there were no stars, a kind of starless tunnel through the Milky Way, and said, "Surely this is a hole in the heavens." This was a matter that was to come up again, too.

Perhaps the grandest perspective that his large telescopes gave Herschel was this — that for the first time, he could study enough stars to come to some overall conclusions concerning the star system as a whole.

For instance, once it was shown that stars had proper motions, that they moved through space, there was no reason to think that the sun was exceptional and motionless. But if the sun moved, could that be demonstrated? Could the speed and direction of the sun's motion be worked out?

With his telescopes, Herschel could detect and measure the proper motion of a larger number of stars than anyone before him could. Ordinarily, one might expect that the motions would be random, as many in one direction as in another. This, however, proved not to be so. In one section of the sky, the stars seemed to be moving generally apart from each other. In the opposite section, they seemed to be moving together.

This could most easily be explained by assuming the sun was itself moving toward the section in which the stars seemed to be moving apart and away from the section in which they were moving together. Herschel suggested in 1805, therefore, that the sun was moving in the direction of the constellation of Hercules at the speed of about 17.5 kilometers (12 miles) per second.

In a way, this was a more disturbing event than the Copernican revolution. Copernicus had dethroned the Earth as center of the universe, but he had replaced it with the sun. The solar system was still the center of the universe, and the Earth, as part of the solar system, still had a share in that soul-satisfying position.

Nor had the work of Kepler, Galileo, Newton, Cassini, or even Halley done anything to disturb that.

Now, however, Herschel had presented logical evidence that the sun was not the center of the universe at all. If the Earth moved as the other planets did, the sun moved as the other stars did. Indeed, for all anyone could tell, after Herschel's observation, there was no center at all and mankind was faced with the rather chilling thought of a universe with no center at all — and in which there could be, therefore, no physical argument for the central importance of mankind.

Yet perhaps something could be determined about the center if one could get a notion of the overall shape of the clustering stars that made up the universe — provided there was a shape at all. Perhaps stars were just randomly distributed through infinite space in all directions as Nicholas of Cusa had thought.

At first glance, it might seem that the stars were indeed randomly distributed over the sky. We can see stars in every direction, and with the telescope we can see more stars in every direction — and still more with each rise in excellence of the telescopes, and in every direction.

Yet this rule must be modified in one way. The Milky Way, which girdles the sky, is extraordinarily rich in extraordinarily faint stars. As early as 1750, the English astronomer Thomas Wright (1711–1786) had suggested a reason for this. He pointed out that the system of stars might not extend outward in every direction forever but only for a limited distance, and that the overall shape of the system might be that of a grindstone or lens. If, from our vantage point on the Earth, we looked along the short axis of the lens, we would see relatively few stars and we would be aware of the darkness of space behind them. If we looked in the direction of the long axis, we would see an immense number of stars fading out into a luminous haze and obscuring the more distant darkness — and it would be this luminous haze that was the Milky Way.

This seemed an attractive and logical thought, and Herschel sought to test it by a more minute observation, that is, by actually counting the number of stars he could see with his excellent telescopes in various directions. To attempt to count them *all* would, of course, be impractical so, in 1784, he took what amounted to a poll of the heavens.

He chose 683 regions, well scattered over the sky, and counted the stars visible in his telescope in each one. He found that the number of stars per unit area of sky rose steadily as one approached the Milky Way. It was greatest in the plane of the Milky Way and least in the direction at right angles to the plane.

This fit right in with Wright's theory and, by actually counting the stars, Herschel could estimate the relative lengths of the minimum and maximum diameter of the star system. He decided that the long diameter of the system was about 800 times the average distance between two stars — say the distance between Sirius and the sun. The short diameter of the system was about 150 times this average distance.

If the stars are scattered through this system in the fashion they are scattered in our own sun's neighborhood, there would be about 300 million stars in it altogether, about 50,000 times as many as could be seen with the unaided eye. Most of these are, of course, in the Milky Way, which could, therefore, lend its name to the entire system. From the Greek name for the Milky Way, the expression "galaxy" came to be applied to the lens-shaped system.

Herschel, therefore, can be considered the discoverer of the Galaxy and to be the first to place a definite shape, size, and star number to the star system of which our sun is a member. Once again, astronomy had enlarged mankind's concept of the universe and once again it was as though the entire universe had been penetrated.

In ancient and medieval times, it had been thought that the Earth itself was the chief portion of the universe, with all the heavenly bodies mere adjuncts. With the invention of the telescope, the Copernican system came to be accepted and the solar system, enormously larger than the Earth, became the essential portion of the universe, with the stars mere adjuncts. Now, Herschel's large telescopes made the Galaxy, enormously larger than the solar system, the essential portion of the universe and there was no reason to think that anything lay beyond to form even adjuncts.

In one respect, Herschel's finding offered some sort of comfort. Since the Milky Way was more or less equally bright through its entire circuit of the sky, it seemed reasonable to suppose that the sun and its attendant planets were at or near the center of the Galaxy and, therefore, of the universe. This was not because of any compelling necessity for the sun to be there — but only because it just happened to be there. Nevertheless, to be near the center of things, for whatever reason, seemed appropriate to self-important mankind.

The Dark Lines

For a generation, Herschel and his large reflectors dominated astronomy, but the difficulty of keeping the metal mirrors polished was as nagging a problem for the wide instruments as chromatic aberration had been for the long refractors. It was clear that if large pieces of perfect glass could be manufactured, out of which large lenses could be made that would never need polishing, the refractor might take the lead again.

The necessary advance did take place, thanks to the Swiss artisan Pierre Louis Guinand (1748–1824). He began as a woodworker, then turned to the making of clock cases, and then to the making of clock bells. In working with metal, he found that he got a more even (or "homogeneous") alloy if he stirred it while it was molten — an obvious fact *after* it was discovered.

Guinand had been interested, in an amateur fashion, in the manufacture of glass as well, teaching himself elementary chemistry for the purpose. In 1798, he began to stir his molten glass and for some years experimented with different kinds of stirrers. Eventually, he learned to obtain glass that was more homogeneous over larger volumes than had ever before been possible. Since the composition of such glass was particularly even from end to end, the manner in which it refracted light was equally even.

Earlier, large pieces of glass had varied in refractivity from point to point so that no true focus could be reached. Attempts to manufacture a lens of more than four inches in width generally ended in uselessness. Guinand, however, began the routine manufacture of lenses six inches in width.

Then, too, it was possible to mix into the glass heavy chemicals which could be relied on, with proper stirring, to spread evenly through the glass. This meant, in particular, that flint glass, with its lead content, could be manufactured in better quality. The stirring even helped to remove air bubbles.

In order to support his experiments, Guinand joined a German optical firm in 1807 and there combined forces with a young optician, Joseph von Fraunhofer (1787–1826).

Fraunhofer extended and improved Guinand's methods and managed to produce a 24-centimeter (9.5-inch) lens of excellent quality which was placed into a telescope that was mounted first at Dorpat, Russia (in what is now the Estonian S.S.R.), and then in the Pulkovo Observatory, ten miles south of St. Petersburg (Leningrad). This refractor, which was 4.3 meters (14 feet) long, was the largest and best refractor that had ever been manufactured and remained so for years.

The Dorpat refractor was not as large as Herschel's great telescopes, but now the shoe was on the other foot. It was the wide reflectors that were large and clumsy (as once the long refractors had been). Herschel's telescopes had to be maneuvered by pulleys and straining muscle power so that far too much of the available time consisted of getting ready and only a little time was left for observation. The Dorpat refractor, on the other hand, was attached to an axis which allowed it to move up and down, while the axis itself was attached to a wheel that could turn horizontally. The whole was so exquisitely balanced through Fraunhofer's meticulous design that the telescope could be moved by the push of a fingertip.

What's more, the Dorpat refractor could be adjusted to a certain up-down declination and then be locked in place. It could next be made to move very slowly by clockwork in a way that just compensated for the rotation of the Earth, so that a single star would remain in focus as it moved across the sky.

Part of Fraunhofer's success with his glass mixes arose from the fact that he carefully studied the refracting properties of every bit of glass he worked with. And in this he encountered difficulties that led him to a discovery far greater than the Dorpat refractor — though, to be sure, that was not recognized at the time.

The difficulty is that the amount of refraction produced by a particular bit of glass varies with the portion of the spectrum that falls upon it. The red light at one end of the spectrum might be refracted through only half the angle that the violet light at the other end of the spectrum is. In order to compare the refraction of one bit of glass with another, Fraunhofer had to use the same color each time, so as to make sure that the differences from glass to glass were due to the nature of the glass and not to the light itself.

Even so, there were variations in refraction within a single color. As one moved along the red part of the spectrum closer and closer to the orange, the angle of refraction grew steadily greater. To achieve the kind of precision Fraunhofer needed, it was necessary to make sure that the same part of the same color was always used. It was difficult, however, to hit the same part each time. There were no landmarks.

At least, there had been no landmarks before Fraunhofer's time. Now, however, there came a change.

Newton, and others who had followed him, had allowed light to emerge through a small circular hole before passing through the prism. The result was that a spectrum was produced which consisted of successive circles of light of successive shades of color. These circles overlapped and blurred.

Fraunhofer, however, had the light pass through a narrow slit before reaching the prism (something Newton himself had suggested, but not done). Fraunhofer's spectra therefore consisted of a succession of vertical lines of light of successive shades of color which overlapped only very slightly.

The spectra from lamps did not show a continuous spectrum as sunlight did. Instead, it produced light of a restricted group of colors so that there were single bright lines, well separated, each an image of the slit. One type of spectrum showed a close pair of lines in the yellow-orange. These seemed to be in a fixed position and Fraunhofer used these lines, successfully, to test the refracting properties of his glass.

The light from lamps, however, was dim and Fraunhofer would have been happier if he could use brilliant sunlight. He wondered if, perhaps, against the general illumination of the solar spectrum there might not be the production of light at different places of greater intensity than usual. By using his slit, then, he could see lines of brightness against a less bright background.

In 1802, an English chemist, William Hyde Wollaston (1766–1828), *had* seen a few marks in the solar spectrum but they had been dark ones, places where light was deficient, and the report had been generally ignored. Now, in 1814, with much better instrumentation, Fraunhofer studied the solar spectrum and found his lines — not bright ones as he expected, but dark ones, as Wollaston had reported. Some, in fact, were almost completely black. Nor were there just a few, as Wollaston had reported, but a great many.

By 1817 he was convinced that what he was observing was a real phenomenon. He counted some 750 lines altogether, and the most prominent of these (which are now called "Fraunhofer lines") he lettered in order, from A in the deep red to I in the deep violet. He was convinced that the lines were always in the same place relative to each other and to the general background of light and that they, too, could be used as landmarks in refraction testing.

The device Fraunhofer used to study the spectrum he called a "spectroscope" ("spectrum-seeing"). It consisted not only of a slit and a prism, but of a small telescope, too, that would focus light upon the slit, and a device to measure accurately the angle through which the light was refracted.

Fraunhofer used his spectroscope to study the light from the moon and from some of the planets and found that those lines he could see in moonlight and planetlight were in the same relative positions as the equivalent lines in sunlight. This was not surprising since the moon and the planets shone by reflected light, so that in observing their light, he was still observing sunlight.

Fraunhofer also turned his spectroscope on some of the brighter stars and so was the first to study stellar spectra. Here he found that the line pattern changed. Some lines duplicated those in the solar spectrum, but others formed strange patterns in ways that varied from star to star. This showed that whatever it was that was causing the lines to exist, it was in the astronomical bodies themselves and not, for instance, in Earth's atmosphere. If the latter had been the case, the stars would all show the same line pattern the sun did.

In studying the action of light passing through a narrow slit, Fraunhofer was aware that the light would bend slightly about each lip of the slit. This means that the light passing through the slit and falling on some opaque barrier would produce a slit of light a little wider than the slit through which it had passed. This phenomenon is called "diffraction."

Fraunhofer thought he might study this effect and learn to allow for it if he began by accentuating it. He placed very thin wires between the lips of the slit, parallel to the lips and evenly spaced. This, in effect, produced a series of successive, very fine slits.

To his surprise, he did not accentuate the diffraction. Instead he found that sunlight passing through the slit produced a bright image, slightly broadened as before, but that on each side of the line of light were a pair of spectra, the outer one fainter than the inner. It turned out that the various parts of the spectrum were diffracted to varying degrees, progressively more and more as one went from violet to red. Dividing a slit into fractions accentuated this spectral difference and produced spectra in reverse to those produced by a prism since red was least refracted but most diffracted.

Fraunhofer had produced spectra without a prism and rightly reasoned he could do it any time he had light passing through anything that was interrupted by finely spaced opaque lines. He therefore made fine parallel scratches on a glass plate with a diamond and produced better spectra than before. He had produced the first "diffraction grating."

Parallax at Last

Fraunhofer did more than produce superb lenses and exquisitely delicate telescope mountings. He made his telescopes into precision instruments by supplying each with filar microscopes superior to anything that had yet been seen in delicacy and accuracy. This, combined with the automatic drive of the telescope that kept stars in focus over a period of time, began to make it possible to measure angular distances to a hundredth of a second of arc for declination and to a thousandth of a second of time in right ascension.

The man to make proper use of this accuracy was the German astronomer Friedrich Wilhelm Bessel (1784–1846), who began life as an accountant but who taught himself astronomy. By 1810 he had become well enough known for his work of recalculating the orbit of Halley's comet to be given the job of supervising the construction of an observatory at Königsberg in East Prussia (now Kaliningrad, and part of the Soviet Union).

Telescopic leadership, which had begun in Italy with Galileo, and which had passed to France with Cassini and to Great Britain with Herschel, now moved on to Germany with Bessel.

Bessel worked hard with every instrument he had in order to correct it for all its minor errors. Where an attachment of the mounting is supposed to be absolutely level, it never is *absolutely*. Right angles are never *exactly* right angles; screw pitches are never *precisely* even all the way across. Bessel used to say that every astronomical instrument was made twice, first in the shop of the artisan who made it as expertly as he could, second in the astronomical observatory where the astronomer carefully worked out its errors and, by meticulously allowing for them, made the instrument into a more nearly perfect device than it had been when it left the artisan's hands.

Bessel used as his basic data Bradley's carefully prepared star catalogue which was the best up to that time. He went on to allow for the shifts in the apparent positions of stars due to their own motion, to aberration of light, to nutation and refraction, and so on, then further allowing for instrumental errors in his own observations.

In 1818 Bessel produced a new and excellent star catalogue containing 50,000 stars. It was by far the largest and best item of that sort produced up to then.

With new levels of accuracy available to him now for plotting the positions of stars and for measuring tiny shifts, Bessel determined to tackle the problem that had been concerning astronomers since the time of Copernicus three centuries before, the problem which had defeated both Bradley and Herschel — the stellar parallax.

For the purpose, he needed a specimen of a new instrument called a "heliometer" ("sun-measure"). It was so named because the first instrument of the sort had been used to measure the diameter of the sun. The French mathematician Pierre Bouguer (1698–1758) had used a telescope containing two equal lenses, each of which produced an image of the sun. By adjusting the positions of the lenses so that the two images exactly coincided, Bouguer could, from the focal length of the lenses and the distance by which they were separated, calculate the angular diameter of the sun with unprecedented precision.

The English instrument-maker Jesse Ramsden improved the device by using two half-lenses. By manipulating these, the images of two stars, ordinarily quite widely separated, could be brought into coincidence, and distances could be measured accurately over a considerable range.

Bessel needed a delicate modification of this and it was up to Fraunhofer to produce it. Fraunhofer arranged to have the two half-lenses adjusted by a delicate screw working against a scale that could be read off by a small microscope.

Fraunhofer died in 1826, at the age of thirty-nine, before the instrument could be finished, but others carried on, and in the end Bessel had it. By 1837, he was ready to observe shifts in star positions (after allowing for all other motions and for instrument error) and thus see if he could detect the elusive parallax.

For his target, he chose a dim 5th-magnitude star in the constellation Cygnus (the Swan). The only name it had was 61 Cygni because it was the sixty-first listed in that constellation in a particular catalogue. Judging by its brightness there was no reason to think that it was particularly close to us nor that it was likely to have a parallax large enough to measure.

In 1814, however, the Italian astronomer Giuseppi Piazzi (1746–1826) had been systematically detecting and measuring the proper motion of stars and had discovered that 61 Cygni moved at the rate of 5.2 seconds of arc per year. This was an amazingly rapid motion, more rapid than any other proper motion known at the time. Since it was moving so much more rapidly than other stars, it seemed reasonable to suppose that it was closer to us than other stars.

As his reference stars, Bessel used two still dimmer ones, one of which was about 8 minutes of arc away from 61 Cygni and the other 12 minutes of arc away. Neither of the reference stars had any detectable proper motion. The combination of dimness and motionlessness made it reasonable to suppose that the reference stars were very far away and would have indetectable parallactic shifts.

Bessel then undertook a careful measurement, to a small fraction of a second of arc, of the distance of 61 Cygni from each of the two reference stars numerous times over the space of a year. Allowing for everything that was not parallax, he discovered that 61 Cygni was changing its position very slightly in exactly the fashion one would expect of stellar parallax.

By 1838 he was able to announce that 61 Cygni made a small ellipse in the sky, mirroring Earth's orbital motion, and that the greatest displacement from the average positions was 0.31 seconds of arc.

This meant that 61 Cygni was 690,000 times as far away from the Earth as the sun was. It was about 150 million million kilometers (65 million million miles) away. Since light travels at about 300,000 kilometers (186,000 miles) per second, it means that it would take about eleven years for light to reach us from 61 Cygni. We can therefore say that 61 Cygni is eleven light-years away from us. This is more than five times the distance that Halley had thought, a century before, might separate us from Sirius.

At last, the stars had succumbed to the persistence of astronomers. For the first time, the distance of a star was measured and instantly the scale of the universe was enormously increased. Since Cassini's measurement of the parallax of Mars a century and a half before, astronomers had grown used to thinking of distances of thousands of millions of kilometers. Now, suddenly, the visualization had to be expanded to millions of millions of kilometers to encompass the stars, and only the nearest stars at that.

The fact that the technique of instrument-making had at last made it possible for Bessel to detect the stellar parallax made it certain that others would try and succeed at about the same time.

At Dorpat, for instance, the German-Russian astronomer Friedrich Georg Wilhelm von Struve (1793–1864) was using Fraunhofer's great refractor to measure the position of the bright star Vega relative to nearby reference stars. He chose Vega, first because it is the fourth brightest star and the second brightest of those stars that could be seen high in the sky in the northern hemisphere and, second, because it had a proper motion of 0.35 seconds of arc per year and any star that had a proper motion at all had to be somewhat close to us. To be sure, Sirius is brighter still and has a still greater proper motion, but Vega is in such a position relative to the Earth that its parallax could be expected to be a circle rather than an ellipse and therefore more easily detected.

Struve could not obtain his results quickly enough to forestall Bessel, who had the honor of being first. Still, in 1840, Struve announced the parallax of Vega to be 0.29 seconds of arc, a little smaller than that of 61 Cygni, so that Vega was a little the farther of the two. Actually, Struve's work was not nearly as precise as Bessel's and the Vega results were a little high. The actual parallax of Vega is less than half that which Struve reported and it is actually twenty-seven light-years away.

In the same decade, a Scottish astronomer, Thomas Henderson (1798–1844), was working on the problem, too. He had an opportunity denied the other two for he was in the southern hemisphere, serving as director of an observatory at the Cape of Good Hope at the southern tip of Africa. There he had an opportunity of observing Alpha Centauri, a star that is not visible in European latitudes.

Alpha Centauri is the third brightest star in the sky, brighter than Vega. Furthermore, its proper motion is 3.7 seconds of arc per year, not quite as high as that of 61 Cygni, but far higher than that of any other bright star. The combination of high proper motion and great brightness seemed a hopeful augury. What's more, Alpha Centauri is a double star with a considerable separation between the two components, as such things go, and yet the two stars completed their orbit rapidly. The rapid completion of the orbit argued that the two components of the Alpha Centauri double star were close together and the fact that they *seemed* far apart in comparison to other double stars, must, again, mean that Alpha Centauri was close to us.

For all these reasons, Henderson was quite confident that if any star could show a parallax, Alpha Centauri was the one. He by no means possessed instruments of the accuracy of Bessel or Struve, but he had indeed picked the right star. It showed a parallax large enough for him to pick up. He completed his observations a long time before Bessel did, actually, but he waited till he had returned to take up a post in Edinburgh before getting to work to complete the mathematical manipulations of the raw data. He did not publish his results till 1839 and the credit goes to the first to publish — Bessel, in this case.

Henderson's announced parallax was 0.91 seconds of arc. Later, more accurate measurements reduced this to 0.76 seconds of arc, but even so that remains, to this day, the largest parallax of any star known. Of all the stars, those of the Alpha Centauri system are the closest known, being at a distance of 4.3 light-years.*

From the known distance of the stars, the actual brightness (or "luminosity") is easily calculated. The brighter star of the Alpha Centauri pair is just about as luminous as our sun, the other is some- what less luminous and 61 Cygni is considerably less luminous. Vega, on the other hand, is considerably more luminous than the sun.

Thus, Copernicus and Nicholas of Cusa were demonstrated cor- rect beyond reasonable doubt. Earth moves about the sun, and the sun is itself a star among innumerable others and, judging by the first measurements made, a star of only average size. It was another blow to man's self-importance.

To be sure, the technique of measuring stellar distance by parallax was sharply limited to those stars less than 100 light-years away — a very small number. As late as 1900, the distances of only seventy- two stars had been determined by this method. All the countless millions of objects beyond had to await techniques more powerful still.

Using his magnificent instruments, Bessel made another discovery

---

* There is a third star, a very dim one, that circles the two components of Alpha Cen- tauri, and this is, at this time in its orbit, a trifle closer than the other two. It is called "Proxima Centauri."

that was second in drama only to the detection of stellar parallax. He studied Sirius in 1844 in an attempt to determine its parallax and noted instead that as it proceeded in the course of its proper motion, it pursued a curved path that could *not* be due to parallax.

Bessel suggested that Sirius was curving out of its straight-line motion because of the gravitational attraction of some other body. If Sirius were indeed an object with a mass of the order of magnitude of our sun, as now seemed certain, it could not possibly be forced to deviate from its path so much except by another mass that was sun-size.

Since Bessel could see nothing in the vicinity of Sirius to account for this, he was forced to postulate the presence of a "dark companion" — nothing less than an invisible star, a star that had grown invisible, perhaps, because it had cooled off and its fires had died. Its mass and its gravitational pull remained, however.

Bessel found that the bright star, Procyon, also moved in a curved path and postulated a dark companion for that star, too.

Thus, we have the paradoxical notion that as telescopes became instruments of precision they proved the agents for the discovery of objects that could *not* be seen.

Herschel, who had died at the good old age of eighty-three in 1822, did not live to see the renewed triumph of refractors. After his death, however, his son, John, carried the torch. The elder Herschel's 122-centimeter (40-inch) reflector had deteriorated to the point where it was useless, but the 61-centimeter (20-inch) reflector was still in good operating order and John Herschel went over his father's work on double stars and nebulae. In 1833, he decided to do for the southern hemisphere what his father had done for the northern.

He went south in January 1834, and for four years his base of operations was at Cape Colony, South Africa, where he had succeeded Henderson. He took the 61-centimeter (20-inch) reflector with him and, using it, swept the southern skies with the same diligence and thoroughness that had marked his father's work. This required considerable hard physical labor, for maneuvering the large telescope was not the easiest task in the world. He studied and described some 2000 double stars and some 2000 nebulae, publishing the results in a great treatise in 1847.

While engaged in this work, John Herschel attempted to do more than estimate the brightness of stars by looking at them — as had been done since the time of Hipparchus in 130 B.C. After all, with the study of large numbers of dim stars by telescope, it became steadily more important to try to reduce the determination of magnitude to some objective method.

Herschel used a small lense to produce a tiny image of the moon, then manipulated the lens until the image seemed to be as bright as the star in question. From this he calculated the brightness of the stars. Meanwhile, at about the same time, the German astronomer Carl August von Steinheil (1801–1870) used similar methods for comparing one star with another, a technique that gave somewhat better results. These were very crude procedures, but they marked the beginning of astronomic "photometery" ("light-measure").

About this time, also, the German physiologist Ernst Heinrich Weber (1795–1878) had worked out the manner in which the eye responded to changing amounts of light. Combining this with the work of Herschel and Steinheil, astronomers were able to tell, for the first time, that a star of one magnitude was about two and a half times brighter than a star of the next higher magnitude.

When John Herschel returned to Great Britain in 1838, he abandoned astronomic observation. It was rather symbolic of the end of an era that in 1839 the 122-centimeter (40-inch) telescope, which had been standing in place for years, had finally grown so rickety as to be dangerous. It was finally lowered and dismantled. Part of the tube had been crushed when a tree fell on it during a storm but the remainder still exists.

And so does the large metal mirror which, in its time, was the wonder of the world.

6. Making Light Do More

The Leviathan

The battle between the reflector and the refractor in the mid-1800s seemed almost to be a battle between Great Britain and Germany respectively. Once Bessel's work had made the refractor a temporary victor, a British astronomer took up the cause of the reflector and determined to surpass even Herschel in this respect.

The astronomer was William Parsons (1800–1867), whose family owned land in Ireland. He graduated from Oxford in 1822, sat in Parliament for a dozen years thereafter, and in 1841 succeeded to his father's title and became 3rd Earl of Rosse. In 1845 he took a seat in the House of Lords. Surely few astronomers of note could boast such evidence of blue blood.

What Rosse was interested in was a project of building the largest telescope the world had ever seen, of using it to make light do more than it had ever done by collecting more of it into one place. He had the room for the telescope on the family estate at Birr, which was located in almost the geographic center of Ireland. He had plenty of money, his time was his own, he had the necessary technical knowledge, and he could train his tenants to do the work.

His first problem was that of casting a large metal mirror without cracking it. Unfortunately, Herschel had never published his own methods for managing this successfully and Rosse had to start from scratch. He spent five years working out a suitable alloy of copper and tin, and then, finding the alloy brittle, decided to cast mirrors in separate pieces which were to be put together by soldering and riveting. The mirror would then be covered with tin which was heated to melting and the whole would be very slowly cooled thereafter.

In the course of seventeen years of experimenting, he succeeded in producing first a 38-centimeter (15-inch) mirror, then a 61-centimeter (24-inch) one, and finally, in 1840, a 91-centimeter (36-inch) one that was almost as large as Herschel's largest.

Rosse designed a reflector for the 91-centimeter (36-inch) mirror that would be Newtonian in nature. He decided that if he tipped the mirror so as to receive the image at the lip of the aperture, according to the Herschelian system, the sharpness of the focus would suffer. Besides that, the observer's warm body, standing at the opening of the telescope in the cool night air, would produce rising currents of warmer air, which would slightly refract light and interfere with seeing.

This is an indication of the troubles arising from the increasing excellence of the telescopes themselves. The amount by which air refracts light depends upon its temperature. If the light of a star passes through layers of different temperature, the final direction of the ray of light as it reaches the telescope is different at different times, as the temperature layers shift and vary. In fact, with slight changes in temperature here and there, the direction of the ray of light could change very rapidly — to only a slight degree, but very rapidly.

This change of direction with time seems to place the star in different positions and even with the unaided eye this can be seen. It is what we mean when we say that a star is "twinkling." When the air is clear and even-temperatured then the twinkling is at a minimum and accurate observations can be made. It is a time of "good-seeing."

Unfortunately, as telescopes grew more and more efficient, slight shifts in position due to changes in air temperature were magnified. A shift that would have been unnoticeable in earlier telescopes were, by the time the mid-1800s telescopes were constructed, visible and annoying.

The telescopes Rosse was planning, then, would not find periods of good-seeing often, and this fact was made worse by the site on which he planned to build it. His estate was in central Ireland and, however desirable the situation might be for some purposes, it was terrible for astronomic observation. It was rarely possible to expect good-seeing before midnight for only by then did the air have a chance to settle down to even temperature and, usually, that was the time for the clouds to come in.

Using the 91-centimeter (36-inch) reflector when he could, however, Rosse satisfied himself that he was using it to better advantage than Herschel had used his giant telescope which had had a 122-centimeter (48-inch) mirror. The years of experimentation had allowed Rosse, apparently, to work out better systems for casting and grinding mirrors. For instance, he had ground the mirror while it was largely immersed in water held at a constant temperature, and the grinding tools were powered by a small steam engine.

With the 91-centimeter (36-inch) reflector a success, in his opinion, Rosse, in 1842, set about an attempt to defeat Herschel in sheer size as well as in mere excellence. He began to cast a mirror double his largest and made one that was 184 centimeters (72 inches) in diameter, a width equal to the height of a tall man. This would be half again as wide as Herschel's largest and would have 2.25 times its area and, therefore, its light-collecting power.

The mirror was cast on April 13, 1842, allowed to cool slowly for sixteen weeks, was ground — and then it cracked just before it could be placed in the telescope. More castings had to be made and it was only the fifth that was satisfactory for use.

By the end of the year, Rosse was constructing the telescope tube. It was made of wooden planks, strengthened by iron hoops. It was 17 meters (56 feet) long and 2.4 meters (8 feet) in diameter. To protect it from the wind, the tube was mounted between two walls of masonry each 22 meters (72 feet) long and 17 meters (56 feet) high. The tube, secure between these two walls, which were lined up in the north-south direction, was itself virtually confined to viewing along the north-south meridian. It could be pointed a little to the east or west, but only 15° at most. To move the tube up and down required the hard labor of two men at a windlass.

Mounting the mirror inside the tube was quite a task, too, since the mirror weighed 3600 kilograms (4 tons) and it had to be inserted in such a way that it would be wedged firmly and would not move. It was not until February 1845 that the telescope could be used and tested.

Still competing with Herschel, Rosse used his 184-centimeter (72-inch) reflector (popularly known as "Leviathan") to study the various nebulae that Herschel had previously studied. These he saw in unprecedented detail and almost at once detected that the object known as M51 in Messier's list had filaments which made the whole seem to be shaped like a spiral. Thus, in 1845, the first of the "spiral nebulae" was discovered. Some fourteen more were discovered by Rosse in the first five years of the Leviathan's existence, so it was clear they were common phenomena.

In 1848 Rosse studied a hazy patch which had first been noted in 1731 by the English astronomer John Bevis (1693–1771). Messier had listed it as number one in his catalogue. Rosse found M1 to be an irregular patch of haze with bright filaments running irregularly through it. The filaments apparently reminded Rosse of the legs of a crab, for he called it the "Crab nebula," a name it bears to this day.

The time was to come when astronomers might well believe that Rosse's Leviathan had earned its keep merely by discovering spiral nebulae and by the first careful study of the Crab nebula. Both objects were to come to be of the highest importance in later times.

Rosse, however, was not to know that, and he had to be satisfied with these feats with no hint of what they would some day come to mean — for that was all the Leviathan did. The telescope had taken three years to build, had cost 12,000 pounds in days when that sum of money meant far more than it does today, and was, technically, an excellent instrument. Because of the horrible weather, however, the telescopes's unmaneuverability, and its inability to see very far to east or west of the meridian, it was nearly useless.

It could view particular objects of interest for only the period when they were near the meridian. It was then necessary to wait for twenty-four hours for a second look, and two successive periods of good-seeing virtually never took place.

It almost seemed, however, as though Rosse were more interested in building telescopes than in using them, anyway, and he certainly achieved his life's ambition of building the largest telescope in the world. If it proved a white elephant it was, at least, indisputably an elephant. It continued to be used, periodically, by Rosse and by others for some eighty years. In 1908, forty-one years after Rosse's death, it had grown rickety and dangerous and it was dismantled.

Rosse's adventure had three important results.

First, it showed that the building of large telescopes was a practical matter. Unlike Herschel, Rosse published his methods and these were used as guides by others and as a base from which improvements could be made.

Second, the sad failure in the battle with weather made it plain that a telescope was useless if the atmosphere did not cooperate, and astronomers began to consider not only the building of a telescope but the selection of a site for it.

Third, it made it clear that although a giant telescope could be built, it could not be used very well unless methods were devised for moving it easily and for pointing it at any part of the sky.

Thus, a Scottish engineer, James Nasmyth (1808–1890), famous for having invented the steam hammer in 1839, interested himself in telescope-making and finally produced a 51-centimeter (20-inch) mirror. This he introduced into a Cassegrain-Newtonian reflector, which he placed on a large turntable. Sitting at his ease, with his eye at the eyepiece near the rear of the telescope, he could, by turning a small hand-wheel, direct the instrument to any part of the sky.

More elaborate were the ambitions of William Lassell (1799–1880), an English brewer who grew interested in astronomy as a hobby. He, like Rosse, wanted to build large reflectors and for that reason visited Rosse's estate in 1844 to inspect the workshops and watch what was going on in connection with the construction of the Leviathan.

In one respect, Lassell had already gone beyond Rosse, for he was the first to apply to reflectors the type of mounting Fraunhofer had placed on the Dorpat refractor. Lassell had built a 23-centimeter (9-inch) Newtonian reflector with such a mounting, for instance, and could maneuver it with unprecedented ease.

After he had learned what he could from Rosse, Lassell built a 61-centimeter (24-inch) reflector and prepared to use it in a way that would have been impossible even three weeks earlier. That chance came about in this fashion:

Since Uranus had been discovered over half a century before, its motions had remained not quite predictable by the calculations based on Newton's law of gravity. Bessel had thought this might be because there was an undiscovered planet beyond Uranus, and that the gravitational pull of this suspected planet was not being taken into account. He died before he could follow up this notion, however.

In 1843 a young English astronomer, John Couch Adams (1819–1892), calculated where a planet might have to be to produce the necessary effect on Uranus. He gave his figures to Great Britain's Astronomer Royal, George Biddell Airy (1801–1892), but Airy was not impressed and did not have the matter checked.

Two years later, a French astronomer, Urbain Jean Joseph Leverrier (1811–1877), took up the same problem and came to a conclusion very close to Adams's. Leverrier gave his figures to a German astronomer, Johann Gottfried Galle (1812–1910). Galle looked in the place indicated by Leverrier's calculations and, on the very first night of his search, September 23, 1846, found the new planet. From its greenish color, it was named for Neptune, the god of the sea.

In some ways, the discovery of Neptune was more dramatic than the discovery of Uranus, for this time it was not accidental. Thought and calculation had discovered the new planet. Great seemed the power of the human mind, and, for the first time since Galileo had turned his simple instrument on the sky, it appeared that the telescope was only a secondary device for astronomers after all. It would be a mistake to think that, however, for without discounting the power of the imagination and mathematical knowledge of Adams and Leverrier, the fact remains that their thought and calculation depended entirely on tiny deviations in Uranus's motion, which were visible only through careful telescopic observation and measurement.

So now Lassell chose to test his new instrument on the new planet 4600 million kilometers (2800 million miles) from the sun. On October 10, 1846, only seventeen days after the planet had been discovered, Lassell observed it and at once detected a tiny body near Neptune which turned out to be a large satellite, eventually named Triton. On September 18, 1848, he discovered an eighth satellite of Saturn, which is now named Hyperion, and in 1851 he discovered third and fourth satellites of Uranus, Ariel and Umbriel.

Caught up in this run of satellite discoveries, Lassell began to search for more and, growing increasingly frustrated by the condition of the atmosphere, determined to move. For the first time, an astronomer decided to establish an observatory not near his home, nor near some place convenient to some supporting patron or government — but in a place where the atmosphere might be suitable for observation. In 1852, therefore, Lassell took his 61-centimeter (24-inch) telescope and went to the island of Malta, which was a British possession.

There he continued his search for additional satellites without success and he decided that he needed a larger telescope that would enable him to see still fainter objects. He had the parts for a 122-centimeter (48-inch) reflector constructed near Liverpool, England, in 1859. They were shipped to Malta and there, in 1861, he erected an instrument with a Fraunhofer-type mounting. It was not as large as Rosse's Leviathan but it was much more easy to handle and therefore incomparably the more practical instrument. Nevertheless, even with it he failed to find additional satellites.

Lassell had been very ingenious in arranging for the movement of his big new telescope. One man could, without undue effort, keep it pointed at a given object by turning a handle once every second, in time to the loud ticks of a clock. Lassell climbed into an observing tower to be high enough to look through the eyepiece. If the telescope in its pursuit of objects in the sky moved away from the tower, the tower could be moved on a circular track by a second assistant and brought within reach again.

If Rosse had proved that large telescopes could be built, Lassell proved that they could be used.

The Permanent Image

It was not enough for light, through being gathered in quantity, to form an enlarged image. It began to dawn on some people that it might be persuaded to make a permanent image.

Bright light induces chemical changes, some of which produce effects that are easily visible. The compound silver chloride is broken down to silver and chlorine and the silver is produced in such fine granules that it looks black. For this reason, silver chloride darkens in the light. The darkening of silver compounds had been known ever since the 1500s, but it was not till the early 1700s that it was recognized that light was responsible for the effect, and not heat.

Was there any way, then, in which sunlight could produce a selective effect, darkening an area of light-sensitive compound here and not there, forming a pattern that would reproduce an image? (The term used for such an effect would be "photography" from Greek words meaning "light-painting.")

Suppose, for instance, that light were made to shine through a transparent object upon a light-sensitive substance beneath. And suppose the object were transparent only in places and opaque in other places. The change in the light-sensitive substance beneath would come precisely in those places which were transparent, and if there were degrees of transparency, this would be reflected in the degrees to which the light-sensitive substance was darkened. If the light-sensitive substance were then protected from further change, the original pattern would have been duplicated (in reverse) by sunlight.

A French artist, Joseph Nicéphore Niepce (1765–1833), was the first to work systematically in such a direction. He used a kind of asphalt which became hard and insoluble on exposure to light and in 1822 he made a copy of an engraving in this manner. It was the first thing that could be called a photograph, albeit a very primitive one.

Niepce also tried to make use of a camera. This consists of an enclosed box with an opening behind which there is a lens. Light, reflected from some object, passes through the lens and is focused on the rear wall of the camera where it produces an image identical to the scene that has produced the light entering the camera (but upside-down). If the light is allowed to fall on a sheet of light-sensitive substance, an alteration will take place in proportion to the quantity of light that falls on each spot and a record of the image is made. It is a "negative" image, for the greatest quantity of light in the original produces the greatest darkening in the image.

Niepce used both the hardening of asphalt and the darkening of silver compounds as the light-sensitive agents in his camera techniques. In 1827, he exposed the view seen from his window to a camera and after an exposure of over eight hours, he had a recognizable image which he presented to the Royal Society. Naturally, anything that took that much time had to remain no more than a curiosity, and Niepce's efforts merely drove him toward bankruptcy.

Similar work was being done by another French artist, Louis

Jacques Mandé Daguerre (1789–1851). In 1829, he went into partnership with Niepce, and after Niepce's death, he continued on his own. He made use of copper plates covered with a thin film of silver. This was exposed to iodine vapor, which converted the silver to silver iodide. The silver iodide broke down more readily than silver chloride did and in this way, Daguerre was able to obtain "daguerrotypes" after exposures of only twenty to thirty minutes.

Other improvements were made rapidly. John Herschel suggested the use of the compound sodium thiosulfate (commonly known as "hypo") to dissolve the unchanged silver salts so that there would be no further darkening on exposure to light. In this way, the image was "fixed" and made permanent.

William Henry Fox Talbot (1800–1877) developed a system of contact printing in 1841. He produced negative images on glass within the camera and then allowed light to shine through them to form a new image on light-sensitive material beneath. The image was again reversed, the negative of a negative, so that it was a "positive" that looked like the original scene. Talbot made use of silver chloride on paper for preparing his positives, so that by 1844 he was able to publish the first book to be illustrated with photographs.

The English-American chemist John William Draper (1811–1882) was the first to use photography on a living subject. In 1839, he dusted the face of his subject with white powder, and on a bright, sunny day managed to make a recognizable photograph after a seven-minute exposure.

He then went on to do what Galileo had done — he took a technological advance produced without astronomy in mind and turned it on the sky. On March 23, 1840, he used a three-inch lens to focus the image of the moon on a light-sensitive plate. He had a clockwork device attached which slowly tipped the lens so as to keep the moon's image focused on the same spot while the moon itself drifted across the sky. In twenty minutes, he had a clear image of the moon — the first piece of astronomic photography.

Other photographs of astronomic interest followed. In 1842 the French physicist Alexandre Edmond Becquerel (1820–1891) succeeded in making the first photograph of the solar spectrum, with some of its dark lines clearly visible. (Draper did the same a few months later.)

The value of photography, if it could be made into a rapid and simple technique, was obvious. Granting the flexibility and delicacy of human vision, it is an impermanent thing. When you are done looking, the impression upon your retina is gone and it can be recalled only imperfectly through memory, or by way of a quick and subjective drawing made at the time. A similar impression on a photographic plate is permanent and objective and can be examined at leisure.

Photographing the Sky

Draper's first photograph of the moon was very primitive, just as Galileo's first telescopic view of the moon was, but the former, like the latter, was pregnant with consequence. The time was to come when the eye was rarely to be at the telescope eyepiece.

As it happened, the growth of the new technique of photography coincided with the advent of telescopic astronomy on a new continent. For the first two and a half centuries after the invention of the telescope, it had remained a purely European instrument. Where professional observations of significance had been made outside Europe, they were made by Europeans who traveled to the spot with instruments designed and built in Europe.

But now the young nation of the new world, the United States, was entering the field. The first American name to become prominent in astronomy was that of William Cranch Bond (1789–1859), a self-educated watchmaker. After seeing an eclipse in 1806, he grew interested in astronomy and established a private observatory that proved to be the best in the nation. His work impressed Harvard College, which appointed him director of the Harvard College Observatory on its completion in 1847.

Bond pioneered in celestial photography, that is, in using a telescope to focus an enlarged image on a photographic plate instead of on the eye. On December 18, 1849, he had taken the picture of the moon, not as Draper had done a decade earlier, through a simple lens, but through a telescope of professional quality. This was a 38-centimeter (15-inch) refractor, which was built with funds raised by public subscription. The telescope is still used today.

This image, taken with a twenty-minute exposure while the telescope was kept focused on the moving moon by clockwork, proved an excellent likeness. It was so impressive, in fact, that Bond's son, George Phillips (1825–1865), took it to London, where the photograph was a sensation at the Great Exhibition held in London that year (the first of the World's Fairs of modern times).

W. C. Bond was helped in his task by a professional photographer (such men already existed, even in the very infancy of the art), John A. Whipple. Together, in 1850, they focused the light of Vega on a photographic plate. This was the first case of a star having its picture taken.

What limited the value of celestial photography at first was the time it took for exposure to be completed. Things began to look up in this respect in 1851, when an English photographer, Frederick Scott Archer (1813–1857), invented the collodion process. Collodion is a solution of cellulose nitrate in a mixture of alcohol and ether. This was coated on a glass plate and, in a darkroom, could be treated in such a way as to be impregnated with silver iodide. The silver iodide, spread through the viscous collodion layer, reacted to light more quickly than in any earlier system. It was the preferred method of photography for twenty years.

The first to apply the collodion process of celestial photography was the British astronomer Warren de la Rue (1815–1889). He used a 33-centimeter (13-inch) reflector which he had, for the most part, built himself, and beginning in 1852, he was able to take pictures of the moon on collodion plates after exposures of only ten to thirty seconds.

Because for such short exposures there was less chance of imperfection in the manner in which the telescope followed the moon, the images he obtained were particularly sharp. He obtained pictures of the moon which were 28 millimeters (1.1 inches) across and which could be enlarged twenty times before becoming too fuzzy for use.

By 1865 he was publishing photographs of the moon that showed, with clarity, virtually every object that could be seen by the eye through a telescope. He made a particular study of the lunar crater Linné because there had been reports of changes seen in its appearance. This was the first attempt to use photography to assist studies by eye alone. De la Rue also took photographs of Jupiter and Saturn, but with far less remarkable results, of course.

The collodion process was particularly useful in photographing faint objects. In 1857 Whipple, who had earlier helped W. C. Bond photograph the moon, used collodion plates to photograph Mizar, the middle star in the handle of the Big Dipper. He used the 38-centimeter (15-inch) refractor, and an exposure of eighty seconds sufficed to record not only Mizar but its faint companion, Alcor. It was the first photograph of a double star and was important for two reasons.

First, it showed that the distance between two very close objects could be measured, at leisure, on a photograph, rather than by dint of meticulous micrometer adjustments by eye. And, indeed, the separation of Mizar and Alcor, as determined from the photograph, matched quite closely the best observations taken by eye.

Second, it offered new methods of measuring the comparative brightness of stars. The devices used by John Herschel and by Steinheil to compare the brightness of a star to that of the moon or to that of another star still made use of the judgment of the eye itself. Using photographs, one could measure the time of exposure required to obtain visible darkening of the plate by a given star, or one could compare the areas of the plate which were darkened by each of several stars.

In 1856, the English astronomer Norman Robert Pogson (1829–1891) pointed out that the average first-magnitude star was 100 times as bright as the average sixth-magnitude star and suggested that this 100-fold difference be defined as the exact measure of a difference of five magnitudes. This meant that every unit magnitude would represent a brightness ratio of 2.512.

In prephotographic days, this might have been little more than an exercise in arithmetic since the accurate measurement of magnitude would have been very difficult to carry through. By means of celestial photography, magnitudes have been measured to accuracies of a hundredth of a magnitude, so that one need not say that Pollux is a 1st-magnitude star — but that it has a magnitude of 1.15.

Naturally, half the 1st-magnitude stars are brighter than average and have magnitudes, therefore, of less than 1. Procyon has a magnitude of 0.35. Magnitudes of less than zero (negative values) are also conceivable, so that Sirius has a magnitude of −1.45. By this system, magnitudes can be stretched to cover astronomic bodies brighter than the stars — the planets, the moon, even the sun, which has a magnitude of −26.72.

Clearly, the one celestial body which could be most successfully photographed had to be the brightest — the sun itself. Already in 1845, before the collodion process had been invented, two French physicists, Jean B. L. Foucault (1819–1868) and Armand H. L. Fizeau (1819–1896), had photographed the sun. With the collodion process, photographs of eclipses in 1851 and 1854 were taken without trouble by various people.

It might have been thought that photographing the sun was merely a stunt, for what of value could be learned from something that was merely a featureless circle of light, with an occasional sunspot present?

Not so! If any had this view it was changed by an amateur German astronomer, Heinrich Samuel Schwabe (1789–1875), a pharmacist by profession. He had a small 5-centimeter (2-inch) refractor, and his schedule required him to do his telescopic viewing by day (a terrible situation for an astronomer). He decided, in 1825, to keep an eye on the neighborhood of the sun and possibly catch sight of some planet closer to the sun than Mercury is. A small telescope viewing the skies by daylight would do the job there.

Schwabe did not find any planet, but he grew interested in the sunspots he could not help but notice on the sun's face. He began sketching them, and did so every sunny day for seventeen years! By 1843 he was able to announce that the sunspots waxed and waned in number according to a ten-year cycle (actually eleven, it has since been determined). This discovery went largely unnoted till it was mentioned in 1851 in a book written by the German scientist Alexander von Humboldt (1769–1859).

Meanwhile, a Scottish-German astronomer, Johann von Lamont (1805–1879), was studying the magnetic field of the Earth independently and showed that its intensity rose and fell in a ten-year cycle. In 1852 a British physicist, Edward Sabine (1788–1883), pointed out the relationship in the two cycles, for Earth's magnetic field rose and fell with the sunspots.

Not only, then, was the sunspot cycle curious in itself but it had an effect on the Earth. These discoveries founded the study of astrophysics — that is, of the physical properties of the stars, of which the sun is one, of course — and showed astronomers that photographs of the sun could be important. John Herschel urged continually that photographs of the sun be made every day so that the sunspot cycle could be studied without the meticulous pains that had had to be taken by poor Schwabe.

The first astronomer to put this suggestion into action was De la Rue. In 1858 he had a telescope built according to his own design for the purpose of photographing the sun. It had an achromatic lens 8.9 centimeters (3.5 inches) in diameter, and a special shutter was included that would allow light to pass through for fractions of a second. The instrument was called a "photoheliograph" ("sunlight-recorder").

Two years elapsed before the instrument could be made to work properly but in 1860, De la Rue was confident enough of its quality to take it to Spain, where a total solar eclipse was to be seen in July. Working with him was the Italian astronomer Pietro Angelo Secchi (1818–1878).

Together, they took photographs of the sun, using the collodion plates. Brilliant prominences, geysers of flame, showed up clearly around the edge of the sun in their photographs.

Nowadays, it seems impossible to imagine such curving arcs of fire as being generated anywhere but from the surface of the sun, yet as late as 1860, this could not be certainly known. The glimpses of such things, by eye, during the moments when the moon was crossing the face of the sun, were insufficient to give details and it could not be certain they did not originate from the moon.

The photographs taken by De la Rue and Secchi, however, fixed the prominences permanently at a given moment and they could be traced, definitely, to the surface of the sun. This was the first astronomical discovery to be made by means of photography.

Analyzing Light

Light, as Newton and subsequent researchers had demonstrated, was no longer mere light. It was a pattern of colors, of bright lines, of dark lines against a bright background. Might the pattern be a code that could be forced to yield information unavailable otherwise?

After Fraunhofer had combined the telescope with the prism (or with the diffraction grating) to produce the first modern spectroscope, astronomers had been wondering about the nature and cause of the dark lines that crossed the solar spectrum. Why were certain wavelengths of light missing?

Fraunhofer himself had noticed that the two closely spaced bright lines produced by heated compounds of the metal sodium seemed to be in the same place as the closely spaced dark lines of the solar spectrum, the dark lines he had labeled "D."

This coincidence was explored further by Foucault in 1849. Foucault blew sodium compounds into the space between two electrodes across which an electric arc was heating the air to white heat. The sodium compounds vaporized naturally and added a yellow color to the glow.

Foucault then allowed sunlight to pass through the sodium-compound vapor before falling upon a prism. He may have expected that the hot sodium-compound glow would supply just those lines missing from the solar spectrum and that the D lines would disappear. Not so! The D lines grew darker, wider, and more pronounced.

This still demonstrated the relationship between sodium and the D lines, of course. Foucault maintained that the sodium atom could give off certain types of light under one set of conditions and absorb those same types under another. In the experiment he had conducted, it seemed to him that the sodium atoms gave off bright lines when it was hot enough to glow but absorbed these same lines from sunlight, which originated at a temperature on the solar surface that was even hotter than the heated sodium atoms in the laboratory.

At the same time, an American physicist, David Alter (1807–1881), was demonstrating the connection between other lines and various elements. Studying the bright lines in the spectra of various heated metals, he found that some lines were sometimes present and sometimes not. These occasionally present lines he attributed to the presence or absence of impurities in the metals being studied. When he mixed two metals, he found that the heated alloy emitted spectral lines characteristic of both metals. He also heated gases such as hydrogen or air and showed that they emitted bright spectral lines as well.

The climax came in 1859 with the work of two German scientists, the chemist Robert Wilhelm Bunsen (1811–1899) and the physicist Gustav Robert Kirchhoff (1824–1887). Bunsen made use of a device which mixed a flammable gas with air intimately and then burned the mixture to yield a virtually colorless flame. Elements heated in such a "Bunsen burner" yielded spectral lines with particular clarity and sharpness since the background of burning gas yielded virtually no light of its own.

Bunsen and Kirchhoff studied the spectra of different elements and presented conclusive evidence showing that each element had its own characteristic spectrum. The spectral lines could be used to identify the elements in any heated substance with certainty. Indeed, where lines appeared that could not be identified as those of any known element, a hitherto undiscovered element must be present. In this way, Bunsen and Kirchhoff detected the element cesium in 1859 and another, rubidium, in 1860. These were the first elements to be detected spectroscopically.

Kirchhoff followed up the work of Foucault in connection with the D lines of the solar spectrum. Instead of allowing sunlight to pass through the sodium vapor, he had the light from sodium vapor fall on the same prism on which sunlight was falling, so that the bright spectral lines of sodium fell upon the solar spectrum. When that was done in such a way that light from both sources entered the prism from the same direction, the sodium spectral lines fell upon the dark D lines, which vanished.

From this and other experiments, he confirmed and extended Foucault's notion that a vapor giving off certain bright spectral lines could absorb those same lines when light from a still hotter source fell upon it.

It followed that the dark lines in the solar spectrum represented light absorbed by the relatively cool solar atmosphere as the light from the hotter regions beneath passed through it. From the position of the dark lines in the solar spectrum, then, the chemical elements present in the sun's atmosphere (or in the atmosphere of any star whose spectrum could be observed) could be determined.

This discovery meant a revolution in telescopic observations.

Until 1860 all one could learn about a star was derived from its light overall — which meant that the star's brightness, position, and motion could be measured, nothing more. Now, for the first time, the light from a star could be analyzed and made to yield more information — its chemical composition, for one thing.

An important lesson was imparted in this way for those who would underestimate the power of the human mind. In 1835 the French philosopher Auguste Comte (1798–1857) had declared the chemical constitution of the stars to be an example of the kind of information science would be eternally incapable of attaining. He died just a little too soon to learn the lesson himself (though he was insane at the time of his death and might not have appreciated the discovery even had he lived long enough).

The connection of the dark lines of the solar spectrum with the chemical composition of its atmosphere fired astronomers into a careful study of the solar spectrum, hitching their telescopes to better and better systems of prisms.

Kirchhoff himself produced a drawing of the solar spectrum that was eight feet long and that listed the positions of the various dark lines in terms of distance from an arbitrary starting point.

This would be a difficult scale for others to use in connection with their own spectra, and something better was devised by the Swedish astronomer Anders Jonas Ångström (1814–1874), who located his dark lines by means of tiny lengths whose significance will be described later in the book. These lengths were given in "Ångström units" where 1 Ångström unit is equal to a ten-billionth of a meter in length. Nowadays, however, a billionth of a meter has come to be known as a "nanometer," so an Ångström unit is equal to a tenth of a nanometer.

Ångström made use of diffraction gratings for his spectra, rather than prisms. For his purposes, this was an improvement. An ordinary prism spreads a given portion of the spectrum over a greater distance in the violet end of the spectrum than in the red end, so that you cannot easily work out the wavelength of a line from its linear position. A diffraction grating allows a more or less even spread over the entire spectrum and that made Ångström's job easier.

A diffraction grating is more efficient and produces a greater spread of spectrum and a sharper delineation of lines the more closely, finely, and evenly the scratches are made in the glass. Ångström's best diffraction grating consisted of glass on which 2000 lines were scratched to the centimeter (5000 to the inch). This was enough to produce a solar spectrum in which 1200 dark lines could be accurately placed.

By 1862 Ångström had studied the solar spectrum sufficiently to be able to identify some of the lines as those produced by hydrogen. This represented the first clear identification of a chemical component of any body other than Earth and the meteors that had fallen upon it.

In 1868, when Ångström published his final map of the solar spectrum, he was able to identify 800 of the lines with one or another of the known elements.

Light passing through a diffraction grating (or a prism, for that matter) suffers diminution because it is absorbed by the glass. In fact, some parts of the spectrum are absorbed more than others so that the glass actually introduces a distorting factor. If light, however, is reflected from a surface with close, fine, even scratches, the same spectral effect is achieved, without distortion and without loss of light.

The American astronomer Lewis Morris Rutherfurd (1816–1892) had devised a lens system for particular use in celestial photographs and in 1860 had tested the first telescope specifically designed to take photographs. He then grew interested in spectroscopy and began to work with such diffraction gratings by reflection.

He coated ordinary glass gratings with a very fine layer of silver and used them for reflection rather than transmission of light. He also ruled fine lines in the kind of speculum metal used for telescope mirrors. His reflection gratings, produced before 1850, showed promise, but they were too small to be of use in astronomic work. (Actually this was no loss, for Rutherfurd's work in this direction came before the astronomic application of spectroscopy was sufficiently appreciated.) In the end, though, Rutherfurd did construct a machine that was capable of ruling diffraction gratings with up to 6700 lines per centimeter (17,000 per inch) far better than anything Ångström had done.

Once it was made clear that the pattern of spectral lines could be made to yield information about the chemical composition of the glowing object from which the lines originated, the effort was expanded from the sun to the stars.

Rutherfurd studied stellar spectra, as Fraunhofer had once done, and also noted the fact that they sometimes differed considerably in pattern from that of the solar spectrum and from each other. He was the first to try to classify them into different types. This was carried through more successfully by Secchi who, in 1867, divided the stellar spectra into four classes and suggested that each was characteristic of a group of stars with distinctive properties.

The English astronomer William Huggins (1824–1910), using a 20-centimeter (8-inch) refractor, studied the spectra of nebulae, of stars, of planets, of comets — of anything, in fact, the light of which he could pass through a telescope and then through some spectrum-producing device.

To be sure, the spectra of even the brighter stars could not be obtained with anything more than a tiny fraction of the detail of the solar spectrum. Enough could be seen, however, to give useful information. As early as 1863, Huggins was able to announce that though stars might show widely different types of spectra, that did not mean that they were made up of elements unknown on Earth. Lines characteristic of known Earthly elements were found in the stellar spectra. (Rutherfurd had demonstrated this at about the same time.)

In 1864 Huggins studied the spectra of certain nebulae which had not been resolved, that is, which seemed, even when seen through the best telescopes then in existence, to be made up of a luminous haze. Many objects that looked like a luminous haze to the unaided eye, or when seen through a small telescope, had been resolved into clusters of separate dim stars by larger telescopes. Some astronomers suspected that *all* nebulae could be resolved if only instruments could be made good enough. They maintained that *all* luminous objects in space were either stars or collections of stars.

When Huggins, however, allowed the light of a nebula in the constellation, Draco, to pass through his telescope and spectroscope, he found no spectrum, only one bright line. The nebula was producing the kind of effect observed on Earth in connection with heated vapors. The conclusion was that some nebulae, at least, were not composed of stars but were vast collections of dust and gas.

Huggins also found lines signifying the presence of hydrogen in connection with some stars and followed up the work of the Italian astronomer Giovanni Battista Donati (1826–1873) in connection with comets.

In 1864, Donati had obtained the spectrum of a comet for the first time. While still some distance from the sun, it shone with reflected light and its spectrum was a faint echo of that of the sun. As the comet drew closer to the sun, however, it substance began to glow and to give off its own light. The pattern of dark lines then changed.

In 1868 Huggins managed to obtain the spectrum of a glowing comet, studied it carefully, and declared it to show lines characteristic of heated hydrocarbons, substances made up of molecules containing both carbon and hydrogen atoms. It was the first time signs of molecules had been discovered elsewhere than on Earth.

But Huggins was able to do more than merely show chemical composition or physical state by means of a spectroscope. Something more could be done from a line of reasoning that dated back to the work of the Austrian physicist Christian Johann Doppler (1803–1853).

In 1842 Doppler studied the relationship of the pitch of a musical sound with the movement of the sound source. A sound source moving rapidly away from an observer (say a sounding whistle on a locomotive) is heard at a lower pitch than it would be if it were standing still. Similarly, a sound source approaching an observer is heard at a higher pitch than it would be if it were standing still.

Doppler accounted for this from an analysis of the nature of sound and did it correctly. Knowing the speed of sound, the speed at which a sound source was approaching or receding could be calculated from the amount of change in its pitch as compared with that of a similar sound source that was motionless.

In 1848 Fizeau pointed out that this "Doppler effect" should apply to light also. Light from a moving light source would shift toward the violet if the source were approaching us and toward the red if it were receding from us. The dark lines would move from their normal positions and one could tell from the extent of the "violet shift" or the "red shift" how fast the source was approaching or receding.

The position of the lines produced in the laboratory, or even present in the solar spectrum (since the sun is at an almost constant distance from us and approaches and recedes only very slowly) can be taken as standard. The position of the lines in the spectrum of the star could then tell us, from their shift, whether the star is approaching us or receding from us and, in either case, how quickly.

Since the speed of light is so great, and any reasonable speed of a star is bound to be small in comparison, the shift in the lines would not be expected to be great. In 1868, however, Huggins studied the spectrum of Sirius carefully and was finally able to detect that one of the more prominent lines in its spectrum was displaced about 1 Ångström unit (no more!) toward the red. From this, he deduced Sirius to be receding from us at the speed of 47.3 kilometers (29.4 miles) per second. This is a bit higher than the value now accepted but is remarkably good for a first attempt.

The most dramatic spectroscopic discovery in the first decade after Bunsen and Kirchhoff had demonstrated the importance of the spectral lines was, however, not really appreciated at first. It came in connection with a solar eclipse visible in India in 1868.

The French astronomer Pierre Jules César Janssen (1824–1907) had traveled there to observe it and, on the day of the eclipse, had studied the spectra of the prominences and found the hydrogen lines easily visible. They were bright lines, for they were light being emitted by the gaseous prominences themselves, without a blanket of absorbing gas between them and the observer.

The day after the eclipse, Janssen wondered if he could still see the hydrogen lines if he pointed his telescope just to the edge of the sun where the prominences would be. He found that the hydrogen lines were still visible and jubilantly exclaimed that the day after the eclipse was the real day of the eclipse for him. In short, although the light of the sun drowned out the light of the prominences to both the eye and the camera, it did not drown out those bright hydrogen lines to the spectroscope.

Yet this was not *the* discovery. Janssen also noted some lines he could not identify. He recorded his observations and sent them to the English astronomer Joseph Norman Lockyer (1836–1920), who was an acknowledged expert on the solar spectrum. (Lockyer had independently demonstrated the ability of the spectroscope to detect prominences even in the absence of an eclipse on the very same day that Janssen had.)

Lockyer, studying Janssen's observations concerning the unidentified bright lines, concluded that they were not produced by any element present on Earth and suggested that there was some element characteristic of the sun which he called "helium" from the Greek word for "sun."

This was not taken seriously, and perhaps should not have been, for there have been many reports of strange spectral lines not attributable to any known element in the century since Lockyer's suggestion. On a number of occasions, new elements have been suggested and it has almost always been discovered that the new lines were due to well-known elements under extreme conditions not easily duplicated in the laboratory.

The one exception to this was the Lockyer suggestion of helium in the sun. The suggestion, ignored in its time, was confirmed in 1895 when the Scottish chemist William Ramsay (1852–1916) discovered a substance on Earth which duplicated, point for point, the spectral lines that Janssen had detected in the sun.

So it came about that nine years after Bunsen and Kirchhoff had pointed the way toward the determination of the chemical constitution of astronomic bodies, a new element was discovered in the sun twenty-eight years before that same element was discovered on Earth.

7. Across the Sea

The American Lenses

The refracting telescope which, thanks to the work of Fraunhofer and Bessel in Germany, had gained new value and reputation, continued to advance through the last half of the 1800s. It reached its peak of perfection, oddly enough, in the United States.

The phrase "oddly enough" is used because surely no one in Europe expected that the position of astronomical leadership which had been held in turn by Italy, France, Great Britain, and Germany would now cross the sea to America. After all, that raw, new nation would seem to have lacked the sophisticated techniques for the purpose. Even the 38-centimeter (15-inch) refractor at the Harvard Observatory, which the Bonds had used to such good purpose, had lenses produced in Germany by the firm of Merz and Mahler, who had succeeded to the techniques of Fraunhofer.

Could the United States declare a telescopic declaration of independence? Could Americans learn to grind lenses of the types required to produce large telescopes of the quality needed to place their astronomers on a par with those of Europe?

One American who could conceive of such a turn of events was Alvan Clark (1804–1887) of Massachusetts. He was a portrait painter by profession but was fascinated by astronomy, so fascinated that he longed to grind lenses. Herschel once had the same longing, but the art of lens-grinding had advanced and new levels of perfection were needed.

Clark recognized the difficulties involved and asked Bond if he might look through the 38-centimeter (15-inch) refractor. Granted this boon, he carefully studied its performance and detected slight errors, slight deviations from the ideal.

Clark closed his studios and devoted himself to learning how to grind lenses that would be better than those of the 38-centimeter (15-inch) model he had studied. Years of painful labor followed, but even when he produced lenses of up to 20 centimeters (8 inches) across that were of excellent quality, he could not sell them. It was difficult for astronomers to trust lenses produced by an American.

Lacking a gift for the soft-soap variety of salesmanship, Clark went about selling his lenses the hard way. He put them into his own telescopes, made observations that required excellent lenses — such as the resolution of close double stars — and announced those observations. The news of Clark's work reached a double-star expert, the English astronomer William Rutter Dawes (1799–1868), in 1851. Dawes followed up these observations, grew enthusiastic, and bought several lenses. One of these ended up in Huggins's telescope and it was with a Clark lens that Huggins did most of his pioneering work in spectroscopy.

By 1859 Dawes invited Clark to London and introduced him to Rosse, to John Herschel, and to others. That was all that was needed. It lifted Clark to astronomic respectability despite his American origin and, after that, his work prospered. He established a factory in Cambridge, Massachusetts, with the help of his two sons, particularly the younger one, Alvan Graham Clark (1832–1897).

In 1860 an order came to the Clarks from the American mathematician Frederick Augustus Porter Barnard (1809–1889), who was Massachusetts-born, but who was then chancellor of the University of Mississippi. Thinking first of the state of his adoption rather than the one of his birth, he wanted a 47-centimeter (18.5-inch) lens, with which to exceed the Harvard Observatory refractor and make his own university the one with the largest refractor in the United States.

The Clarks understood the task and by 1862 two such lenses were ready. They had reached the stage of final testing: that of setting up a rough and ready setting for the lens and then testing it on the sky to see how delicately it could see hard-to-observe objects. Alvan G. Clark pointed one of the lenses at the star Sirius in the course of this test and found a tiny spark of light in its neighborhood concerning which he could find no record on the star maps.

Repeated observations made it clear that the dim star observed near Sirius was not the result of an imperfection in the lens. Rather, it was seen precisely because the lens was so good. It was in exactly the position in which the famous dark companion of Sirius (postulated by Bessel) would have had to be in order to account for Sirius's movements. The younger Clark had, in fact, discovered the dark companion, which turned out to be not completely dark, and had thus confirmed Bessel's work.

For this, Clark received a medal from the French Academy of Sciences and if anything were lacking to assure the international recognition of the American firm, that supplied it.

The lens, thus made famous, never reached its Mississippi destination, however, for within a year of Barnard's order, Mississippi had seceded from the Union and the American Civil War had broken out. The lens went to Chicago instead and was mounted in a telescope at the Dearborn Observatory of the University of Chicago. There the American astronomer George Washington Hough (1836–1909) used it to study double stars and to carry through long-sustained observations of the planet Jupiter.

The Civil War ended in 1865 and the nation entered an era of great prosperity and optimism. In every direction, nothing seemed too great for American accomplishment and the United States took the lead in every direction in producing superlatives, a lead it was to keep down to the present. It is not surprising that the superlatives involved scientific instruments as well — notably telescopes.

In 1870 the Canadian-American astronomer Simon Newcomb (1835–1909) had $50,000 placed at his disposal by the American government in order that the biggest and best telescope available at that price might be obtained for the U.S. Naval Observatory, which he headed. Naturally, he turned to the Clarks.

The Clarks accepted the new task and, a couple of years later, the Naval Observatory had a refractor some 13 meters (40 feet) long with a lens that was 66 centimeters (26 inches) across. The lens, which weighed 45 kilograms (110 pounds), was the largest and best that existed in the world at that time. What this representative of the new American technical virtuosity could do was demonstrated by the American astronomer Asaph Hall (1829–1907).

Hall had little formal education, since he had to work at carpentry when he was a teen-ager in order to support a fatherless family.

Like so many others in the history of astronomy, however, his desire to view the heavens forced him into self-education and in 1857 he managed to become an assistant to Bond at the Harvard Observatory at a salary of three dollars a week.

In 1863, however, Hall had proved his worth to the point where he was appointed professor of astronomy at the Naval Observatory and he was there when the 66-centimeter (26-inch) refractor was put in operation.

In 1877 a dramatic moment was at hand. Mars was going to pass through a point in its orbit that would bring it just about as close to Earth as it could possibly get. All the telescopes of the world were pointed in its direction and one question concerning the planet was whether it possessed satellites. All the outer planets then known possessed satellites — Saturn possessing eight, Jupiter and Uranus four apiece, and Neptune one.

Of the inner planets, Earth had one satellite, of course, but the others had none. At least none were observed and, if any existed, they must be very small.

Small objects near Venus or Mercury would be difficult to observe since those planets were rarely far from the sun and, at their farthest, both they and any satellite they might possess would be in the crescent phase. A small satellite would then be all the more difficult to see so that the two innermost planets were not popular objects for satellite searches.

Mars did not present such difficulties. Viewed in the midnight sky, it (and any satellites) would present fully illuminated surfaces to viewers on Earth. There was therefore much enthusiasm for a satellite quest in connection with that planet.

The task would not be easy, however, and everyone knew that. Since no satellites of Mars had yet been seen, they must be very small, or very close to the overpowering brilliance of the planetary body, or both. If close, they must revolve about Mars in a very short period. Tiny, rapidly moving bodies lost in the glare of Mars would be difficult to see.

(Interestingly enough, the problem had occupied the Irish satirist Jonathan Swift [1667–1745], and plays a part in his *Gulliver's Travels,* which he published in 1726. There he reported that astronomers in his fictional land of Laputa had discovered such satellites. Since

Swift understood the astronomy involved, he made them small, close to Mars, and revolving with a short period. He also imagined there to be two, possibly choosing that figure because Earth had one satellite and Jupiter four, so that Mars in its intermediate position ought to have an intermediate number.)

Hall began to search the neighborhood of Mars for small satellites at the beginning of August 1877. He worked his way systematically inward toward Mars's surface. By August 11, he was so close to Mars that its glare was beginning to interfere with his observations. He decided to give up, went home, and told his wife of his decision.

Mrs. Hall said, "Try it just one more night."

Hall agreed to do so and on that "one more night" discovered a tiny moving object near Mars. Unfortunately, clouds came in and he had to wait for five agonizingly suspenseful days for another chance to look. On August 16 he could see once again and definitely observed a satellite. On the seventeenth he found another.

There were two Martian satellites, which he named Phobos ("fear") and Deimos ("terror") after the two sons of Mars, the god of war in the classic myths.

So there turned out to be, after all, two satellites of Mars as Swift had guessed, and they had very much the properties that Swift had described. This, however, was a tribute not to any mysterious powers of foresight that Swift might have had (some have jokingly suggested he was a Martian and had firsthand knowledge) but to his astronomical good sense.

What the discovery, a most dramatic and well-publicized one, did was to further advance the reputation of the Clarks and to mark the rapid advance of astronomical techniques in the United States.

This is not to imply, however, that important work wasn't being done in Europe at the same time — even with smaller refractors.

In the same 1877 approach of Mars, for instance, the Italian astronomer Giovanni Virginio Schiaparelli (1835–1910) studied the face of Mars with a refractor containing a lens (made by Merz and Mahler) of only 21.5 centimeters (8.5 inches) in diameter.

It was his intention to produce a map of the markings on Mars. The first attempt to draw a picture of Mars's appearance, as seen through the telescope, had been in 1636 by Gaetano Fontana (1645–1719). Cassini made an attempt to do the same in 1666. Understandably, these early attempts were extremely sketchy. The first drawing of the Martian surface which could actually be dignified by the word "map" was produced in 1830 by the German astronomer Wilhelm Beer (1797–1850).

Schiaparelli outstripped Beer completely, however, producing a map that was not to be improved on fundamentally for a century. He established the basis for naming Martian features by using Latin words taken from the geography and mythology of the Mediterranean area in ancient times.

One observation which he made at the time created an enormous stir over Mars, an even greater one than that caused by Hall's discovery of the two satellites. He noted straight dark lines on the Martian surface, lines that crisscrossed in a complicated pattern. These he referred to as "canali," Italian for "channels," a neutral word meaning, at most, narrow waterways. Somehow the word became "canals" in English, signifying artificial structures built by intelligent beings.

For the first time, there seemed real astronomical evidence for that mainstay of fictional speculation — intelligent life on other worlds and for nearly a century there was talk of a possible Martian civilization. It was assumed by many romanticists that there was a dying race of Martians trying, with their gigantic canals, to make the most of their small planet's dwindling water supply.

(This was of key importance to the history of science fiction, for it led to *The War of the Worlds* by the English writer H. G. Wells [1866–1946], published in 1898. Dealing with an invasion of Martians seeking a younger, more watery home on Earth, Wells's romance was the first important story of interplanetary warfare ever written.)

Refractors at the Peak

The success of the large refractors built by the Clarks inspired competition in Europe. In France, the astronomical brother team of Paul Pierre Henry (1848–1905) and Prosper Mathieu Henry (1849–1903), with the help of an instrument-maker, P. Gautier, constructed a 62-centimeter (24.5-inch) lens in 1891.

Then there was an Irish father-and-son team, Thomas Grubb

(1800–1878) and Howard Grubb (1844–1931). The elder Grubb was an engineer who turned to the task of telescope-making. At first, his work involved reflectors, but in the 1880s the younger Grubb turned to refractors. In 1893 he produced a 71-centimeter (28-inch) lens which was used in the refractor at Greenwich and which, for a time, outclassed in size the Clark instruments.

The Clarks did not relinquish their lead in size for long, however, partly through the whim of the American financier James Lick (1796–1876). Lick, having made a great deal of money in real estate during the California gold rush of 1849, was anxious to leave behind him a sum of money that could be used to memorialize himself and his name. He knew nothing about astronomy, apparently, and had never seen a telescope, but he had somehow gained an appreciation of the value of advancing knowledge of the heavenly bodies. He therefore announced in 1874 that he would leave $700,000 (far greater in real value than a present-day sum of that amount) for the specific purpose of building a bigger and better telescope than any yet existing.

There was some question, at first, as to the kind of telescope the money ought to go for, but it was finally decided to build a 91-centimeter (36-inch) refractor, and the Clarks set to work. It took years to get the glass and grind the surfaces. There were many failures, and the younger Clark had to go to Paris to negotiate for glass of higher quality than any he had yet obtained. Finally, after fourteen years and a cost of $50,000, the lens was prepared.

On January 3, 1888, the lens, mounted in a telescope some 18.3 meters (60 feet) long, was used for the first time in an observatory that had been established on Mount Hamilton in northern California, about 21 kilometers (13 miles) east of San Jose. The elder Clark had died just a few months too soon to see the new telescope in operation.

Lick had died years before, but his name lived on in the Lick Observatory, whose importance to astronomy has been such that the financier's name was preserved and honored to a greater extent than he could possibly have expected. He was preserved in a more literal sense, too, for his remains were interred (at his dying request) in the brick pier on which the telescope is mounted.

The 91-centimeter (36-inch) refractor was at once turned on Mars by Edward Singleton Holder (1846–1914) who headed the Observatory and by his assistant, James Edward Keeler (1857–1900). It was hoped that in this way a new and better view of Schiaparelli's canals would be obtained, but the results were disappointing. The details seemed lower in quality than those observed by older and smaller instruments and, of course, no canals could be seen.

There was talk, at once, that this demonstrated the uselessness of large telescopes — that the imperfections of seeing brought on by temperature variations of the air, to say nothing of other factors, were enhanced more than the image was enlarged as lenses grew larger and larger. What one saw, the argument went, would come closer and closer to a blur.

This was not so, of course. A large refractor couldn't see nearly as well as its theoretical limit — which would come if there were no air at all between itself and the object it was looking at — but if its lens were an excellent one, it could still do better than a smaller instrument would. Besides, if planetary surfaces were not the real forte of a large refractor, there remained the smaller and more distant objects in space, where it did far better.

This was demonstrated by Edward Emerson Barnard (1857–1923). In 1892, using the Lick refractor, he did something no astronomer had done since Galileo's time. He discovered a fifth satellite of the planet Jupiter. Oddly enough, it has no official name (and neither do eight more Jovian satellites discovered in the twentieth century). It is sometimes called "Jupiter V" because it was the fifth satellite of Jupiter to be discovered, and sometimes "Barnard's Satellite." The name Amalthea, honoring a nymph (or goat) who fed Jupiter in his infancy, was suggested by the French astronomer Camille Flammarion (1842–1925) and is often used but has never been made official.

The discovery was a tribute to the excellence of the refractor — and to Barnard's abilities as a keen-eyed observer. (He is reported to have detected craters on Mars in the 1890s but did not make his finding public since he considered it too dubious. It took an additional three quarters of a century and enormous advances in technology before anyone else saw them.)

Amalthea is a small body, only 110 kilometers (70 miles) in diameter, and much tinier than the four moon-sized bodies that Galileo had detected with his first primitive instrument. Furthermore, Amalthea is closer to Jupiter than any of the other satellites, only 108,000 kilometers (67,000) miles above Jupiter's surface. To detect a body so small and dim, and so close to Jupiter's own overwhelming brightness, called for excellence on the part of both lenses, that of the telescope and that of the eye — but it was done. Amalthea is the last object in the solar system to have been discovered by eye. Since 1892 all such discoveries have been made by a camera attached to a telescope.

In 1895 John Martin Schaeberle (1853–1924), using the Lick refractor, detected the "dark companion" of Procyon which Bessel had predicted from its gravitational effect a half century before. It was a dim spark of a star of the 13th magnitude.

Schaeberle also designed a telescopic camera with a 12.5-centimeter (5-inch) lens, placed in a tube 12 meters (40 feet) long. He took this to Chile with him to study the eclipse of April 16, 1893. With this instrument he managed to demonstrate that the corona of light that appeared around the eclipsed sun was a real object and not an illusion, and that it was part of the sun — its outer atmosphere, in fact.

The Lick refractor, by the way, demonstrated the practicality of constructing a large telescope at mountain heights. The site of Lick Observatory is 1400 meters (4250 feet) above sea level, and a telescope at that height leaves much of Earth's atmosphere below it — and the densest and dirtiest part at that. Of course, the price is paid in the difficulty of getting men and supplies up the mountain and in the increased coldness of the nights.

The new refractor also established California as a site for large telescopes, a distinction it has held ever since.

As a matter of fact, the University of Southern California decided it wanted a telescope even better than the Lick Observatory's. An order for a 101-centimeter (40-inch) lens was placed with Clark. After Clark had invested $20,000 in the project, however, the plan fell through. The university could not raise the money.

At this point, the American astronomer George Ellery Hale (1868–1938) came to the rescue. He was a young assistant professor of astrophysics at the just established University of Chicago and he greatly desired a large telescope. Since Clark had the raw glass all

Hans Lippershey was a Dutch lens grinder who made what may have been the first telescope and then went into the business of selling them. Rumors of his work stimulated Galileo to build a telescope of his own.

Galileo and two of his early telescopes. Beginning in 1609 Galileo discovered objects in the heavens never seen before and showed that science should be based on observation and not on philosophical argument. The telescopes are about the size of a sea captain's long spyglass of a later year. The rack on which these telescopes are displayed in the Science Museum at Florence provides a sense of the scale.

This illustrative insert has been prepared by Dr. Dow Smith in association with Itek Corporation.

Johann Kepler in 1609 announced that the planets move about the sun in ellipses and stated the first two of his mathematical laws which describe the motion. His important contribution to telescopes came two years later when he described how to make a telescope with two convex lenses instead of one convex and one concave as used by Galileo.

In 1668 Isaac Newton built the first reflecting telescope. His diagram compares the appearance of what Newton described as a weathercock 300 feet distant as seen with the reflector at thirty-eight times magnification with the view from a refractor at fourteen times magnification. The length of focus was about twelve inches.

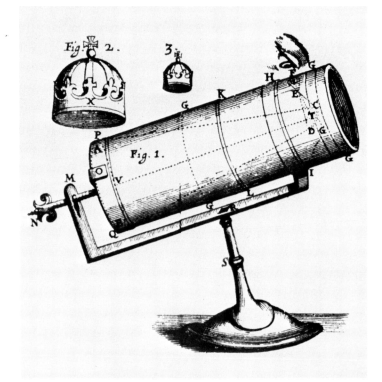

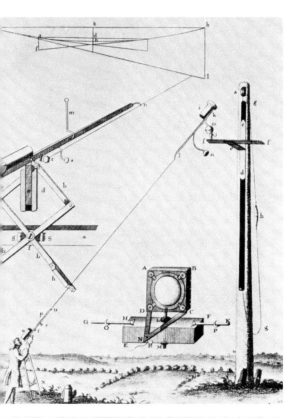

Christian Huygens, nearly half a century after Galileo, applied Kepler's ideas for a new telescope design and in 1659 built this tubeless telescope, 123 feet long, with which he discovered the rings of Saturn.

In spite of Newton's achievement, reflecting telescopes were not important in astronomy until the time of John Hadley, who showed this 6-inch-aperture (62-inch-focus) telescope to the Royal Society in 1721. It was the first reflector with performance comparable to Huygens' 123-foot-focus long refractor.

William Herschel in the late 1700s built the first really large reflecting telescopes. He made voluminous contributions to astronomy and is best known as discoverer of the planet Uranus and of binary stars. The 48-inch-diameter, 40-foot-focus telescope shown here was his largest.

William Lassell showed how to apply Herschel's developments in mirror-making to really practical telescopes. He built this 48-inch-diameter in England in 1861 and took it to Malta where the skies were clear. He was first to use Fraunhofer's idea of an "equatorial" mount on a large telescope. *Royal Astronomical Society*

In 1845 Lord Rosse completed his 72-inch-diameter telescope which the public named "Leviathan." With it he discovered the Crab nebula, but he was ahead of his time. The really efficient use of such large telescopes would need better materials and improved technology for mounting the instrument. *Itek Corporation*

NEWTONIAN TELESCOPE

eye
eyepiece
primary image
parabolic mirror
light from star

GREGORIAN TELESCOPE

parabolic mirror
elliptical mirror

CASSEGRAIN TELESCOPE

hyperbolic mirror
parabolic mirror

SCHMIDT TELESCOPE

aspheric plate
spherical mirror
spherical image

Classical reflecting telescope types. Many variations and combinations of these are possible.

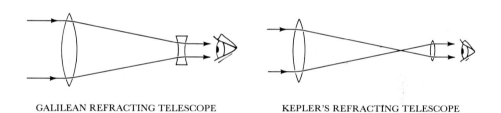

GALILEAN REFRACTING TELESCOPE

KEPLER'S REFRACTING TELESCOPE

The basic types of classical refracting telescopes. Galileo's gives an erect image. Kepler's telescope in this simple form used for astronomy gives an inverted image.

blue focus
red light focus
red and blue images coincide

CONVEX LENS

CONCAVE LENS

COMBINATION

Principle of achromatic doublet. The combination of a convex lens with a concave lens of a higher dispersion glass can produce a lens which behaves like a convex lens but eliminates the colored rings in the image of a star formed by a simple convex lens.

Joseph von Fraunhofer was a superb optician and instrument maker. He built prism spectrographs good enough to see the narrow dark absorption lines in the sun's light now called Fraunhofer lines. He studied the diffraction of light and almost single-handedly founded the field of grating spectroscopy. He was the first to mount a telescope so that one axis of movement is parallel to the earth's axis, the important "equatorial" mount. Working with the glass-maker Guinand he designed and made the 9½-inch lens for his great Dorpat refractor, which for many years remained the largest in the world. *Deutsches Museum print*

Stimulated by the Harvard 15-inch, Alvan Clark and his sons in Cambridge, Massachusetts, developed the art of lens-making to a high degree. They made the huge 36-inch-diameter for the Lick telescope, which was put into operation in 1888. This has been exceeded in size only by their own 40-inch lens for the Yerkes Observatory about ten years later. These telescopes, still in use, remain the largest refractors in the world. *Library of Congress*

In 1847 a 15-inch refractor was installed at the Harvard College Observatory. It had been made in Germany by the firm of Mertz and Mahler and incorporated new advances in lens design and the latest optical glass. This telescope was used by G. P. Bond and J. A. Whipple in 1850 to take the first photographs of stars. *Harvard College Observatory*

The era of modern giant reflectors began on
Mount Wilson in California when in 1908 as a
result of the vision and drive of George Ellery
Hale, the 60-inch telescope went into operation.
This was only four years after the first smaller
telescopes had been taken by pack burro to the
summit. The telescope has a glass mirror and an
equatorial mount arranged in a symmetrical form.
Hale Observatories

In 1917 the 100-inch Hooker telescope was put
into operation at Mount Wilson, again under
Hale's leadership. It had three times the light-
gathering power of the 60-inch. *Hale Observatories*

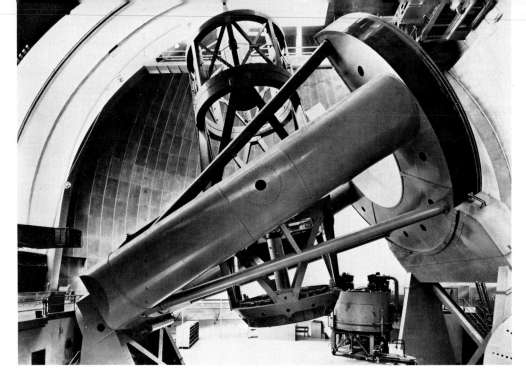

In 1928 George Ellery Hale proposed a telescope with a mirror diameter of 200 inches (nearly 17 feet). As the project developed it caught the imagination of the public and received worldwide publicity. Since its completion in 1948 this telescope has added greatly to man's knowledge of the far distant parts of the universe. *Mount Wilson–Palomar Observatories*

Alvan Clark and sons used this machine to polish the 36-inch Lick telescope mirror. The two reciprocating arms move the pitch-faced polishing lap (similar to the one seen on the floor) while the lens in its wooden cradle is rotated from below. This principle of operation has been used in both the very early and most modern machines, though often only one crank is used and the single drive arm extends beyond the work to a support in which it slides. *Scientific American* cover, September, 1887

This optical grinding and polishing machine at Sir Howard Grubb Parsons and Company in England is the largest in the world. It is here being used to grind the blank for the 150-inch mirror for the Anglo-Australian telescope. *Sir Howard Grubb Parsons and Company Ltd.*

A polished mirror with a diameter of 1.8 meters (6 feet) made of ultra-low-expansion (ULE) fused silica from the Corning Glass Works who fabricated this lightweight blank. The mirror consists of a faceplate and a backplate separated by a cellular core about a foot in depth, visible through the polished surface. Such mirrors are suitable for use in space. *Itek Corporation*

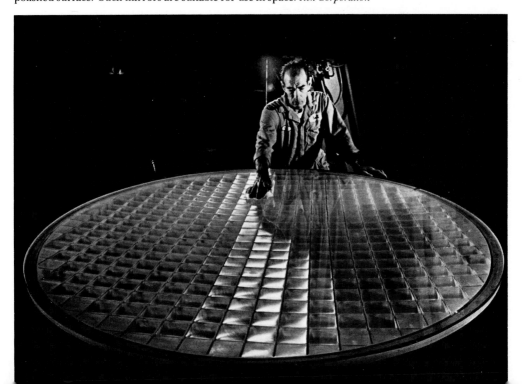

By placing a thin glass corrector plate of special shape at the center of curvature of a spherical mirror, Bernhard Schmidt demonstrated an entirely new kind of telescope, the first which could take sharp pictures of stars over a wide field of view. Schmidt is shown here in his workshop polishing one of the corrector plates.
A. A. Wachman

The Baker-Nunn Camera was designed for the Smithsonian Astrophysical Observatory to photograph artificial satellites. Instruments like this 1957 model and later versions are in operation around the world. James G. Baker, the optical designer, used Schmidt's principle, though in a more complex form with a correcting "plate" having three glass elements with four aspheric and two spherical surfaces. This was necessary to provide sharp images over the wide field of view for light from the violet through the deep red.

Smithsonian Astrophysical Observatory

The Snow telescope was carried by mule train to the top of Mount Wilson in 1904, the first major telescope designed for observing the sun. A moving mirror (heliostat) directs the light into the telescope so as to provide a stationary image of the sun at the slit of a spectrograph. By scanning the slit across the image the astronomer can obtain a picture of the sun in a single wavelength of light. In the background are two tower telescopes specialized for solar observation. The taller tower (150 feet) is used to measure the magnetism of the sun's surface. *Hale Observatories*

The Robert R. McMath solar telescope at Kitt Peak, Arizona, is the largest of its kind. The diagram shows how light is directed toward the 60-inch primary mirror of the telescope by the moving heliostat mirror and then by the smaller flat mirror into the laboratory which houses the spectrograph. In solar telescopes the mirrors are exposed to the direct rays of the hot sun creating major problems for the telescope designer. The sloping telescope tube extends into the ground for a distance greater than that visible above ground. *Kitt Peak National Observatory*

from sun

moving
80-inch
heliostat mirror

fixed flat mirror

ground level

image of sun

60-inch
primary mirror

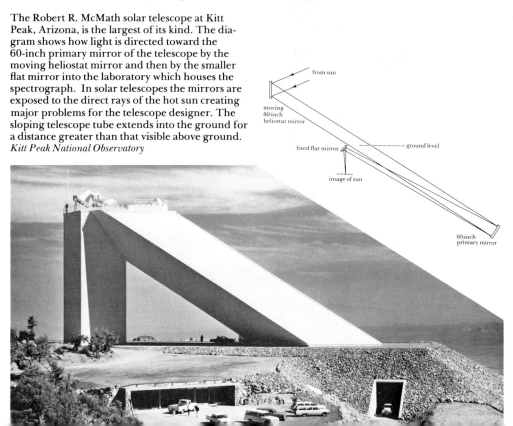

This unusual telescope was designed to detect high-energy gamma rays from deep space by collecting the light emitted as the radiation enters the earth's atmosphere. It is at the Smithsonian Astrophysical Observatory on Mount Hopkins in Arizona. The peak of the mountain can be seen inverted in the 34-foot-diameter mosaic mirror. *Smithsonian Astrophysical Observatory*

Radio astronomy began when Karl Jansky of the Bell Telephone Laboratories used this apparatus in 1932 to show that radio waves were reaching the Earth from the center of our galaxy. The antenna "looked" in a horizontal direction only and scanned the celestial dome by combining the earth's motion with rotation of the antenna on its circular track. *Bell Telephone Laboratories*

The 210-foot-diameter tracking antenna at NASA's Goldstone Deep Space Communication Complex in California is used primarily for tracking and communicating with distant space vehicles. It is exceeded in size among fully steerable dishes only by the pioneering Jodrell Bank telescope in England. Since going into operation in 1966 its astronomical chores have included the radar mapping of Mars and Venus as well as the precise determination of planetary distances. *NASA*

This radio telescope at Arecibo in Puerto Rico (1963) was made by reshaping a natural valley to support a metal mesh a thousand feet in diameter. It is the largest dish in the world. The microwave detector supported by cables from the three towers can be moved to provide limited ability to scan the sky in addition to that provided by the motion of the earth. *U.S. Air Force*

The Orbiting Astronomical Observatory (OAO-3) is shown here during preparation prior to launching at the Kennedy Space Center in 1972. The two-and-a-half-ton automated observatory carried out extensive experiments. The Princeton telescope and spectrometer has an aperture of 80 centimeters (about 32 inches) and gathered important information about the nature of interstellar space, including the widespread distribution of molecular hydrogen and the presence of carbon monoxide. *NASA*

The Helios A Solar Probe is shown here during systems checkout. It was launched in a *Titan III* booster in December 1974 to study interplanetary space toward and in the vicinity of the sun which it approached to within 28 million miles. The spacecraft was designed and built in Germany and is controlled from the German space center near Munich using data gathered by the NASA deep space network. At its first approach to the sun it was exposed to a level of solar illumination ten times that at the Earth. *NASA*

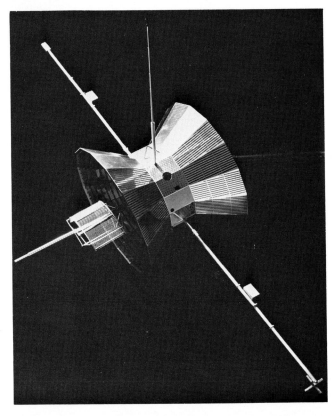

This is an artist's concept of the NASA Large Space Telescope (LST) being carried as a payload of the Space Shuttle in the 1980s. The LST, the first major observatory in space, will be a long-life-time telescope which can be repaired and refurbished while in earth orbit through visits of the shuttle. It is expected to be the most powerful telescope ever built and to remain in orbit for at least ten years. If major repairs should be needed it can be returned to Earth and relaunched later. *NASA*

Once in space, the LST, shown here in orbit in artist's concept, will begin an extensive program of astronomical observation. Free from the disturbing effects of the Earth's atmosphere it would, with the proposed 2.4-meter aperture, be able to see ten times further into space than the best telescope on earth. Such an instrument can be expected to provide answers to many as yet unanswered questions about the universe and almost certainly make new and quite unanticipated discoveries. *Itek Corporation*

set for the lens (and nothing else that could possibly be done with it) all Hale needed was the money.

Hale was a determined person and he found his prey in the form of the financier Charles Tyson Yerkes (1837–1905), who had gained control of the Chicago trolley system and was making enormous sums out of it in ways that some thought were corrupt. There was no reason why some of this possibly tainted money could not be put to the benefit of science and Hale hounded Yerkes until, bit by bit, the financier found he had promised $349,000 toward the telescope and a surrounding observatory.

Hale chose a site at Lake Geneva, Wisconsin, about 130 kilometers (80 miles) northwest of Chicago, and there the Yerkes Observatory came into being. It was only 73 meters (240 feet) above sea level, but Hale had had bad experience with mountaintop observatories — too many storms, he felt. Furthermore, the winters in the Chicago area were cold enough at sea level, with temperatures of $-11°$ C. ($-20°$ F.) not unheard of. To go a mile high or so would be unbearable. (Even in California, mountain heights had their problems since it is impossible to heat the observatories without producing temperature differences in the air about the telescope and thus make seeing impossible.)

The 101-centimeter (40-inch) lens was finished in October 1895. It weighed 230 kilograms (500 pounds) and was placed into a telescope over 18 meters (60 feet) long. The whole weight was some 18,000 kilograms (20 tons), yet it was so well balanced that it could be moved with slight pressure to survey any part of the sky.

On May 21, 1897, the new refractor was used for the first time, and the younger Clark died on June 9, 1897, just three weeks after the crowning glory of telescopic refraction had gone into action.

And it *was* the crowning glory. The history of refracting telescopes which, for three centuries, from the day of Galileo to the day of the Clarks, from 1609 to 1897, had produced bigger and better instruments now came to an end — at least as far as advances in size were concerned. In 1897 the refractors at Yerkes and at Lick, both with lenses produced by the Clarks, were the first and second largest refractors in the world. Three quarters of a century later, they are still the first and second largest refractors in the world, and there are no plans to outdo either.

The reason is a simple one. The lenses had grown so large that certain deficiencies had become important, deficiencies that would increase if still larger lenses were attempted and more than cancel out any gains to be expected from the increase in light-gathering power. Despite the outcries against the large refractors when the one at the Lick Observatory on Mount Hamilton had gone into operation, it and the Yerkes refractor had both done excellent service, but the limit was reached.

For one thing, it is difficult to get large lumps of glass so entirely free of imperfections as to make it suitable for telescopic lenses. The larger the lens you want, the larger (in rapidly mounting progression) the difficulty of getting the glass — and all the advances in technology throughout the nineteenth and twentieth centuries have not made it easy to get a piece of glass large enough to surpass the Clark refractors.

Secondly, the larger the lens, the heavier it must be. Since light had to pass through all of it, if it was to be useful, it had to be supported only at the edges. With support only at the rim, the center of a heavy lens begins to sag and the whole lens starts to deform. The deformity was small enough in the 101-centimeter (40-inch) refractor to bring on no intolerable interference with the attainment of a sharp focus. A still larger lens, however, was bound to lose sharpness through sag.

Clark himself had remained optimistic. He had argued that larger pieces of glass could indeed be obtained if one were only patient, that absorption of light could be minimized, that the sagging of a lens would not introduce serious problems. He was also sure that it was the reflectors that had come to the end of the road in view of the misadventures of Rosse's Leviathan. Even while the 101-centimeter (40-inch) refractor was being completed, Clark was making plans for a lens 152 centimeters (60 inches) across.

But he died. No one else had Clark's faith in refractors or his skill and patience in endlessly polishing lenses — so nothing beyond the Yerkes refractor was ever planned. The refractors had come to the end of the road, at least as far as sheer size was concerned, and the leadership turned once again, and this time permanently, to the reflectors.

The New Mirrors

During the nearly two-century history of reflecting telescopes from Newton to Rosse, the metal mirror was what represented the bottleneck to its advance. The bronze of which it was composed had a tendency to corrode and had to be repolished periodically with the loss of enormous quantities of time and labor. There were metals that would have been more resistant to corrosion, but every one of them would have been heavier and much more expensive than bronze.

That, under these conditions, the reflector competed as stubbornly and as successfully as it did against the refractors of such masters as Fraunhofer and the Clarks was remarkable. Part of the reason lay in the fact that, despite everything, a refractor was longer, larger, and more expensive than a reflector of the same light-gathering power.

As long as reflectors kept their metal mirrors, however, they could advance little further, and instruments such as that of Lassell were not likely to be improved on much more. If there were an escape from the metal mirror, it would have to lie in the direction of glass, a substance that was light, cheap, noncorrodible, capable of taking a high polish and more easily ground into shape than metal was. Yet glass was transparent and reflected relatively little light. It was superlative for lenses precisely because of that; how then could it be used for mirrors?

In Roman times, the notion had arisen of backing a piece of glass with a sheet of metal. The surface of the metal which made immediate contact with the glass was never touched by air and did not corrode. What's more, it took on the smooth flatness of the glass. Furthermore, it was the glass that supplied the bulk and strength of the system and the metal backing could be very thin. In that case, tin or silver could be used for the purpose without undue expense. These metals, being white, would introduce less color distortion than bronze or gold mirrors would.

The technique was improved in the Middle Ages and by the sixteenth century Venetian glass blowers, then the best in the world, could make colorless glass backed by a thin film of a mixture of tin and mercury ("tin amalgam"). Such a mirror was much better than one of polished metal alone.

In 1691 the art of making plate glass was introduced in France. This new variety of glass had both sides flatter and more nearly parallel than had ever been achieved before. The use of plate glass further increased the excellence of mirrors and the Hall of Mirrors at Versailles (which does not astonish us now) was a wonder of the world when it was established.

By the time Newton had devised the first reflecting telescope, then, the metal-backed glass mirror had reached a pitch of considerable excellence. Why could not something like that have been used in telescopes?

The metal-backed mirror was useless for telescopes because, for one thing, light would have to travel through the glass of the mirror in order to strike the metal film and be reflected, and then travel through the glass again on its return. The glass would thus have to reach an even higher pitch of perfection than was required of lenses, since light would have to traverse the glass mirror twice and the glass lens only once. Then, too, the glass surface itself would reflect some light, not much, but enough to produce a ghost image and ruin everything.

A glass mirror simply had to reflect light from its surface, as metal does, not from its rear. There would then be only one reflection and the quality of the glass making up the bulk of the mirror could fall short of perfection appreciably without bothering anyone.

Suppose, then, you produced a "metal-fronted" glass with a film of tin amalgam, or other metal, on the front surface. The light would then be reflected by the metal directly and it would never pass through glass to be distorted or absorbed.

Such a metal-fronted mirror was not difficult to conceive and James Short, the first man to produce a paraboloid surface in metal mirrors, tried to produce a metal-fronted glass mirror in the 1730s. He failed to get useful results, however, and went back to metal. The trouble is that when the front of the mirror is coated, the highly polished side of the film faces the glass while the light hits the *other* side, which is rough and dull. If you will slip a mirror out of its frame and look at its back you will find the thin metal coating to be dull and gray on the side away from the glass and nothing will be reflected in it. If you were to try to polish it, you would find it so thin, that you would polish it away altogether.

The turning point came in 1856, when the German chemist Justus von Liebig (1803–1873) worked out a system for applying a thin silver coating to glass. He made use of a solution of silver ammonium nitrate so adjusted, chemically, that it was on the point of decomposing and precipitating metallic silver in very fine granules. To bring the precipitation about, he then added a sugar solution and poured the mixture on a smooth glass surface that had been thoroughly cleaned with strong chemicals. The silver precipitated on the glass slowly to form a thin, but compact, film that was strong enough to take a light buffing and become sufficiently polished to reflect light efficiently.

The silver, thus layered on the glass, produced so thin a film that its use was not prohibitively expensive even on the largest mirrors. Properly polished it became a metal-fronted glass mirror that could be used for astronomical purposes.

A silver-fronted glass mirror is lighter than a solid metal mirror, and even though the silver might corrode, this is no tragedy. It is less likely to do so than bronze and when it does, it need merely be dissolved away and a new film precipitated on the glass and then gently polished. The glass itself will keep its shape indefinitely and only mechanical failure, such as cracking through temperature change or chipping through mechanical impact, will alter that fact.

Liebig did not himself apply his method to telescopic mirrors. That was left for Steinheil and Foucault, each of whom did it independently, the former in 1856 and the latter in 1857. With that, the reflecting telescope moved forward to compete with the refractors from a new and far more advantageous position, since not only did better mirrors become possible, but (even more important) larger mirrors became practical.

Foucault, in 1859, produced something else that gave the art of mirror-making another lift.

The grinding of the mirror is a tedious process that is begun with curved grinders moving against the face of the glass while rotating and also moving laterally in a complex pattern. The actual grinding material is a series of finer and finer powders of hard materials that can scratch into the glass or metal. Finally, the grinding tool is covered with pitch and then finer and finer jeweler's rouge (consisting of microscopic particles of iron oxide) is used until a highly polished curved surface is obtained.

This surface is spherical to start with but additional polishing is applied to calculated portions of the mirror, mostly around the rim, to introduce a slight flattening that will convert the curve to the paraboloid shape that will succeed in bringing all the reflected light from every part of the mirror into a sharp focus.

Once that is all done, how can one be sure that the curve is really perfectly paraboloid (or varies just enough from the paraboloid to make up for tiny local imperfections in the glass) without actually going to the prohibitive trouble of mounting it in a telescope and putting it to the actual test — then regrinding, mounting it again, and so on.

Halley, as mentioned earlier in the book, had used a pinhole of light at the focus of the paraboloid which, if the mirror were perfectly formed, would light the entire surface uniformly.

Foucault invented a very simple and satisfactory improvement on the process. He placed the lighted pinhole slightly to one side of the focus, so that the light radiated out in all directions to the mirror and was then reflected to a point just on the other side of the focus. There it could be seen by the eye and the entire mirror would seem uniformly bright since light would be coming from every part of it.

He next moved the edge of a knife blade in front of his eye from one side to cut the light rays from the pinhole. When this is done, the mirror goes uniformly dark all over. If any part of the mirror curves too gently or too sharply, the uniformity will be gone — either one spot will remain light when all the rest is dark or one spot will grow dark while all the rest is light. These spots can be located and the mirror ground to correct the imperfections.

The Foucault test is even more precise than is needed since it will detect irregularities in the range of a ten millionth of a centimeter. The test is so delicate that if the mirror is touched by a finger, the warmth of that finger will cause a local expansion that will produce a change in the mirror's shape of exceeding smallness — yet one that is easily made visible by the test.

The combination of a silver-fronted glass mirror and Foucault's test made the metal mirror obsolete. One last large reflector of the older type was built in 1862 and set up in Melbourne, Australia. The Australians wanted a 122-centimeter (48-inch) mirror but were unwilling to trust what they considered the insufficiently tried silver-fronting technique and insisted on a metal one. They got what they wanted, the telescope being manufactured by Grubb.

When the new reflector was set up, however, the mirror quickly tarnished and it was clear it would have to be sent back to Great Britain for repolishing. Attempts to do the job in Australia were not successful and the telescope was useless. After that, there was no way in which the metal mirror could win out in the astronomer's mind over glass.

Of course, it would be useful to have an example of a silver-fronted glass mirror that clearly did the job well. One of the pioneers in this respect was Henry Draper, who had been trying to grind metal mirrors with disappointing results. He heard about the new mirrors from John Herschel and began to try the technique at once. He modified Liebig's method for forming the silver deposit and got even harder films that could withstand polishing better.

He labored over the glass, too, in order to minimize even slight and temporary temperature variations in it during the course of forming the mirror. In 1862, the same year in which the Melbourne reflector proved such a failure, Draper's 39-centimeter (15.5-inch) silver-fronted glass mirror proved successful. In 1867 Draper began the construction of a 71-centimeter (28-inch) silver-fronted glass mirror. It was not till 1872 that he was satisfied with what he had, but thereafter it worked very well indeed.

In 1877 a 120-centimeter (47-inch) silver-fronted glass mirror was installed into a telescope in France. This reflector is still used today.

In Great Britain, Andrew Ainslie Common (1841–1903), who had been working with a 14-centimeter (5.5-inch) refractor, decided he needed a larger instrument. After considering the possibilities of larger lenses, he decided to switch to a silver-fronted glass reflector. For the purpose, he employed the instrument-maker George Calver, who made many mirrors of the new type. To Common's order, Calver made a 91-centimeter (36-inch) mirror which was mounted in a telescope in 1879.

Common and Calver tried to make a 153-centimeter (60-inch)

mirror for a still larger telescope but they never quite got that to the pitch of proper perfection.

But even as the Clarks were triumphing with their large refractors, it was clear to many astronomers that the silver-fronted glass mirrors were allowing the reflectors to close in again, and that the future lay with them.

The New Star Maps

Even as the large telescopes, both refractors and reflectors, were dominating the field of astronomic instrumentation in the latter half of the nineteenth century, observation by eye was rapidly losing almost all its importance. It did not do so, however, without producing a monumental last work.

In the 1840s and 1850s, the German astronomer Friedrich Wilhelm August Argelander (1799–1875), at Bonn Observatory, used an 8.5 centimeter (3.4 inch) refractor, with the lens produced by Fraunhofer, to pinpoint the positions of all the stars he could see down through the 9th magnitude. He kept the telescope fixed to a particular latitude and recorded each star as the Earth's rotation carried it past the field of view.

Between 1859 and 1862 he published the giant *Bonner Durchmusterung (Bonn Survey)* in four volumes, locating the positions of 457,848 stars from the north celestial pole to 2° south of the celestial equator. It was a gigantic job which was gradually extended into the south celestial hemisphere till by 1930 it covered the entire sky. The whole catalogue was reissued by astronomical demand in 1950.

Still, it remains the last star map to be produced by direct visual observation through a telescope.

Even before the *Bonner Durchmusterung* was published, George Bond was pointing out that what was needed for star mapping was photography. A photograph of the stars in a portion of the sky would produce a permanent record. If the position of any star in the photograph was known, the positions of all the rest could be calculated at leisure.

The application of photography to the stars, however, was not easy. Photography of the sun, the moon, and the planets was successful even in the 1860s, but the stars were far dimmer and to make their feeble glow imprint itself on the photographic plate was a problem indeed.

One who attempted to produce stellar photographs was Rutherfurd, whose observatory was in the back yard of his home in New York at 2nd Avenue and 11th Street. There he had a 28.5 centimeter (11.2 inch) refractor. (He had tried a silvered glass reflector but was disappointed in it as far as photography was concerned.) Using his refractor, he took a series of photographs of star groups and double stars, with exposures of up to three minutes. Another American astronomer, Benjamin Apthorp Gould (1824–1896), worked at an observatory at Córdoba, Argentina, between 1870 and 1884 and there photographed the stars of the southern hemisphere.

The trouble was, though, that the collodion process of photography used a plate smeared with a wet solution and while this was quite suitable for the short exposures that were sufficient for the brighter celestial objects, it was not adequate for conditions where long exposures were absolutely necessary. The "wet plate," drying with time, failed before dim stars could be recorded, so that the work of Rutherfurd and Gould could not compete with the use of the eye.

In 1871, however, the British chemist Richard Leach Maddox (1816–1902) used gelatin in place of collodion as a solvent for the silver compound. Gelatin sets into a jellylike material dry to the touch, and it holds on to its moisture strongly enough not to lose it under ordinary conditions, so that it does not dry out with time and can be used for long exposures. It is with this "dry-plate" technique that stellar photography became practical.

The dry plate was less sensitive at first than the wet plate, but by 1876 methods had been worked out for heating the gelatin first and bringing the silver compounds closer to the edge of silver precipitation. By 1880 the dry plate had become some sixty times as sensitive as the wet plate at its best had ever been. What's more, whereas the wet plates had had to be prepared just before use and developed immediately after, the dry plates could be bought ready-made and used whenever desired. They could then be developed at any time after use, even long after.

Another shortcoming of photography in the wet-film days, as compared with the human eye, was that the silver salts on the film did not respond equally to all parts of the spectrum. They were most easily precipitated by the violet end of the spectrum. Red and orange light scarcely affected the film. To be sure, almost every star has enough light of all colors in its radiation to affect the film, but those which were red-orange in color showed up far more faintly in photographs than they appeared to the eye.

In 1873, however, the German chemist Hermann Wilhelm Vogel (1834–1898) found that if certain dyes were added to the emulsion, they would absorb the red end of the spectrum and the silver salts would then be more sensitive to that end. In this way, the entire range of the spectrum could be made available for study.

The new dry-plate technique produced its first important result almost by accident. In 1879 the Scottish astronomer David Gill (1843–1914) had taken over the post at the Cape of Good Hope observatory. In 1882 a great comet was visible in the sky and Gill decided to photograph it. He used an ordinary camera which he strapped to his telescope.

He got an excellent photograph of the comet but what pleased him far more was that he also got an excellent photograph of the background of stars. It immediately occurred to him that he might make the kind of photographic star-map survey that astronomers had been speculating about for twenty years — all the more so since the great *Bonner Durchmusterung* had left the south celestial hemisphere untouched.

Gill obtained a better camera, adapted to the task, and over a period of years swept the sky, taking photographs of each bit of the far southern portion of it. The Dutch astronomer Jacobus Cornelius Kapteyn (1851–1922) took on the task of interpreting these photographs. He calculated all the positions — a ten-year task — and in 1904 published the *Cape Photographic Durchmusterung*, a catalogue of 454,000 stars within 19° of the celestial south pole.

Work similar to that of Gill was done in the northern hemisphere by the Henry brothers in France, and in 1886 and 1887 they obtained stellar photographs of astonishing excellence, using a 34-centimeter (13.4-inch) refractor.

Though the work of Gill and the Henrys superseded the centuries-long technique of star mapping by eye, this did not mean that visual observation through the telescope had come to an end altogether. Even if we place amateur observations to one side, there remain delicate measurements to be made of the separation of closely spaced binary stars and of the changing separations of stars due to the parallax of one of them. In this field, refractors still hold their own in an age when the reflector is, generally, king. Refractors generally show a sharp image over a larger field than a reflector of similar size does.

Still, photography has another advantage over the eye in addition to the former's production of a permanent record. The photographic plate gathers light cumulatively. Something that is too faint to be seen by eye remains unseen no matter how long we look at it. The retina of the eye is constantly clearing its impressions and starting over so that we can see something only if it is bright enough to activate the retina in a small fraction of a second.

The photographic plate, on the other hand, records the light in terms of a chemical reaction, the mark of which remains indefinitely. And to the initial reaction are added progressively additional reactions as light continues to strike a particular point on the plate. If an object, then, is too dim to make a perceptible mark on the plate at first, it will eventually make one if exposure is continued long enough.

This means that a photographic plate exposed to the same portion of the heavens through the same telescope for longer and longer periods will show more and more stars, as dimmer and dimmer stars affect it. Naturally, the presence of relatively bright stars will produce reactions that spread over an area of the plate, that overexpose portions of it, in other words, and eventually the general dim illumination of the sky will fog the plate, so the process can't be continued indefinitely. Nevertheless, any telescope can make more stars visible photographically than it can do so optically.

In the case of stars, it is only the number that is affected by lengthening time of exposure. It is something more in the case of nebulae, those little foggy patches of light scattered here and there among the stars. A nebula can be a cloud of dust and gas or a conglomeration of stars so distant that they cannot be made out individually. In either case, there are brighter and dimmer portions to the nebula and the whole has some distinct shape.

By means of photography, portions of the nebula that are too dim to be seen by eye become apparent and a more nearly true picture of its shape can be obtained. In some cases, the whole is too dim to be seen by the eye, even through a good telescope, and it is only by photography that it first becomes apparent.

Consider the Pleiades, for instance, the most notable star cluster visible to the unaided eye. Six stars, set closely together in the constellation Taurus are visible, though many more can be seen by telescope. In 1885, the Henry brothers took a photograph of the Pleiades that showed some fogginess about the two brightest stars of the group.

About the same time, the English astronomer Isaac Roberts (1829–1904), who had planned a thorough program of stellar photography and then found himself caught up in nebular photography instead, recognized the fact that telescopes intended for time-exposure photography had to be constructed to more careful specification than was required for optical observations. In order to gather light on a particular point on the photographic plate, there must be no shaking of the stand or flexing of the tube, since that would produce fuzziness over a period of time. The longer the period of time in question, the smaller the amount of shaking and flexing that would suffice to ruin everything. Furthermore, the driving mechanism that moves the telescope in time with the heavens has to be all the more precise since tiny errors would mount up unacceptably over an exposure of minutes, where no difficulty would be involved under optical investigation.

Roberts modified his 51-centimeter (20-inch) reflector to meet his requirements and in 1886 showed that the Pleiades cluster was enmeshed in a cloudy, filamentous cloud. The obvious explanation was that it was a vast thin cloud of dust in which the stars were embedded and which diffused and reflected the starlight it received.

That same year, he discovered something more interesting still when he photographed the Andromeda nebula. Till then, it had seemed, to the eye, a dim oval haze of light and nothing more even in the best telescopes. The photograph caught the outer regions of the nebulae that were too dim to see by eye and showed quite clearly that the outer regions had a spiral structure. The Andromeda nebula, in other words, seemed to be of the same species as the Whirlpool nebula, discovered forty years earlier by Rosse.

The spiral nature of the Andromeda nebula, which is seen almost edge-on, was much harder to detect than that of the Whirlpool nebula, which is seen full-face. Even so, Robert's 51-centimeter (20-inch) reflector could do what Rosse's 184-centimeter (72-inch) Leviathan would never have been able to do. Photography made the difference.

The American astronomer James Edward Keeler continued the work on nebular photography, and he had one advantage that Roberts did not have. Keeler worked in Lick Observatory at Mount Hamilton, California, where the seeing was much better, much more often, than in England. Keeler also had the 92-centimeter (36-inch) reflector.

Between 1898 and 1900, Keeler began to photograph hundreds of faint nebulae and produced several important results. In the first place, he demonstrated once and for all that reflectors were superior to refractors for photographing dim objects and that helped insure that the twentieth century would be exclusively reflector as far as the building of large telescopes was concerned.

Keeler also showed that the nebulae were far more common than had been thought. Keeler's careful photography of the heavens showed there were at least 100,000 of them, ten times the quantity that had earlier been estimated. Furthermore, Keeler showed that most of them had a spiral structure. The "spiral nebulae" were shown to make up a common astronomical species.

Yet however well photography served in the glamorous regions of the stars and nebulae, it came to be of increasing service within the solar system, too. It served to map the moon in instant detail and to record, permanently, the appearance of the planets. In addition, it made possible the discovery of new objects.

In 1891 the German astronomer Maximilian Franz Joseph Cornelius Wolf (1863–1932) adapted the technique of photography to the wholesale discovery of asteroids. By keeping the telescope moving with the apparent motion of the stars, each star appeared on the photographic plate as a sharp point. Any asteroid, crossing the field of vision, did so, inevitably, at some motion relative to the stars, so that it appeared as a streak of light.

Over the space of a generation, Wolf discovered 582 asteroids in this way and his successor, Karl Reinmuth, discovered 980.

Wolf discovered Achilles, the first of the "Trojan asteroids," in 1906. This is one of a group of asteroids that travels in Jupiter's orbit, in step with that mighty planet and in such a way that Jupiter, the sun, and the asteroids form an equilateral triangle. Such a triangular arrangement had been shown to be stable by the Italian-French astronomer Joseph-Louis Lagrange (1736–1813) in 1772, but this was the first actual example of the situation found to exist.

Another important asteroid discovery was made, photographically, in 1898, by the German astronomer Gustav Witt. This was the asteroid Eros, which proved to have an orbit that was closer to the sun, in part, than that of Mars. Its orbit approached closer to that of Earth than any of the major planets and when both bodies were properly situated, Eros could be as close as 22.5 million kilometers (14 million miles) to Earth. It was the first of the so-called "Earth-grazers" to be discovered.

8. Reflectors Take Over

Stellar Spectra

If one could photograph the light of a heavenly object in the ordinary way, one could also photograph that light once it was spread out into a spectrum. Naturally, it is harder to photograph a spectrum than the source itself, because the light of the source is spread out over an area in forming the spectrum and is therefore dimmer at every given point than the spectrum is. This means that longer exposures are required to photograph the spectrum of a star than the star itself, and it also means that without the development of silver-fronted glass mirrors which made large reflectors possible, and without the development of sensitive dry-plate photography, the spectra of anything more than those of a few of the brightest stars could not have been studied.

The necessary advances in technology were made, however, and astronomers were straining to move forward. Clearly, there would be no end to the convenience of having numerous stellar spectra permanently recorded, to be studied at leisure.

Such was the eagerness of astronomers that the history of stellar spectra begins before the technology had become adequate for the purpose. As early as 1863, Huggins had focused the stellar spectra he was trying to observe on a photographic plate, thus producing the first spectral photographs of the stars Sirius and Capella. The photographs were faint and showed no lines. The wet plates used were inconvenient and the telescope was not steady enough to produce a good focus.

In May 1872 a more successful photograph of a stellar spectrum was taken by Henry Draper. He used his 71-centimeter (28-inch) reflector and brought the light of Vega through a quartz prism and then onto a photographic plate. Here, too, no lines were visible, but in August of that year, Draper tried again and this time he obtained a photograph of the spectrum of Vega which showed the existence of four lines. It was the first time that stellar spectral lines had been photographed.

The German astronomer Hermann Karl Vogel (1841–1907) began work on spectrography in 1873 and was the first to make a real specialty of it. Beginning in 1888, he used his spectrographs to determine the velocities of approach or recession of many stars with, for the first time, good accuracy.

Even without spectrography, enough stellar spectra had been observed visually to make it possible to suggest that their natures varied widely among themselves and that stars could be grouped into stellar classes. The advent of spectrography enormously strengthened this view and Draper's work was crucial here.

Before he died in November 1882, at the age of eighty-five, Draper had made spectrographs of dozens of stars. Edward Charles Pickering (1846–1919), the director of Harvard College Observatory, studied the spectrograms Draper had left behind, painstakingly measured the positions of the lines, and compared them with those of the sun's spectrum. By such labor, he showed, for instance, that Arcturus and Capella were of the same spectral class as the sun.

Pickering then went on to initiate a huge program of stellar spectrography, making use of the idea of an objective prism. Instead of having the light of a single star pass through a prism near the telescope focus, he placed a narrow prism just in front of the telescope objective. In this way, every star whose light reached the photographic plate at the other end reached it as a spectrum. Many spectra were thus recorded on a single plate.

By 1889 Pickering had made a complete spectrographic survey of the stars of the northern hemisphere and was setting up an observatory at Arequipa, Peru, in order to continue the survey in the southern hemisphere. A quarter of a million stellar spectra were eventually obtained and were included in the *Henry Draper Catalogue* (which was not completed till 1924).

The growing spectrographic survey was more than a mere collection. For one thing, it served the same function in the heavens that the careful cataloguing of plant and animal species did on Earth. The biological cataloguing of the species carried through in the eighteenth century showed such an intricate pattern of relationships among the species that it was almost inevitable that a theory of biological evolution was worked out in the nineteenth century.

In the same way, the spectrographic survey of the late nineteenth century resulted in the grouping of stars into spectral classes in an ever more refined and meaningful way, and this gave rise to notions of stellar evolution that were to reach fruition in the twentieth century.

The major portion of the delicate work required to classify the stellar spectra into main groups was that of Annie Jump Cannon (1863–1941). The letter listing of the spectra and of the classes of stars, O, B, A, F, G, K, M, N, R, S (in order of decreasing temperature), together with transitions indicated by dividing each letter into numerical divisions was originated by her.

A fellow astronomer, Antonia Caetana Maury (1866–1952), had evolved a spectral classification superior to Cannon's but one that was a little too complicated to come into general use. The failure here was made up by a remarkable discovery she was able to announce in 1889 as a result of her photography of the spectrum of the star Zeta Ursae Majoris.

This star, better known as "Mizar," is the middle star in the handle of the Big Dipper. In the days of naked-eye observation of the heavens, it was the best known "double star," for near it, just far enough to be seen separately, if one's eyes were acute, was the dimmer star, Alcor.

Mizar and Alcor were not double in the sense of really being near each other. They just happened to be in very nearly the same direction from Earth, with one much farther than the other. In 1650, using the telescope, the Italian astronomer Giovanni Battista Riccioli found that Mizar was itself two stars that were impossible to see separately without the telescope. The two stars that made up Mizar were really close and physically related, the kind of star which Herschel, a century and a half later, was to call a binary — two stars revolving about a common center of gravity.

The two binary components are Zeta Ursae Majoris A and Zeta Ursae Majoris B, with A the brighter, and it was the spectrum of A that Maury was studying. When comparing plates of the spectrum taken at different times, she noted that some of the brighter lines were sometimes double, sometimes single.

A closer study of the various plates showed that each bright line was really two that, as time passed, separated, came together, crossed, separated in the other direction, came together, crossed, and so on.

Since a line shift toward the red means a star is receding and a line shift toward the violet means it is approaching, it seemed clear that Zeta Ursae Majoris A had to be two stars, since one star could not both approach and recede simultaneously. The two stars were so close together that the best available telescope would fail to separate their images. They circled each other in an orbit which appeared nearly edge-on from Earth's point of view so that as one star was approaching, the other was receding, and this was revealed in the spectrum.

Zeta Ursae Majoris A was thus shown to be a "spectroscopic binary." H. K. Vogel discovered another spectroscopic binary in 1890 and then devoted himself to a search for further examples. Over 1500 spectroscopic binaries are now known.

In 1908 the American astronomer Edwin Brant Frost (1866–1935) discovered that Zeta Ursae Majoris B was also a spectroscopic binary. Mizar is, therefore, a four-star system, two spectroscopic binaries circling each other as an ordinary binary (and with a fifth and unrelated star seeming close to it in the sky as seen from our terrestrial stage).

With the increasing importance of spectroscopy, it is not surprising that attempts were made to improve the means by which spectra were formed. The prism was not susceptible of much improvement, but diffraction gratings were.

In 1881 the American physicist Henry Augustus Rowland (1848–1901) developed concave gratings of lines on metal. This not only dispersed the wavelengths to form a spectrum but focused the light so that no lenses or mirrors were required as part of the spectroscopic system. Light did not have to pass through glass and be partly absorbed or strike a mirror and be only partly reflected. The spectra were therefore brighter.

Rowland proceeded to rule lines more finely in this gratings than anyone had before. He scored up to 8000 lines per centimeter over a stretch of 15 centimeters (20,000 lines per inch over a stretch of 6 inches). As a result he prepared a map, between the years 1886 and 1895, of the solar spectrum that was some 12 meters (40 feet) long, in which the precise location of some 20,000 lines could be determined. Some of Rowland's gratings are still in use.

The Spectroheliograph

The next step was taken by Hale, who had made the Yerkes refractor possible. Indeed, he took the step even before that large refractor had come into view. While he was still a student at Massachusetts Institute of Technology (from which he graduated in 1890), he began thinking of a device by which an object could be photographed by the light of some specific *part* of its spectrum.

It wasn't likely that this could be done in the case of the stars generally, since so little light was delivered by them that, once that light was spread out over the spectrum, no single part of it would yield much additional information if the star were photographed by that alone. This was especially so since a star is virtually a point source of light and only all of it can be photographed whether by part or by all its spectrum.

But what about the sun? It is an extended body so that small portions of it could be photographed, and it was bright enough so that even the light of a small part of its spectrum would suffice. Before he was out of college, Hale had the principle of the device needed to do this clearly in his mind. It was something he called a "spectroheliograph" (the stem "helio" coming from the Greek word for "sun").

In the spectroheliograph, light from a portion of the sun's outermost rim makes its way through an appropriately placed slit and is focused by way of a telescope through a prism. The spectrum so formed falls on a photographic plate which is covered by an opaque lid containing a slit. The slit is so placed that only a small, carefully chosen portion of the sun's spectrum reaches the photographic plate.

151

The portion of the sun's outermost rim is thus photographed at one end of the photographic plate by the light, let us say, of a portion of the red end of the spectrum. The two slits now move in synchronous fashion, so that a progressively farther-inward portion of the sun is photographed on a progressively farther-inward portion of the photographic plate, always by the same portion of the spectrum.

The end result is that the photograph of the entire sun is taken by the kind of light produced particularly strongly by, say, hydrogen atoms or by calcium atoms. One could in this way note the varying concentrations of hydrogen or calcium from point to point on the sun's face. A similar device was worked out, independently, by the French astrophysicist Henri Alexandre Deslandres (1853–1948) and both were in operation about 1891.

Where photographs of the sun by ordinary light show a bright sphere that is featureless except for the comparatively dark sunspots, the spectroheliograph by calcium light shows the disc to have a mottled appearance, with bright areas around the sunspots. By hydrogen light the sunspots are less marked, but flares and other disturbances show up clearly as dark dots and lines.

Once Hale had arranged for the construction of the Yerkes refractor, he tried to fit it with a spectroheliograph but found that an instrument needed for the purpose was too large and cumbersome and results were mediocre.

It seemed to him that a different kind of structure was necessary. There had to be a "solar telescope," one which could be fixed in place, with an adjustable "coelostat," a mirror that would reflect the sun's image into the objective steadily as the sun moved across the sky. In that case the spectroheliographic equipment could also be fixed in position on stone or concrete piers, and much better results could be expected.

The first instrument of this sort which was built was destroyed in a fire and a second had to be constructed. This second one, called the "Snow telescope" because it was made possible by a grant of $10,000 from a Miss Helen Snow, was successfully completed in the autumn of 1903.

There was nothing wrong with the Snow telescope itself, but the images received were too fuzzy to be useful because of the quivering of air subjected to different temperatures from place to place as it heated and cooled.

It seemed to Hale that, for the proper study of the sun, a mountaintop would be preferable, since there the air would be distinctly thinner than at or near sea level and there would be less interference with temperature change. And, if some mountain were going to be chosen, it might as well be one in a relatively warm area and one where the incidence of sunny days was high. What about southern California?

Some years before, William Henry Pickering (1858–1938), the younger brother of E. C. Pickering, had spoken highly of the telescopic view from Mount Wilson, which was 1800 meters (5900 feet) high and about 48 kilometers (30 miles) northeast of Pasadena. He had established a small observatory there.

Hale, after investigating possible sites, concurred in the view of Mount Wilson's suitability. In 1904 various instruments, including the Snow telescope, were brought to Pasadena and then lifted to the mountaintop along a narrow, winding, steep road that was more than 10 kilometers (6 miles) long.

Observing the sun was still a problem. The air was thinner than at sea level but it was not entirely absent. Changing temperature distorted the crucial figures of the lenses and mirrors, too.

Hale had to take numerous measures to minimize disturbance. He tried to restrict viewing to the morning and evening hours, to shield the mirrors from direct sunlight except at the moment of viewing, and so on. He also built a tunnel into which he could place a vertical telescope, outfitted with a spectroheliograph, keeping the whole thing underground.

Despite the difficulties, results were most useful. The spectroheliographic work at Mount Wilson showed that the spectral lines produced in the regions of the sunspots were more intense than in the undisturbed sections of the solar surface. That would be expected if the sunspot regions were at lower temperatures than other parts of the sun and therefore more efficiently absorbed light passing through them.

What was more curious was the observation in 1908 that some of the lines in the sunspot regions were doubled. Hale and his co-workers interpreted this in accordance with the work of the Dutch physicist Pieter Zeeman (1865–1943). In 1896 Zeeman had shown that an ordinary single spectral line will be split into several components when the light source is between the poles of a strong electromagnet.

What Hale was observing then was a "Zeeman effect" in the spectral lines of sunspots, and it was clear that those spots were embedded in a strong magnetic field many times stronger than Earth's magnetic field. It was the first observation of magnetic effects elsewhere than on Earth.

Just as the Earth has a north magnetic pole and a south magnetic pole, so do the sunspots. In 1913, when one eleven-year sunspot cycle ended and the next began, it turned out that the new sunspots, as judged by their spectral lines, had the north and south magnetic poles reversed as compared with the old sunspots. Such a reversal, apparently, takes place in each new cycle, so that magnetically the sunspot cycle is twenty-two years long.

In 1926 Hale made the spectroheliograph more flexible by arranging to have the slits oscillate back and forth so that separate views of a portion of the sun by a specific part of the spectrum could be seen as a succession of closely spaced "stills." The result in such a "spectrohelioscope" was precisely what one has in a motion picture film. The stills melt together as they are viewed and astronomers could see flares and prominences on the sun grow and subside.

Stellar Evolution

As the twentieth century opened, interest was rising in the question of the evolution of the stars, of their changes in the course of time, of their birth and development and death.

The first breakthrough in this direction began with the consideration of the surface temperatures of stars. From experience on Earth, it was to be expected that with higher temperatures there was some tendency to have the emitted light shift color away from the red end of the spectrum. It was to be expected, then, that yellow stars were hotter than red stars and that blue white stars were hotter still. In 1893, however, the German physicist Wilhelm Wien

(1864–1928) showed just how spectra would change with temperature and it became possible to use the spectra to make quite accurate measurements of stellar temperatures.

It was, for instance, possible to tell from the spectra, from the distribution of energy among the various parts, from the nature of the spectral lines present that the surface temperature of the sun was 6000° C., while that of the white star, Sirius, was 11,000° C., and that of the blue white star, Alpha Crucis, was 21,000° C. On the other hand, red stars can have surface temperatures as low as 2500° C.

Once the matter of stellar temperatures came to the fore, the Danish astronomer Ejnar Hertzsprung (1873–1967) noted a peculiar phenomenon. Allowing for differences in brightness due to distance, he noted that some red stars were exceedingly luminous and some were exceedingly dim. Since both types of star had similar spectra, both had to possess the same comparatively low surface temperature and both had to have similar luminosities per square mile of surface.

The only way to account for the enormous brightness of some of the red stars was to suppose that their surface was extremely large and that the low luminosity per square mile was made up for by the vast number of square miles available. Hertzsprung began to speak of "red giants" and "red dwarfs," therefore, and the most interesting point to be made in this connection was that there were *no* red stars of intermediate size.

As long as everything about stars seemed distributed in random fashion, as long as there were stars at all distances, at all temperatures, with all kinds of spectra, it was hard to make order out of the stellar population and decide whether there was any definite way in which stars changed in the course of time.

Hertzsprung had now pointed out for the first time a gross lack of randomness — very large cool stars and very small cool stars and nothing in between. At once theories of stellar evolution arose. Could stars, for instance, form as large volumes of gas, barely red hot, condense and grow hotter until they are blue white stars of medium size, and then continue to shrink and cool off till they were small stars barely red hot? *

* This turned out to be a wrong view of stellar evolution, but even a wrong view is of importance if it entices scientists into thinking about a problem.

In order to determine what the course of stellar evolution might be, it was necessary to wring as much detail from stellar spectra as possible and Hale, having been satisfied with Mount Wilson as a site for astronomical observation, determined to build large reflectors there in order to accomplish that.

As it happened, Hale's father had obtained, some years before, a 153-centimeter (60-inch) mirror-blank from Paris, and had paid $25,000 for it. It had originally been intended for Yerkes Observatory, which had agreed to supply the telescope itself plus a building to house it in. Lack of funds brought that hope to the ground but in 1903 Hale had managed to obtain a grant from Carnegie Foundation, and now he set about constructing the telescope and the necessary housing on Mount Wilson.

In charge of the design was George Willis Ritchey (1864–1945), who had worked with Hale at Yerkes. Ritchey in his initial grindings of the mirror plate became the first to use "Carborundum," or silicon carbide, for this purpose. Carborundum had first been formed by the American inventor Edward Goodrich Acheson (1856–1931) in 1891, and it proved to be harder than any other substance known at that time, excepting only diamond (and, of course, Carborundum was much cheaper than diamond). Carborundum had six times the cutting power of emery, a form of aluminum oxide which had previously been used at this stage.

Extraordinary precautions were taken to keep the room in which the grinding was taking place dust-free and at constant temperature and by December 1908 the 153-centimeter (60-inch) reflector was ready for work. Only Rosse's Leviathan had been larger, but there was no comparison really. Considering the excellent seeing on Mount Wilson and the ease with which the new reflector could be manipulated, the fact that Rosse's mirror had been larger and its light-gathering power 1.5 times greater went for nothing. Hale's new telescope was infinitely the superior of the Leviathan. It was, indeed, the most useful telescope built up to that time. With four hours of exposure, stars as dim as the 20th magnitude could be photographed and stellar spectra could be obtained with better definition than ever before.

Meanwhile a new system of focusing had been developed for reflectors. Light was reflected by two or more small, flat mirrors to a point outside the telescope in such a way that although the telescope moved, this was compensated for by the mirror arrangement, and the focus remained in the same place. This "coude system" (a French word meaning "bent like an elbow" to describe the bending of the light by reflection) was invented by the Austrian-French astronomer Maurice Loewy (1833–1907) in 1894.

It made it far easier to use instruments such as cameras, spectrographs, and spectroheliographs in connection with reflectors, since those instruments could now be placed at the stationary focus.

One of the advances made possible by Hale's reflector came in 1915 when the American astronomer Walter Sydney Adams (1876–1956) used it to take the spectrum of the tiny companion of Sirius (Sirus B), the one that had been deduced by Bessel and first seen by Clark.

Rather to Adams' astonishment, the spectrum clearly showed that the surface of Sirius B was at a temperature of 10,000° C. as hot as that of Sirius itself, and considerably hotter than that of the sun. But if Sirius B had a surface as hot as that of Sirius, the two stars should be equally luminous and they were certainly equally distant from Earth. Why, then, did they not appear of equal brightness?

The situation was the reverse of that of the red giants. The red giants, with cool dim surfaces, had to be enormous in order to emit enough light to seem as bright as they are. Sirius B, with a white-hot surface, had to be pigmyish to seem as dim as it was. In fact, Sirius B would have to have a diameter of not more than 27,000 kilometers (17,000 miles) and be no larger in size than the planet Uranus. It was a "white dwarf" star.

The mass of Sirius B, however, had to be roughly equal to that of the sun, judging from the manner in which it made Sirius itself wobble in its path. If the mass of the sun is condensed into the size of the planet Uranus, the result is a star with a density 8000 times that of the dense metal platinum.

Such a result would have seemed ridiculous not many years before—so ridiculous that Adams's observations would have seemed so obviously wrong that they would have been dismissed out of hand. As it happened, however, it had been discovered in 1896 that the uranium atom was constantly giving off radiations and this led to a course of chemical and physical research that showed that the various atoms of matter were made up of still smaller "subatomic particles."

In 1911 the New Zealand–born British physicist Ernest Rutherford (1871–1937) had clearly demonstrated that the atom's mass is concentrated into a tiny "atomic nucleus" far smaller than the atom itself. This atomic nucleus was surrounded by almost massless electrons. If, then, under the pull of gravity, the atomic structure was smashed, if the light electrons were, so to speak, brushed aside and the heavy atomic nuclei came closer together than they could in the case of intact atoms, it was quite possible for the density of matter to become far greater than anything seen on Earth.

It was this which made the enormous density of Sirius B acceptable. It also meant that an astronomic observation of a dim object nearly nine light-years away offered striking confirmation of a sophisticated physical theory of atomic structure worked out on Earth.

Then, too, the discovery of the small size and superdensity of Sirius B was the first step toward working out the details of the final stages of stellar evolution into a variety of condensed objects of which the white dwarfs were, in fact, the least strange.

The Mount Wilson reflector was used also on objects of the solar system, and in particular, on Mars.

Mars, the second closest to ourselves of the planets of the solar system, had gained a new interest in 1877, the year in which Hall had discovered the two Martian satellites and Schiaparelli had reported the existence of the Martian canals.

The canals were by no means universally accepted. E. C. Pickering, for instance, who watched Mars carefully, could not see the canals, and neither could E. E. Barnard, an excellent observer.

The French astronomer Camille Flammarion was, on the other hand, enthusiastic for the canals, writing a book proclaiming the existence of intelligent life on Mars in 1892. In 1894 Percival Lowell (1855–1916), the scion of a well-to-do Boston family, entered the fray on the side of Flammarion.

Lowell had enough money to establish an observatory where he could be sure of clear nights and clean air — not in California as Hale was to do but in Flagstaff, Arizona. He observed Mars assiduously for a period of fifteen years, first with a 46-centimeter (18-inch) refractor and then with a 61-centimeter (24-inch) refractor which he put into action in 1896. These were excellent telescopes, built by Clark, and by using them Lowell was able to map intricate canal patterns, which he sometimes saw in doubled form and which seemed to meet in "oases."

He wrote popular books on the subject, the first of which was *Mars,* published in 1895, in which he upheld the claim that there was intelligent life on that planet.

On the whole most astronomers did not accept the Lowell view, but everything rested on what could be seen on the Martian surface. Some astronomers could see the canals but some could not. Those who could not insisted the canals were optical illusions, with the eyes manufacturing straight lines out of irregular markings. Those who could see the canals, however, blamed the failure of others to see them on less-than-perfect vision or less-than-adequate telescopes or both.

Nor could the new technique of photography help. Photographs of the Martian surface were invariably fuzzier than one could see by eye, because of the graininess of the film and because the necessary length of exposure gave time for temperature variations in the atmosphere to fuzz the fine detail slightly.

In 1905, when Mars was again making a close approach, Lowell redoubled his observational efforts and then in 1906 and 1908 published two more books on the subject, *Mars and Its Canals* and *Mars as the Abode of Life.*

Naturally, there were high hopes that the new reflector might settle the matter. In 1911 Barnard, perhaps the keenest-eyed astronomer in history, went to Mount Wilson and used the great telescope for a month. He saw no canals but, on the other hand, there was no indication that the vision of the surface through the new reflector was perceptibly better than through smaller instruments.

Indeed, the large reflectors of the twentieth century, though immeasurably useful in their studies of the stars, never earned their keep as far as planetary observations were concerned. The turbulence of the air limited the detail that could be seen and enlarging the image enlarged the turbulence, too. When the time came that the problem was indeed settled and the controversy over the Martian canals was finally put to rest, it was to be through advances as far beyond the telescopes of 1911 as those were beyond the unaided eye.

Dwarfing the Leviathan at Last

The accomplishments of the Mount Wilson reflector did not satisfy Hale. He was after bigger game and after bigger telescopes to catch that game. He had built the 153-centimeter (60-inch) reflector largely because a mirror-plate of that size had been available, but he had set his sights higher.

Even while that reflector was being built, a Los Angeles business-man, J. D. Hooker, had promised Hale $45,000 toward a 212-cen-timeter (84-inch) mirror. Anxious to have his name attached to the largest telescope ever built (one even larger than Rosse's Leviathan) and to make sure that it would not be too soon surpassed, he even increased the grant to make a 254-centimeter (100-inch) mirror pos-sible.

It wasn't at all easy to get a piece of glass weighing nearly 5000 kilograms and of the requisite quality. The same glassworks in France that had supplied the 153-centimeter mirror was, how-ever, willing to tackle the larger job. They were the only ones who were.

Meanwhile, the American astronomer and telescope-maker John Alfred Brashear (1840–1920) was engaged in the most ambitious un-dertaking of his life. He had been among the first to devise a prac-tical method of silvering telescope mirrors and his technique is still used by amateur telescopists. He also produced the fine surfaces on which Rowland ruled some of his most closely spaced gratings for spectroscopic work. Now he, too, was engaged in an attempt to outclass the Mount Wilson telescope. He was producing a 183-cen-timeter (72-inch) mirror for a reflector to be set up at the Dominion Astrophysical Observatory, located some 11 kilometers (7 miles) north of Victoria, British Columbia.

The first mirror-plate produced for Hale's 254-centimeter (100-inch) reflector arrived in Pasadena in 1908, but it was dismissed as useless. It had innumerable tiny air bubbles and the glass had par-tially crystallized so that it was doubtful if it could withstand polish-ing at all let alone be brought to the necessary perfection of curva-ture. The glassworks in France produced other mirror-plates, each one imperfect, and then World War I began and all chance of doing anything for the duration disappeared.

In sheer desperation Hooker returned to the first mirror-plate he had received. Close examination showed that the air bubbles were not near the surface and might not, perhaps, affect the polishing — and that the partial crystallization might not affect it either. At any rate, it was decided to try. Month after month, the polishing went on while the tube and the controls of the telescope were designed and constructed.

While this went on, Brashear's mirror and the telescope housing it (which had also been delayed by World War I) was completed and put into operation in 1918. It was the largest telescope in the world when astronomers looked through it for the first time and the first to match Rosse's great telescope. It was, of course, infinitely superior to Rosse's instrument and it marked a new advance in that it made use of an aluminum mirror-coating rather than a silver one. An aluminum film reflects some 82 percent of the light that falls on it as compared with 65 percent for a fresh silver coating.

But Hale's project was succeeding, too. Despite early misgivings everything worked. In the end, the 254-centimeter (100-inch) mirror was completed and proved excellent. The entire telescope, weighing 90,000 kilograms (100 tons), could be handled easily and made to follow the stars with great precision.

The Hooker telescope came into operation toward the end of 1918, and this brought to a close the very short reign of Brashear's instrument as the largest in the world. The Hooker telescope was the first to dwarf Rosse's Leviathan — after three quarters of a century.

The Hooker telescope was the first instrument, and the only one for three more decades, that could supply the necessary information that would serve to determine the actual size of the Galaxy and our own location in it.

The story of the conquest of the Galaxy begins, of course, before the coming of the Hooker telescope, even long before. It begins with the discovery of certain variable stars whose light dimmed and brightened regularly. In 1784 the Dutch-English astronomer John Goodricke (1764–1786), a deaf mute who died at twenty-one, noted the regular variability of the star Delta Cephei, the light of which rose and fell in a distinctive pattern every 5.37 days.

As time went on, other stars were discovered that varied in the same regular pattern that Delta Cephei did, with periods of anywhere from two days to forty-five days, a period of about a week being particularly common. The stars of this sort were called "Cepheid variables" or just "Cepheids" after the first example of this sort which had been known. By the time the Hooker telescope had come into operation about 170 Cepheids were known.

Some Cepheids were brighter than others and some had longer periods than others. There seemed no correlation between the two, since there could be bright Cepheids and dim Cepheids with periods over the entire range, too.

Of course, the brightness depended upon the distance of the stars as well as upon their intrinsic luminosity. If the distances of the Cepheids were known, the actual luminosity of the stars could be worked out and then some relationship between luminosity and period could be worked out. The trouble was that not a single Cepheid was close enough to have its distance determined by the method of parallax.

In 1912, however, the American astronomer Henrietta Leavitt Swan (1868–1921), working at the observatory in Arequipa in Peru, initiated a new type of Cepheid study. From Arequipa it is possible to study sections of the sky invisible from observatories farther north, and she was particularly interested in photographing the two Magellanic clouds.

These objects, which look like detached portions of the Milky Way, were first described in 1521 by the chronicler accompanying Magellan's voyage of circumnavigation of the globe — whence their names. They are clusters of stars that seem to be separate from the main body of the Galaxy — satellite galaxies, so to speak.

Leavitt, studying the smaller Magellanic cloud, became interested in the Cepheid variables, hundreds of them, which she could see there. If the smaller Magellanic cloud was indeed very far from us, and was separated from us by a distance compared with which its own thickness is small, then all the Cepheids it contains would be at roughly the same distance from us. (Just as all the people in Chicago are at roughly the same distance from New York, regardless of what part of Chicago they may be in.)

In that case, the variation in brightness of the Cepheids in the smaller Magellanic cloud reflects their luminosity, since there are no differences in distance to confuse the issue. In 1912 Leavitt noticed that in the smaller Magellanic cloud, the brighter a Cepheid, the longer its period, the relationship being quite a regular one.

This luminosity-period relationship could be used as a yardstick for distances far greater than those that could be plumbed by parallax. If two Cepheids vary in period, the relative luminosities can be determined, and it can be assumed that the fainter of the two must be further away. Indeed, the relative distances of all Cepheids can be determined.

The reason for the luminosity-period relationship was worked out by the English astronomer Arthur Stanley Eddington (1882–1944). He began with the assumption that the sun, and the stars generally, were gaseous throughout. (This had been suggested first in 1911, by reasoning from the nature of the spectra, by the American astronomer Charles Greeley Abbott [1872–1973].) In that case, Eddington reasoned that the gravitational pull inward, tending to collapse the star, was balanced by the expansive effect of the central temperatures, and this would have to be in the millions of degrees to serve the purpose.

The more massive the star, the greater the internal temperature and, therefore, the brighter the star. This "mass-luminosity law" was finally announced in 1924. Eddington also showed that under certain conditions there could be an oscillation in which, first, the gravitational pull inward predominates and then the temperature-expansion effect forces the surface layers outward. The Cepheids dim and brighten in a regular way because of this pulsation. The more massive the star, the brighter, and, at the same time, the slower the pulsation — hence Leavitt's luminosity-period relationship.

Even before Eddington had worked out the rationale behind the Cepheids, the American astronomer Harlow Shapley (1885–1972) had put them to magnificent use.

He was interested in globular clusters, dense packings of anywhere from 10,000 to 1,000,000 stars. The first of these clusters had been discovered by William Herschel and by the opening of the twentieth century nearly a hundred were known. The odd thing about them was that they were not distributed evenly across the sky, or even evenly along the Milky Way (which contains the vast majority of the stars of the Galaxy). Instead, almost all were in a particular half of the sky, and one third of them were within the bounds of a single constellation, Sagittarius, which makes up only 2 percent of the sky. The first to comment on this maldistribution was John Herschel, the son of William.

Shapley suggested that the globular clusters were, in actual fact, symmetrically distributed, themselves forming a larger "cluster of clusters" centered about the center of the Galaxy. It was we, ourselves, who produced the asymmetry. It was our sun and the solar system that were located far from the center of the Galaxy. Therefore, looking in the direction of Sagittarius where, presumably, the center was located, we took in most of the globular cluster of clusters.

This argument, which was the first to suggest that our solar system was located far from the center of the Galaxy, ran counter to the fact that the Milky Way formed a more or less uniform band about the sky. From this observation, astronomers ever since Herschel's time had argued that the solar system must be located near the center of the Galaxy.

Shapley therefore needed good observational evidence before his hypothesis could be taken seriously. For this, he used the new Hooker telescope and began a painstaking program of photographing globular clusters and locating the various Cepheids within them. Arguing that a Cepheid of a certain period would have the same luminosity no matter which cluster it was in, the difference in brightness of Cepheids of a given period in various clusters would indicate the difference in distance.

In this way, Shapley could form a three-dimensional model of the clusters and could show that they were indeed globularly distributed about some center far from the solar system. It seemed only logical to suppose that center to be the center of the Galaxy.

But how, then, account for the even band of the Milky Way around the sky? To be sure it was particularly bright in the direction of Sagittarius, but if the galactic center were in that direction, the Milky Way should be enormously more bright there.

As it happens, there exist patches in the sky where no stars can be seen. These had been noted in the Milky Way by William Herschel, who had said of one, "Surely, this is a hole in the heavens."

As more and more of these regions were studied, it began to seem more and more improbable that such regions, unexplainably empty of stars, could exist in such numbers and that all should just happen to be so angled that we could look into the "hole." By 1919 Barnard had listed the position of 182 such dark regions.

Barnard (and, independently, Max Wolf) concluded that those "holes" were dark nebulae, regions of dust and gas that lacked any stars within them to light them as the Orion nebula was lighted. The dark nebulae hid the stars behind them, and it was easy for Shapley to use this newly presented suggestion to argue that these dust clouds, concentrated in the Milky Way region, hid and blocked off the light of the galactic center and left us with the vision of only our neighborhood of the Galaxy, within which there seemed an evenly distributed Milky Way.

By a statistical analysis of the speed of recession or approach of many Cepheids, Hertzsprung had estimated the distances to certain Cepheids in 1913, and therefore by use of the luminosity-period relationship, the distance to any Cepheid could be calculated. It turned out that the Cepheids are large, bright stars. A Cepheid with the common period of a week is 600 times as luminous as the sun.

Shapley made use of Hertzsprung's findings to determine the actual (and not merely relative) distance of the clusters. In 1920 he announced the first picture of the "asymmetric galaxy," one which we still accept as correct.

His suggested dimensions have had to be reduced somewhat as later data and analyses were made, and we now accept the fact that the Milky Way galaxy is a lens-shaped object about 100,000 light-years across its long diameter, with a globular nucleus about 16,000 light-years in diameter at its center, and with far-stretching spiral arms in one of which our solar system is located.

The solar system is about 27,000 light-years from the center of the Galaxy and our spiral arm is about 3000 light-years thick in our position. The sphere of globular clusters centered about the center of the Galaxy has an overall diameter of 100,000 light-years. It was eventually also shown that the Galaxy consisted of over a hundred billion stars, all rotating about the center in a stately average period of some 230 million years.

Shapley had also used the Cepheid yardstick, in 1918, to show that the large Magellanic cloud was about 155,000 light-years away from us and the small Magellanic cloud about 165,000 light-years. The former, some 40,000 light-years in extreme diameter, contained no more than 5 to 10 billion stars and the small Magellanic cloud only 1 to 2 billion stars.

The Hooker telescope, which thus revealed the true size and nature of the Galaxy for the first time, also made possible some astonishing discoveries concerning individual stars.

In 1881 the German-American physicist Albert Abraham Michelson (1852–1931) had invented the "interferometer." This was a device which could take a single ray of light, split it in two, and bring it back together again in such a way that the two rays would "interfere" with each other, producing alternate bands, or "fringes," of light and dark. From the appearance and disappearance of such fringes, and from the width of each, enormously delicate inferences could be made.

By 1890 Michelson knew that if the light from a star was thus split in two and brought together again, conclusions could be drawn about the actual diameter of the star. If the star were a point source, all the rays of light would be parallel and no fringes could be obtained. The larger it was, the more nonparallel the rays of light would be (the rays from one side of the star would approach from a slightly different direction than would those from the opposite side) and this would show up in the interferometer.

What was needed was a telescope large enough to magnify the size of a star to the point where the delicate interferometer could begin to produce the necessary fringes. With the coming of the Hooker telescope that was supplied.

In 1920 an interferometer arrangement was connected to the telescope and used, first, to measure the distance between close binaries more delicately than could be done directly either by eye or by camera. Then, on December 13, 1920, the attempt was made to measure the diameter of Betelgeuse, one of the bright stars of Orion. It was chosen because its combination of brightness and redness made it appear, according to Hertzsprung's reasoning, to be a very large star.

Hertzsprung proved to be correct. Betelgeuse was found to have a diameter of 0.045 seconds of arc. This is too small to be directly measured by optical observation (it would take 40,000 objects this size, side by side, to stretch across the face of the full moon). Nevertheless, allowing for the distance of the star, this tiny apparent diameter meant that Betelgeuse had an actual diameter of 300,000,000 miles, about 350 times the diameter of the sun.

Other red giants were found to be of similar size. Mira had a diameter calculated to be 400,000,000 miles.

The measurement told astronomers nothing they were not prepared to accept from less direct observations, but it was a dramatic event that made the front page of the *New York Times*. And it was one more way of putting the solar system, the Earth, and mankind into its proper negligible place in the universe.

9. Beyond the Galaxy

The Andromeda Nebula

The most important accomplishment of the Hooker reflector, however, was to unveil the scope of the universe beyond the galaxy. As the twentieth century opened, it seemed that the Milky Way galaxy, that vast spiral-shaped cluster of over a hundred billion stars, together with its attendant satellites, the Magellanic clouds, actually represented all there was to the universe. There was nothing in the sky that definitely seemed to lie beyond the Galaxy.

If there was one object that seemed suspicious in this respect it was the Andromeda nebula, a small object of the 4th magnitude that looks like a faint fuzzy star to the unaided eye. In the telescope it has the foggy appearance of a nebula, but, unlike the Orion nebula, it contained, as far as anyone could see, no stars that would account for its light.

The spectroscope heightened the problem. It was to be expected that clouds of luminous gas might eliminate light in only a few selected portions of the spectrum rather than all across it as stars do. The spectrum of the Orion nebula was studied by Huggins, for instance, and was found to produce a spectrum of a few bright lines, including a particularly strong one in the green.

The light of the Andromeda nebula, on the other hand, seemed to be a drab white, lacking the delicate touches of color that appeared in those nebulae that, like heated gases in the laboratories on Earth, emitted light in only a few lines. In 1899 the German astronomer Julius Scheiner (1858–1913) managed to obtain the spectrum of the Andromeda nebula and found it to be very much like the spectra obtained for stars. He maintained, therefore, that the Andromeda nebula was a cluster of stars, and that meant that the nebula was extraordinarily far away and might represent another galaxy like our own.

Since Keeler had, at that time, estimated that there were some 120,000 spiral nebulae within reach of his telescope, some astronomers began to wonder if the Milky Way galaxy were only one of a very large number of galaxies scattered through a much larger space than that occupied by our galaxy alone.

In 1913, however, the American astronomer Vesto Melvin Slipher (1875–1969) obtained the spectrum of the nebula about the Pleaides (which was indisputably part of the Galaxy, and as indisputably a collection of gas) and showed that it had the spectrum typical of stars. The Pleiades nebula simply reflected the light of the stars it included and so, perhaps, did the Andromeda.

But if that were the case, where were the stars? In all the studies of the Andromeda nebula before 1913, only once had a star been seen in the same section of the sky in which it was to be found and it was a special case. It was a "nova," a "new" star.

Such stars had very occasionally been seen in pretelescopic days, when they did indeed seem new since nothing appeared in the spot before the nova became visible and nothing appeared there after it had faded away. The telescope, however, made it obvious that novas were not really new stars but merely dim stars that, temporarily, grew many times brighter, then faded away again. It became apparent, by the twentieth century, that these were cases where stars exploded.

In 1885 a nova appeared in the central portions of the Andromeda nebula. There was no way of being certain that it was really part of the nebula. It might have been a star much closer to us than the nebula was, but one in the same line-of-sight direction. In any case, this nova, later called "S Andromedae," grew as bright as the 7th magnitude before fading away. It was nearly bright enough to be made out by the unaided eye, and this alone seemed to militate against the Andromeda nebula being very far away. How could a single star be so bright as to be seen from far beyond the limits of our galaxy? It was nearly as bright, in fact, as the whole Andromeda nebula and how could that be, if the nebula were really a galaxy?

In 1901 a nova appeared that was indisputably in our own galaxy, in the constellation of Perseus, so that it was called "Nova Persei." It reached a maximum brightness at magnitude 0 when it was the third brightest star in the sky. It happened to be fairly close to us and its parallax could be determined. It was about 100 light-years away.

In 1911 the American astronomer Frank Washington Very (1852–1927) made the assumption that Nova Persei and S Andromedae were actually of the same luminosity and that the latter was so much dimmer only because it was so much farther away. On that basis he estimated that S Andromedae was 1600 light-years away, close enough to make the Andromeda nebula part of our own galaxy, provided that S Andromedae were indeed part of the nebula.

If S Andromedae were not part of the Andromeda nebula but merely existed in the same line of sight, the nebula might still be much farther away and well outside the Galaxy. The thing to do, then, was to search for more novae in the Andromeda nebula. If it were actually within the galaxy, it would be a relatively small object and it was unlikely that more novae (which are quite rare phenomena) would appear there. If, on the other hand, the Andromeda nebula was very far away and of galactic dimensions, a number of novae might be noted.

The American astronomer Heber Doust Curtis (1872–1942) undertook to settle the point. In 1917 he, and other astronomers, too, notably Ritchey at Mount Wilson, found that novae could be seen easily in the Andromeda nebula and in other spiral nebulae, too, and in surprising numbers. By 1918 Curtis had discovered so many novae in the Andromeda nebula that it seemed to him impossible to suppose that it was a relatively small object in our own galaxy.

What's more, all the novae detected by Curtis were far, far fainter than S Andromedae had been. Either S Andromedae had not been part of the nebula but had been much closer — or else it was a "supernova," not to be compared with ordinary novae like Nova Persei. Curtis compared the brightness of the ordinary novae of the Andromeda nebula with that of Nova Persei and announced the distance of the nebula to be 500,000 light-years, making it an extragalactic object.

There grew to be an intense debate on the subject. Curtis led those astronomers who maintained that the spiral nebulae were independent galaxies separated by hundreds of thousands of light-years from each other. Shapley led those who insisted that the spiral nebulae were galactic objects.

There seemed no way of coming to a hard decision on the matter since all the evidence was tenuous. If one could only look at the Andromeda nebula through a telescope so powerful that it could actually show the apparent fog of light to be made up of clusters of exceedingly dim stars that could then be made out separately, the argument would be over at once.

The new Hooker reflector at Mount Wilson was the telescope needed for the job and the man who undertook the necessary observations of the Andromeda nebula was the American astronomer Edwin Powell Hubble (1889–1953). Starting in 1919, Hubble produced painstaking photographs of the Andromeda nebula and finally showed it, indeed, to be composed of a powdering of extremely faint stars.

The problem was settled, and the Andromeda nebula was a galaxy of stars like our own and, thenceforward, was called the Andromeda galaxy. The implication was that the other spiral nebulae visible in telescopes were, indeed, spiral galaxies, and that there were also elliptical galaxies lacking the spiral arms. Our own Milky Way galaxy by no means represented the universe, after all, but was only one of countless galaxies that together made up a far larger universe than anyone could have predicted on any but the most speculative grounds before the coming of the Hooker reflector.

But if the Andromeda galaxy is far outside our own — how far would that be? The only method for determining galactic distances lay in the study of Cepheids, and Hubble began hunting for any star in the vast and distant Andromeda galaxy that could be considered a Cepheid. Only the most luminous and longest-period Cepheids could be seen at the distance of the Andromeda galaxy, but that would be enough.

In 1923 Hubble located the first star he could show to be a Cepheid and thereafter he discovered dozens. It was clear that those Cepheids had to be part of the Andromeda galaxy, for if they were simply ordinary stars much closer than the Andromeda but lying in the same line-of-sight, it was statistically improbable that so many should be found.

Hubble assumed that the light of the Cepheids in the Andromeda galaxy was not dimmed by dust clouds and that the luminosity-period relationship was the same throughout the universe and did not apply to our galaxy alone. Both assumptions seemed quite reasonable and Hubble compared the brightness of the Cepheids of the Andromeda galaxy with those of similar period in the Magellanic clouds. To account for the lesser brightness of the Cepheids in the Andromeda galaxy, Hubble decided that the Andromeda galaxy would have to be over five times as distant as the Magellanic clouds and was some 800,000 light-years away.

This was by far the largest distance ever worked out for a specific object by astronomers, but it was clear that the Andromeda galaxy was only one of the nearest of the galaxies and that in the universe as a whole, distances in the many millions of light-years would have to be taken into consideration.

As a matter of fact, there was some reason to think that Hubble's determination of the distance of the Andromeda galaxy was an underestimate. If the Andromeda galaxy were at that distance, its actual size (judging from its apparent width as seen in the Hooker reflector) would be 40,000 light-years in diameter, less than half the width of our own galaxy, even after Shapley's first estimates of our galaxy's diameter had been scaled down.

As a matter of fact, as other distances were calculated, it began to seem that all the galaxies were markedly smaller than our own and that we just happened to live in an unusually outsize galaxy. This seemed too lucky to be true and, indeed, it wasn't true, as was discovered after 1942.

In that year the Hooker telescope was still the largest and best reflector in the world. In that year also, the world was at war, and the city of Los Angeles and adjacent suburbs were blacked out.

The growing urbanization of the United States (and, indeed, of the world) was slowly filling the night with the diffuse glow of artificial lighting and was making it steadily more difficult for astronomers to see. Thanks to the blackout, though, there were a couple of years in which the nights on Mount Wilson were darker and better than they had been for some years in the past or were to be for an indefinite number of years into the future.

Seizing the opportunity was a German-American astronomer, Walter Baade (1893–1960). Until then Hubble and others had been able to resolve only the outer spiral arms of the Andromeda galaxy into individual stars. Baade, in 1942, was able to make out the stars of the nucleus of the Andromeda galaxy, a more difficult task.

It turned out that there was a distinct difference between the stars of the spiral arms and those of the nucleus. The brightest stars of the spiral arms tended to be brilliant blue white stars, and star populations in which this was true Baade referred to as "Population I." The brightest stars of the nucleus of the Andromeda were dimmer and redder, and that star population he called "Population II."

Baade followed the lines of blue white stars, using them to mark out the spiral arms of the Andromeda galaxy. He suggested that a similar study would trace the spiral arms of our own galaxy. In 1951 the American astronomer William Wilson Morgan, working at Yerkes Observatory, followed this suggestion and, for the first time, marked out sections of the spiral arms of the Milky Way, including the one in which the solar system is located.

The stars of the globular clusters of our own galaxy and of the Magellanic clouds are largely Population II, and it was the Cepheids of this type of star that were used by Leavitt to work out the luminosity-period relationship. What's more, it was the Population II Cepheids that Shapley used to work out the dimensions of the Milky Way galaxy and the distance of the Magellanic clouds.

The Cepheids used by Hubble to determine the distance of the Andromeda galaxy (and from that the distance of the other galaxies) were, however, those very bright ones of the Population I Cepheids of the spiral arms. Did the luminosity-period relationship hold for both populations?

By 1952 Baade was able to announce that the relationship did *not* hold for the two populations equally. A modified relationship was worked out for the Population I Cepheids and on that basis it turned out that the Andromeda galaxy (and all the other galaxies) were some three times farther away than had been thought. The Andromeda galaxy is about 2,300,000 light-years away from us and the scale of the entire universe of galaxies was correspondingly increased.

At this new and larger distance, the Andromeda galaxy had to be correspondingly larger to appear the size it did in our telescopes. It turned out to be rather larger than the Milky Way galaxy. All the other galaxies had to be allowed a larger size and our own galaxy turned out to be merely an average member of the class after all.

The Expanding Universe

Once the Hooker reflector had revealed the larger universe of the galaxies, it became possible to attempt to work out the properties and evolution, not merely of individual stars or galaxies but of the universe as a whole. The new studies of "cosmology," dealing with the properties of the universe as a whole, and of "cosmogony," dealing with the origin and evolution of the universe, became possible.

The theoretical basis for such studies had come about in 1916, when the German-Swiss physicist Albert Einstein (1879–1955) announced his General Theory of Relativity which made it possible for him to set up equations that would describe the bahavior of the universe as a whole.

Einstein's picture of the universe differed from Newton's earlier and simpler one only in a few hard-to-measure ways. For one thing, the Einsteinian picture predicted a certain variation in Mercury's orbit which had already been observed and which could not be explained by Newtonian calculations.

For another, Einstein predicted that light, passing a massive body, would be bent out of its path by a very slight amount. This could be tested during a solar eclipse, when the light from stars near the eclipsed disc of the sun, having passed near the sun, would nevertheless be visible.

On March 29, 1919, a solar eclipse was scheduled to take place at just the time when more bright stars were in the vicinity of the eclipsed sun than would have been there at any other time of the year. The Royal Astronomical Society of London made ready for two expeditions, one to northern Brazil and one to Principe Island in the Gulf of Guinea off the coast of West Africa. The positions of the bright stars were measured hastily and as accurately as possible while the light of the sun remained blanked out.

If light were bent in its passage near the sun, those stars would be in positions that would differ slightly from those they would occupy six months later, when their light passed nowhere near the sun as they rode high in the midnight sky. The comparison of positions backed Einstein.

These two observations, that of Mercury's orbit and that of stellar positions during an eclipse, made use of ordinary telescopic observations of a type that had long been possible.

Einstein's third prediction was something else. According to his relativistic scheme, light moving against the pull of a gravitational field would lose energy. The lines in stellar spectra should therefore shift toward the red for this reason, much as they would in the case of a receding light source. The "Einstein red-shift" would, however, be very small. Light leaving the sun would shift so slightly as a result of the solar gravitational field that the result would be immeasurable by the techniques of the time.

W. S. Adams, who had first demonstrated the nature of Sirius B, thought that the Einstein red-shift might become large enough to measure in the case of that superdense white dwarf. At the surface of Sirius B, after all, the gravitational pull is 2500 times that at the surface of the sun.

In 1925 Adams used the Hooker reflector to check the spectrum of Sirius B with great care. After allowing for the motion of Sirius B in its orbit around Sirius, and through space, he found a residual red-shift that agreed with Einstein's prediction. This was the third and most sophisticated demonstration of the correctness of the theory of relativity. And, assuming the theory to be a close description of the properties of the universe, Adams' finding was another way of demonstrating the enormous density of a white dwarf such as Sirius B.

The Hooker reflector was useful in a still more dramatic finding concerning the universe of the galaxies, as a result of a line of investigation that began before it was built and before the nature of the galaxies was discovered — before even Einstein had announced his General Theory of Relativity.

In 1912 Slipher had studied the spectral lines of what was still, at that time, thought of as the Andromeda nebula and noted a shift toward the violet. This signified a motion toward us at a speed of 200 kilometers (125 miles) per second. (Actually, that motion is relative to the Earth, but the solar system is moving toward the Andromeda nebula on the sun's long voyage around the center of the Milky Way galaxy. The Andromeda nebula is moving toward that galactic center at a speed of only 50 kilometers [37 miles] per second.)

Slipher then went on to measure the velocities toward us, or away from us, of other spiral nebulae and by 1917 had obtained values for fifteen of them. On a purely random basis, one might expect that half of them, more or less, would be approaching us and half of them would be receding from us.

Not only did the recessions seem much more numerous than one would expect, they seemed greater, too. The average speed of recession was 640 kilometers (400 miles) per second, far higher than the speeds of the stars, generally, within our galaxy. That was a little point in favor of the galaxies *not* being part of our galaxy, as Hubble was soon to prove.

Once the Hooker reflector came into use and Hubble began to make the photographs that settled the Andromeda dispute, Slipher's measurements seemed more important than ever and the work of determining the velocities of the galaxies was taken up by the American astronomer Milton La Salle Humason, using the new telescope.

While Slipher continued his work and extended his findings to forty-one galaxies by 1925, Humason obtained the spectra of fainter and fainter galaxies. Neither could find another example of an approach toward us on the part of any galaxy but the two that had earlier been measured, the Andromeda and one other close one. All the rest, without exception, were receding. What's more, the fainter they were, the more rapidly they were receding, apparently.

In 1928 Humason studied the spectrum of a galaxy called NGC 7619 and got a value of a recession at the rate of 3800 kilometers (2400 miles) per second, and by 1936 he found the spectra of a cluster of galaxies in Ursa Major to give evidence of a recession at the velocity of 40,000 kilometers (25,000 miles) per second, nearly one-seventh the speed of light. He had reached his limit, though, for he had to use ten night exposures to get spectra of the dimmest galaxies he was dealing with.

Hubble, working along with Humason, had been painstakingly making estimates of the distances of the galaxies in several ways. He had made use of Cepheids in the closest. For those too far away to reveal any Cepheids, he made use of any stars he could see and assumed those were as luminous as the most luminous stars in our galaxy. For those still farther, he assumed the galaxies as a whole were as luminous as the average of those galaxies he had determined.

By 1929 Hubble was able to make use of the velocity determinations of Slipher and Humason, along with his own estimates of galactic distances to show that the velocity of recession was proportional to the distance from us. If Galaxy-1 was three times as far from us as Galaxy-2, then Galaxy-1 was receding from us at three times the velocity at which Galaxy-2 was receding.

At first blush it would seem that this puts us in a suspiciously privileged spot. Why the recession from *us?* The easiest way to explain it is to suppose that the entire universe is expanding, that the distances between each galaxy and its neighbors is widening. In that case, no matter which galaxy you are standing on, it would seem that every other galaxy was receding and that the further a galaxy was, the faster it was receding.

In that case, though, why were at least two of the nearer galaxies approaching? The answer eventually proved to be that galaxies frequently occur in clusters, within which the together-pulling influence of gravitation is dominant so that all circle some center of gravity and so that any two might be approaching each other at some times and receding from each other at other times. The Milky Way galaxy, the Andromeda galaxy, and a number of other generally smaller galaxies are all part of the local group. It is the clusters-of-galaxies together with individual galaxies that happen not to be part of some cluster that constantly move apart in this grand universal expansion.

Hubble's vision of the expanding universe has been accepted by astronomers generally, and it is the first observation of change in the universe as a whole — the predominant and fundamental change — and it was the gift of the Hooker reflector. This completed the triumphs of this telescope which, for its time, contributed a series of findings more startling than that of any other telescope except for Galileo's very first ones.

Why should the universe be expanding? From a theoretical standpoint, the Dutch astronomer Willem de Sitter (1872–1934) had shown, in 1917, that one could deduce from Einstein's General Theory of Relativity that the universe would have to be expanding. He deduced, again from purely theoretical considerations, that the universe might have a diameter of 4 billion light-years and might contain 80 billion galaxies.

From Hubble's demonstration of increasing speed of recession with distance (as modified by Baade's increase of the scale of the universe), it would now appear that at a distance of 12.5 billion light-years galaxies would be receding, relative to ourselves, with the speed of light. Nothing beyond that could be observed. The observable universe has a diameter of 25 billion light-years and the number of galaxies it contains is uncertain.

A more dramatic and easily grasped picture of the expansion of the universe than that of De Sitter's working out of equations was advanced by a Belgian astronomer, Georges Lemaître (1894–1966). In 1927, by which time the picture of the expanding universe was clear even though Hubble had not quite demonstrated the proportionality of speed of recession and distance, Lemaître suggested that the universe had begun as a condensed glob of matter (the "cosmic egg") which had exploded. The present expansion of the universe is the still visible consequence of that vast explosion long ago. This suggestion, which the Russian-American physicist George Gamow (1904–1968) was to call the "big bang theory," still holds today, in its essence.

From the speed with which the galaxies are receding from each other, one could work backward to see when, in the past, it was that they were all together. Early figures were 2,000,000,000 years, but this was highly suspect since geologists were quite certain that the Earth had existed in its present state for some 4,600,000,000 years. Baade's expansion of the scale of the universe, however, put the time of the cosmic egg at least 6 billion years in the past.

Special Telescopes

The success of the Hooker reflector led to the design and building of other large reflectors in the course of the 1920s and 1930s. Unfortunately, the parabolic mirrors of the large reflectors have an intrinsic flaw.

Although they could, at best, make visible extraordinarily faint objects with splendid accuracy, this "at best" was true only for light that entered the telescope and struck the mirror in a line of rays parallel or nearly parallel to the axis (that is, to a line perpendicular to the center of the mirror). This was true for objects at or near the center of the field of view of the telescope. For objects at a distance from the center, "coma" develops. The star images look like tiny comets with tails pointed away from the center. This effect increases as the distance from the center increases, and it gets worse as the mirror involved is larger.

This means that the excellent photographs made possible by a large reflector can be taken only over a small area of the sky toward which the telescope is directly pointing. Regions to the side of that small area, in any direction, are too distorted for use. The larger the telescope, in fact, the smaller the area of the sky that can be viewed with precision at one time.

Thus, to use the Hooker reflector to make star maps would require an immense number of separate photographs, each one covering only a tiny patch of the sky about equal in size to that of the full moon. Anyone in his right mind would use a smaller telescope for the purpose and sacrifice the dimmest objects. Nor was it only a matter of maps. If the sky were to be rapidly scanned in a search for specific members of a particular class of object, the Hooker reflector, or any large reflector, would be inefficient for the job.

A solution to the problem was reached by a Russian-German optician, Bernhard Voldomar Schmidt (1879–1935), whose early interest in experimentation was satisfied at a high price. Setting off a supply of gunpowder, which he had crammed into a steel pipe, he created a most satisfactory bang and also blew off his right hand and forearm. In later life he had to grind his mirrors and lenses one-armed.

In the 1920s Schmidt conceived of a compromise between reflectors and refractors, instruments that made use of both mirrors and lenses. The mirror he used was a spherical one. Such a mirror, if used with a circular diaphragm at its center of curvature, does not produce coma; it does, however, produce spherical aberration, which is worse. To take care of spherical aberration, Schmidt added a "corrector plate," an oddly shaped lens that could be placed at the center of curvature of the sphere and through which the light would pass. The corrector plate has a complicated shape, thickest in the center, less thick at the edges, and least thick between the edges and the center. It is so designed as to refract the light passing through it in just such a way as to make up for the spherical aberration introduced by the mirror, without introducing coma or much chromatic aberration.

The result is that a telescope built about such a mirror and lens can take a good photograph of objects over a wide field of the sky. So much information can be gained in such a short time, thanks to the wide field, that such a device can be profitably used even in places with relatively poor climates. The instrument is called a "Schmidt telescope" or, since it is used exclusively for photography, a "Schmidt camera."

Schmidt built his first Schmidt telescope in 1930, and instruments of this sort amazingly increased the efficiency of the large reflectors. A Schmidt telescope could make a survey of a wide field, producing single photographs containing the images of as many as 1,000,000 stars and 100,000 galaxies, and if anything in that field looked suspicious or interesting, the giant reflector could then zero in upon it, with its unexcelled probing ability.

The Schmidt telescope also has its shortcomings, of course. In order to minimize coma it must be at least twice as long as an ordinary telescope with the same size of mirror. This is because the corrector plate is at the center of curvature of the mirror; the focus of the mirror (changed very little by the presence of the plate) is halfway between the center and the mirror. Then, too, the corrector plate is hard to make and, finally, in order to make a good photograph in a Schmidt telescope, the photographic plate must be curved into a spherical form, which introduces a considerable complication.

The largest Schmidt telescope in operation now has a mirror that is 200 centimeters (79 inches) across, with a corrector plate that is 134 centimeters (52.8 inches) across. It is located at the Karl Schwarzschild Observatory in Jena, East Germany. It is doubtful whether any attempt will be made to build a still larger one.

About the time the first Schmidt telescope was devised, another special kind of telescope came into use, too. This kind involved the sun.

Around the sun is a thin, dim outer atmosphere that is utterly invisible under ordinary conditions. No one would have suspected its existence but for the extraordinary coincidence that the disc of the moon as seen from the Earth is almost exactly the size of the disc of the sun as seen from the Earth — and that there are times when the moon moves exactly in front of the sun in a total eclipse of the latter body. At such a time, the brilliant light of the solar disc is obscured and then, and only then, can the outer solar atmosphere shine out in pearly light like a crown around the dark disk of the obscuring moon. Indeed, it is called the "corona," the Latin word for "crown."

The corona is of complex structure and the tantalizing glimpses of it, a few minutes at a time, during occasional eclipses, whetted astronomical curiosity. Attempts were made to obscure the brightness of the solar disc at the point of focus — a kind of artificial eclipse within the telescope — but that never worked. The trouble was that light from the sky generally was scattered or diffused into the telescope from all directions.

The problem was solved by a French astronomer, Bernard Ferdinand Lyot (1897–1952), who realized that the main culprits as far as diffusion was concerned were the glassy components of the telescope itself. The smallest bubble or imperfection in the lens or the mirror surface, the least amount of dust managed to scatter enough light to drown out the corona. Lyot therefore devised his telescope with the utmost care in excluding dust and imperfections and then put it high in the Pyrenees Mountains in order to cut down light scattered from the atmosphere.

In 1930 he had a device called a "coronagraph" that could block out the sun so efficiently and with so little in the way of diffused light that he could take pictures of the brighter portions of the corona routinely on any sunlit day.

By 1937 Lyot's photographs showed the corona to be rotating at about the same speed as the solar disc itself. Close attention to its spectral lines showed that certain unusual ones, which had in the past been attributed to a hitherto-undiscovered element named "coronium," actually belonged to atoms of common elements, such as iron, which were at an extraordinarily high temperature. In fact, in 1942 it was shown that coronal temperatures were in the range of 1,000,000° C. (The average temperature of the sun's disc is only about 5700°.)

The largest coronagraph now in use is at Sacramento Peak Observatory, at Sunspot, New Mexico. It has a 40.5-centimeter (16-inch) lens completely free of all defect. At the same observatory there is a solar telescope 76 centimeters (30 inches) in diameter that is evacuated in order to eliminate distortion by air at different temperatures within the tube.

A larger solar telescope, one that is not evacuated, was put into operation about 1960 at Kitt Peak National Observatory near Tucson, Arizona. It has a focal length of 91 meters (300 feet) and produces an image of the sun that is 1 meter (3 feet) in diameter. It is fixed in direction, two thirds of it is underground, and it is cooled to the temperature of its surroundings. A 204-centimeter (80-inch) mirror, made of a substance little effected by heat changes, is kept 33 meters (100 feet) above the surface, reflecting sunlight into the tube.

The New Leviathan

Hale retired from active astronomical work in 1923, after a series of nervous breakdowns, but even in retirement he thought of new and larger telescopes. The great astronomic frontier now, thanks to the Hooker telescope, lay among the distant galaxies, and Hale did not hesitate to speculate on the possible usefulness of a 762-centimeter (300-inch) telescope. That seemed, however, a little too great a jump and a 508-centimeter (200-inch) reflector seemed the more realistic goal.

Hale began raising money for it, as successfully as he had earlier raised money for his other reflectors. He had originally intended to place the new telescope on Mount Wilson with its predecessors, but Mount Wilson was no longer what it had been in the days when he had first arrived there. The advance of Los Angeles and its suburbs was polluting the skies with dust and night light, something which was particularly disturbing where extended exposures were required, as for photographing the very distant galaxies.

Eventually, therefore, a new site, Mount Palomar, was chosen. It was about 145 kilometers (90 miles) southeast of Mount Wilson.

A 508-centimeter (200-inch) mirror would be not only wider but also thicker and heavier than anything ever used before in any telescope, and that introduced problems in itself. Even tiny temperature changes produced expansions and contractions in a large lump of glass which would upset the precisions of the paraboloid reflecting surface. Could something be done to minimize this?

Glass is composed of a mixture of sodium silicate and calcium silicate plus, in special cases, silicates of metals such as potassium, lead, and so on. It might be viewed as a mixture of various metal oxides added to silicon dioxide or "silica." Ordinary sand is an impure silicon dioxide (quartz) and it is the basic material out of which glass is formed.

Silicon dioxide itself can exist in a transparent, glassy form called "fused quartz" or "fused silica," and it occurred to Hale that quartz might be used instead of glass for the new, large mirror. Quartz is harder than glass, is less easily scratched, and takes a high polish. More important still, it expands or contracts very little with change in temperature. Temperature changes which would utterly distort a glass mirror would scarcely affect one of quartz.

Unfortunately, quartz is difficult to work with. It melts at a higher temperature than glass does and, at its melting temperature, it already has a perceptible tendency to evaporate so that bubbles will form in the melt. Experiments with quartz were finally abandoned in 1931. (Nevertheless, quartz plays a role in modern instruments. The 204-centimeter [80-inch] mirror of the Kitt Peak solar telescope is made of fused quartz.)

There are forms of glass, however, that, while not as good as quartz, are much better than ordinary glass is when it comes to resistance to distortion with temperature change. One of these is Pyrex, a type of glass that had been developed not many years before at Corning Glass Works in Corning, New York. It is a trade name for a glass containing boron oxide. A given temperature change affects Pyrex five times as much as it would quartz, but only one-third as much as it would ordinary glass — and Pyrex is easier to work with than ordinary glass.

As another innovation, it was finally decided to cast the 508-centimeter (200-inch) mirror not as a solid cylinder of glass but as a relatively thin piece of glass with an intricate system of ribbing in the back. This made the weight of the mirror less than half what it would have been if it were solidly thick, without reducing the strength and rigidity by much. Furthermore, it reduced the thickness of the glass in such a way that no point within the mirror was more than five centimeters (two inches) from the surface. This meant that temperature change would equalize over the glass volume that much more quickly and would further reduce the effects of distortion.

In order to produce the ribbed effect, however, the molten glass had to pour over and between cores of material which sometimes broke loose as the high temperatures melted the cement holding them to the base.

After many tests on smaller discs, the first full-size disc was poured on March 24, 1934, at Corning. The molten liquid, 59,000 kilograms (65 tons) of it, was poured into the mold little by little, while kept at a high, constant temperature, and then allowed to cool very slowly. One problem was that a few of the 114 cores came loose. When it was all done, those cores were embedded in the body of the glass and tests showed various strains in the blank as a result. The disc was kept as a spare (and is still on display in the Corning Museum in Corning, New York) while a second disc was prepared.

This time the cores were improved and bolted into place with chrome-nickel steel, while a special cooling system was used to keep the interior of the cores from becoming too hot. On December 2, 1934, the second disc was poured successfully. Ten months were allowed for very slow cooling so that the final mirror would exist without bubbles or strains. During this period of cooling, the mirror survived the flooding of a nearby river that forced the shutting off of the temperature control for three days, and it also survived a slight earthquake shock.

The disc then had to be sent across the nation from Corning, New York, to Mount Palomar, California, by railroad. The train moved only by day, at a speed of never more than twenty-five miles an hour, and across a special route which offered no difficulties with tunnels, bridges, and underpasses, since the disc was, after all, well over 5 meters (17 feet) across if one counts the case it was in. There were many places where passage was possible with only centimeters to spare.

The disc arrived in Pasadena in perfect condition and Hale had the satisfaction of viewing the huge object that was to become the new Leviathan of astronomy and the culmination of the efforts that began with Galileo's small spyglass three and a quarter centuries before. The disc had a central aperture, small in comparison to the total diameter, but at 101 centimeters (40 inches) across, that hole was itself as large as the greatest refractor lens in existence.

There then began the long, long task of grinding and polishing. An indication of the enormous size of the task lies in the fact that to bring the flat surface to the approximate curvature, the center had to be deepened by 10 centimeters (4 inches) and a total of 4500 kilograms (5 tons) of glass had to be removed. Altogether, thirty-one tons of abrasive were consumed in the whole grinding process. The mirror, when finally ground into shape, weighed 14,500 kilograms (16 tons).

Hale died in 1938, long before the mirror was ready for use — but when it was finally placed in a telescope, that telescope was named for him, and rightly so.

Other tasks, as great as the grinding of the blank itself, involved the designing of the tube that was to house the mirror and the auxiliary optical equipment, the engineering of methods that would make the huge instrument responsive to delicate adjustments, to say nothing of the design of the huge dome that was to house the instrument.

World War II, of course, delayed things, but finally in January 1948 the Hale telescope was used for the first test sightings and on June 3, 1948, it was dedicated. Final grindings were then made to correct a slight imperfection in the curvature at the outer edge and, in October 1949 the mirror received a new coating of aluminum. (The American physicist John Donovan Strong had developed a new and improved method, in 1931, for depositing aluminum on glass in a vacuum.)

The Hale reflector made it possible to photograph and resolve distant objects much better than did the Hooker reflector. It could photograph objects as dim as the 23rd magnitude — objects only 1/6,000,000 as bright as the dimmest object visible to the unaided eye. It could detect faint galaxies that were hundreds of millions of light-years away from us.

However, it had an even more limited field of vision than the Hooker telescope did. It has been estimated that to map the entire sky with the Hale reflector, tiny spot by tiny spot, would take 10,000 years. To correct this deficiency a large Schmidt telescope with a 122-centimeter (48-inch) corrector plate, second in size only to the one in Jena, was built for use in association with the Hale.

In addition, new devices have been developed to increase the ability of telescopes to make out dim objects. In 1946, just two years before the Hale telescope went into operation, the "photomultiplier tube" was invented. This device is based on the fact that light which strikes surfaces coated with certain chemicals will bring about the emission of electrons. The emitted electrons can be made to bring about the emission of still others and in the end the effect of the light may be multiplied a millionfold. The light from faint stars that will not affect the eye, or even the photographic plate without excessively long exposures, will produce electron emission which can be detected speedily. The photomultiplier will work with light intensities only a hundredth of those which will effect a photographic plate in the same time.

With the Hale reflector gathering four times the light that the Hooker reflector did, with better diffraction gratings, with faster cameras and more sensitive photographic plates, and with photomultiplier tubes, the new reflector could do in less than an hour what the old telescope took night after night to do. What's more, the Hale telescope has so large a mirror that if a cage is placed at the focal point large enough to contain instruments and even an observer, the light blocked out is only a bearably small fraction of the total.

By 1956 exposures of up to thirty hours or more had obtained spectra of galaxies a billion light-years away. Red-shift measurements that could be measured with an accuracy of 0.5 percent showed those distant galaxies to be receding at a speed of 60,000 kilometers (37,000 miles) per second — one-fifth the speed of light.

Yet although the Hale reflector could see farther than the Hooker reflector and could make out more, it did not introduce the revolutions in man's outlook on the universe that the smaller instrument had. The Hooker telescope had made it possible for man to gauge the size and nature of his own galaxy, the nature and motions of the outer galaxies, and had presented the vision of an expanding universe originating from a cosmic explosion in the dim past. The Hale reflector merely confirmed all this.

What is more, the Hale reflector, like the Yerkes refractor a half century before, seemed to herald an end to the growth of a particular type of telescope.

To be sure, other large reflectors have been built since 1948 but none have surpassed the Hale Leviathan. At Lick Observatory a 305-centimeter (120-inch) reflector was installed in 1958, making use of a disc that had been poured at Corning in preparation for the climactic forming of the great Hale mirror.

Some six instruments with mirrors that lie between the Lick reflector and the Hale reflector in size are in various stages of preparation around the world. Among them are two in Chile and one in Australia, which will bring the giant eyes to the southern hemisphere.

One instrument is in preparation that, if successfully brought to actual use, will be larger than the Hale telescope. This new super-Leviathan is being built in the Soviet Union. For over ten years a 600-centimeter (236-inch) reflector has been on the drawing boards. When completed, the new reflector will be set up near Zelenchukskaya on Mount Pastukhov in the Caucasus, at an elevation of 2080 meters (6830 feet). The mirror was poured near Moscow in a special foundry built for the purpose and was allowed to cool very slowly for two years. Advantage has been taken of the experience of the Hale mirror, for the new, larger one, is also of Pyrex and is also ribbed in the back. The mirror reached the site of the observatory in early 1970, and installation then began. The telescope itself, built and assembled near Leningrad, is 25 meters (82 feet long) and though it weighs 77,000 kilograms (850 tons) is easily movable.

This new reflector, even if it is successfully put into operation, will probably not lead to much of an astronomical advance. The successful solution of the engineering problems involved in handling glass and metal of such size will not help in other respects.

The atmosphere itself has become the limiting factor. Its absorption of light, its clouds and mists, its temperature changes are all among the dominating source of troubles where distances and dimnesses of the kind penetrated by the Hale reflector are concerned.

The telescopes that have descended from the first ones built by Galileo and Newton have reached their limits. If man's probing of the universe was to continue, then some new instrument involving a new revolution in technique must come into being — and it did.

10. Beyond Light

Widening the Spectrum

For uncounted thousands of years, the only information reaching mankind from the skies was by way of the light of the visible bodies located there.

Nor did anyone conceive that there might be more than that, that there might be light coming from objects in the sky, light that could not be seen. The very notion that there was such a thing as light that could not be seen would surely have struck anyone as a ridiculous paradox.

The first indication that such a thing could exist came in 1800 when William Herschel was studying the heating effect of various parts of the solar spectrum. He placed a thermometer in various parts of the spectrum and noted the temperature rise. It would have been natural to suppose that a thermometer placed beyond the spectrum would show no temperature rise since there was no sunlight visible there. When, however, Herschel placed the thermometer just beyond the red end of the spectrum, he found the heating effect actually greater there than anywhere within the spectrum.

Apparently, there were rays of sunlight that were refracted even less than red light was, and those rays the human eye could not detect. These rays came to be called "infrared radiation" ("below the red").

Light did more than affect the eye. It brought about a breakdown of silver chloride, liberating metallic silver and, in this way, darkening the white compound. (It was this which a couple of decades later became the basis of photography.)

The German physicist Johann Wilhelm Ritter (1776–1810) studied the effect of different portions of the spectrum on this breakdown.

It was known that the violet end of the spectrum was more effective in breaking down silver chloride than the red end was, but in 1801 Ritter found, to his amazement, that the silver chloride broke down most rapidly when placed beyond the violet end of the spectrum where the eye could see nothing.

Ritter had discovered rays in sunlight that were refracted even more than violet light was, and these were called "ultraviolet radiation" ("beyond the violet"). As the nineteenth century opened, then, it became clear that the solar spectrum did not represent the entire range of sunlight. There was radiation beyond either end, radiation to which our eyes were insensitive.

In 1803 the English physicist Thomas Young (1773–1829) demonstrated that light consisted of tiny waves of varying wavelengths, and the French physicist Augustin Jean Fresnel (1788–1827) worked out the mathematical details in 1814.

To recapitulate some of the material in Chapter 8, the wavelengths of light are too small for any ordinary measure of length to be used conveniently. Ångström, in his study of the solar spectrum, made use of a unit equal to a ten billionth of a meter, and that is called, in his honor, an "Ångström unit," abbreviated Å.

It turned out that the wavelength of light was shortest at the violet end of the spectrum and increased steadily to the red end. The wavelength at the extreme violet end was just under 4000 Å, while at the extreme red end it was just over 7000 Å. The longest wavelengths were thus almost twice the shortest so that, by analogy with the situation with sound waves, the light spectrum can be said to extend over one octave.

Ten Ångström units are equal to a "millimicrometer" (a thousandth of a millionth of a meter), which nowadays is termed a "nanometer." In nanometers, the proper metric unit, the purple region of the spectrum centers about the 410 mark, while for the remaining colors the central wavelengths are blue, 470; green, 520; yellow, 580; orange, 600; and red, 650.

Each different kind of atom emits light at characteristic wavelengths and, under other conditions, absorbs light at those same wavelengths. The dark lines of the solar spectrum represent wavelengths of light absorbed by the relatively cool atoms in the solar atmosphere.

Viewed from the standpoint of the wave theory of light, it would seem that the sun (and, presumably, other stars as well) emitted light in a broad range of wavelengths and that the eye was only capable of receiving a restricted portion of that range.

The eye's specialized ability is not surprising. At the temperature of the sun's surface, the peak of the radiation is in the middle of the visible range, so that in the course of evolution the eye adapted in such a way as to react to the kind of light that was available in highest concentration. Indeed, at a wavelength of 556 nanometers, we have both the peak of solar radiation and of optical sensitivity.

What *is* surprising is that the atmosphere happens to be transparent to just this peak range of solar radiation. There is no fundamental reason why it should be. After all, while it permits the wavelengths in and near the solar spectrum to pass, wavelengths markedly longer or shorter do *not* pass through the atmosphere.

The short wavelengths of the ultraviolet are absorbed by ozone, an energetic form of oxygen, which is found in the upper atmosphere. The result is that at the Earth's surface, no wavelengths less than 292 nanometers are received from the sun or from other objects in the sky.

The long wavelengths of the infrared are absorbed by water vapor in the Earth's atmosphere and by carbon dioxide, and in general there are only a few widely separated wavelengths that are received from the sun and other objects in the sky longer than a wavelength of 1400 nanometers.

Had it been otherwise and had the range of transparency been differently placed, the world might have been much dimmer than it is, the sense of sight less important — and astronomy might never have developed.

The interference of the atmosphere did not prevent astronomers receiving half an octave of ultraviolet and a whole octave of infrared, in addition to the well-known octave of what had now to be called "visible light." Could these extensions of the spectrum be dealt with as the visible spectrum could?

In 1850 the Italian physicist Macedonio Melloni (1798–1854), having found that crystals of sodium chloride are much more transparent to infrared radiation than glass is, constructed lenses and prisms of that substance and showed that infrared radiation could be refracted, spread into a spectrum, and show all the behavior of ordinary light. It was the final evidence that "invisible light" differed from ordinary light only in wavelength, that it could be treated as ordinary light and made to yield information.

Of the two types of beyond-the-visible-spectrum light, ultra-violet offers a smaller problem. It can be easily photographed even though its region of the spectrum seems black to the eye and indeed is automatically included in any spectrograph, provided it is not absorbed.

That means that the recording of the ultraviolet portion of the spectrum places additional constraints on telescopic equipment. Even that part of the ultraviolet which can get through the atmosphere may not survive passage through glass. Glass absorbs light more readily as the wavelengths grow shorter. The thickness of the lens of the 102-centimeter (40-inch) Yerkes refractor absorbs virtually all of the ultraviolet radiation of the sun. Consequently, the study of the ultraviolet portion of the spectrum requires reflectors, and furthermore, it requires an aluminum-fronted mirror rather than a silver-fronted mirror since aluminum is a far more efficient reflector of ultraviolet than silver is.

The influence of light upon chemicals becomes less as the wavelength becomes longer. It is harder to photograph the long-wave orange and red light and still harder to photograph infrared radiation. The first to succeed in doing so was the English chemist William de Wiveleslie Abney (1843–1920) who, in 1874, worked with dyes sensitive to the red end of the spectrum and beyond.

In the late 1930s the American astronomer Charles W. Hetzler, using the Yerkes refractor and infrared-sensitive film, detected a number of cool stars with surface temperatures of from 1000° C. to 2000° C. At such temperatures, stars deliver only small quantities of visible light but larger amounts of infrared radiation.

Infrared radiation can also be detected by having it induce some effect that produces a change in an electric current, something that can be measured with delicate precision.

Rosse was the first to take advantage of this. He used a "thermocouple," which is a junction of two different metals. A small current flows across this junction and the size of that current increases with temperature. By focusing infrared radiation upon the thermocouple, the temperature is made to rise by an amount proportional to the quantity of radiation. By measuring the small electric currents induced in a thermocouple placed at the focus of a reflector, Rosse could measure the infrared radiation emitted by the full moon. (Again, large lenses do not transmit enough infrared radiation to allow the procedure to work with refractors.)

In 1880 Langley devised the "bolometer," in which a blackened metal foil is heated by infrared radiation focused upon it by a reflector. Its electrical resistance varies sharply with temperature and this can be measured so delicately that a temperature change of a ten thousandth of a degree can be detected.

In the 1920s the American physicist William Weber Coblentz (1873–1962) placed a bolometer in a vacuum, thus multiplying its sensitivity. He was able to measure the infrared radiations of stars for the first time.

One difficulty in measuring infrared radiation is that whereas objects must be red hot in order to emit visible light, they need be only warm to emit infrared radiation. The atmosphere is also transparent to infrared radiation in the regions of 4000 and also 10,000 nanometers. Even the walls of the telescope tube are warm enough to give radiation at these wavelengths. There is thus infrared arriving at the image from all directions. This "background radiation" can blot out dim sources in the sky, and astronomers working with the infrared have problems like those they would have in trying to observe stars by visible light in the daylight.

To do very fine infrared work, therefore, astronomers in the last few decades have taken to refrigerating all the equipment used, sometimes down to temperatures quite close to absolute zero. (This is the equivalent to darkening a room in order to detect faint sparks of light.)

There are advantages, too, in the infrared. In general a telescopic mirror has to have a shape deviating from the mathematical ideal by amounts in the range of the wavelength of the light you want to observe. Since infrared radiation has longer wavelengths than visible light, the mirrors used can be a little sloppier.

For instance, to work in the infrared region, astronomers at the California Institute of Technology began with an aluminum dish that was approximately paraboloid. They then poured a slow-setting resin into it and kept the dish at a constant rapid rotation for three days. The resin, whirling with it, assumed a paraboloid shape and set, permanently, in that shape. The final result was not accurate enough to handle visible light but could deal adequately with infrared.

The mirror is then rocked gently twenty times a second while everything else is held steady. Under such conditions, the general smear of infrared radiation from the background produces an electric current with one kind of characteristic while the tiny sources in the sky, moving back and forth, produce an electric current with another kind. The latter then stand out against the background.

With the sophisticated instruments of today, tens of thousands of infrared sources in the sky have been detected, along with much information that could not have been obtained as easily by way of ordinary light. Molecules (made up of groups of atoms) have characteristic absorptions in the infrared portion of the spectrum and in this way one can detect carbon dioxide in the atmosphere of Mars and ammonia in that of Jupiter with great certainty.

Through the middle of the 1880s, astronomers could easily suppose that even if visible light were not the whole of the spectrum, it represented a large portion of it. They might suppose that even though there were signs that the atmosphere cut off the shorter wavelengths of the ultraviolet radiation and the longer wavelengths of the infrared radiation, there might be very little beyond the cutoff points.

The first real broadening of the optical horizon came by 1870, when the Scottish mathematician James Clerk Maxwell (1831–1879) worked out a complete theory of electricity and magnetism, one that still stands in full beauty today. He showed that the two phenomena were different aspects of a single "electromagnetic field." He also showed that periodic variations in such a field produced "electromagnetic radiations" of which light was one variety. By Maxwell's theory the radiations could come in any wavelength from far less than the observed ultraviolet to far more than the observed infrared. There was an enormously broad "electromagnetic spectrum" of which visible light made up only a very small part.

It was only theory at first, but soon enough Maxwell's suggestions came to be backed by firm evidence. In 1888 the German physicist

Heinrich Rudolph Hertz (1857–1894) was able to produce, detect, and study electromagnetic radiation with wavelengths far higher than those of the infrared. These very long wavelengths studied by Hertz were originally referred to as "Hertzian waves" but eventually came to be known as "radio waves."

Then, in 1895 the German physicist Wilhelm Conrad Roentgen (1845–1923) discovered a form of radiation which he called "x-rays." These were definitely shown, in 1912, to be electromagnetic radiation with wavelengths much smaller than those of ultraviolet light by the German physicist Max Theodor Felix von Laue (1879–1960).

In 1896 the French physicist Antoine Henri Becquerel (1852–1908) discovered the phenomenon of "radioactivity," though he had no way of knowing at the time that this was caused by atoms of the heavy metal uranium giving off a constant emission of radiation and particles. In 1900 the French physicist Paul Ulrich Villard (1860–1934) demonstrated that part of this radiation was unaffected by a magnetic field and might therefore be a form of electromagnetic radiation. This was shown to be so and Rutherford called them "gamma rays." They had a wavelength even less than those of x-rays.

A span of electromagnetic radiation was therefore known, in the early decades of the twentieth century, reaching from gamma rays at the short-wavelength end through x-rays, ultraviolet radiation, visible light, infrared radiation to longer and longer radio waves. The whole covered dozens of octaves of which only *a single octave* is occupied by the entire spectrum of visible light.

In 1905 Einstein showed that all these forms of radiation traveled in wave packets which acted like particles in some ways and which he called "photons." Interpreting these in the light of a theory worked out by the German physicist Max Karl Ernst Ludwig Planck (1858–1947) in 1900, it could be demonstrated that the energy of the photons increased as the wavelength decreased. This meant that gamma rays were the most energetic form of electromagnetic radiation and that the energy decreased through x-rays, ultraviolet radiation, visible light, infrared radiation, and then finally the radio waves which are least energetic.

By modern concepts of the electromagnetic spectrum, the range of ultraviolet radiation from 400 to 300 nanometers, which is all the atmosphere will allow to pass, is only the "near ultraviolet." Beyond that is the "far ultraviolet" (300 to 200 nanometers) and the "extreme ultraviolet" (200 to 1 nanometers).

The x-rays lie beyond, with wavelengths of from 1 to 0.01 nanometers, while the gamma rays have wavelengths below 0.01 nanometers. (The boundary lines are man-made and arbitrary, of course, and what is convenient to consider the far ultraviolet at one time might be convenient to consider the near x-rays another.)

In the other direction lies the infrared radiation. The range from a wavelength of 700 to 2500 nanometers is the "near infrared." Since 1000 nanometers equals 1 micrometer, we might say that the near infrared range is from 0.7 to 2.5 micrometers. From 2.5 to 50 micrometers is the "intermediate infrared" and from 50 to 1000 micrometers is the "far infrared."

Beyond the infrared lies the radio-wave region with wavelengths of more than 1000 micrometers or, which is the same thing, with wavelengths of more than 1 millimeter.

The shortest radio waves are sometimes referred to as the "microwave" region, which extends from 1 to 500 millimeters (or from 0.1 to 50 centimeters). Beyond that are the still longer waves of the radio spectrum.

Radio Waves

One might suppose that the sun and the other stars in space would deliver radiation throughout the many octaves of the electromagnetic spectrum and that to be limited to the two and a half octaves of visible light and the immediately neighboring regions on either side was to limit the knowledge available to astronomers intolerably — but the thought did not seem to bother astronomers for more than half a century after Maxwell had advanced his theory.

After all, the sun's peak radiation was in the visible-light region and it might be supposed that on either side of the visible spectrum the quantity of radiation fell off rapidly. The intensity of very-long-wave and very-short-wave radiation from the sky would probably be negligible and so, therefore, would be the information they could carry.

To be sure, some people did speculate about the possibility of radiation from objects in the sky that would lie far outside the usual bands of wavelength. Even then, the speculations dealt only with the sun, since that seemed the only object capable of bathing Earth in significant quantities of such radiation. The American inventor Thomas Alva Edison (1847–1931) and the English physicist Oliver Joseph Lodge (1851–1940) both speculated on the possibility of radio waves from the sun. These speculations came about the turn of the century, but they were not followed up. For one thing, astronomers lacked the instruments to deal with radio waves.

Such instruments were being developed, however, though not in connection with astronomy.

When Hertz first produced radio waves, he did so by means of an alternating electric current surging first this way, then that, and leaping across a small air gap with each surge. The radio waves produced in this fashion could, in turn, produce an electric current in a wire that was held at a distance. These were the first "antennas," a term used for a wire or other structure used to send out or receive radio waves. It was by measuring the properties of the electric currents produced in antennas that one could determine the properties of the radio waves producing those currents.

The Italian electrical engineer Guglielmo Marconi (1874–1937) devised improved antennas for sending and receiving beams of radio waves. Using them, he could send messages in pulses without the use of long, connecting wires ("wireless telegraphy") over increasing distances. On December 12, 1901, he succeeded in having radio-wave pulses sent from the southwestern tip of England and detected in Newfoundland. That date is usually considered the birth of "radio."

The Canadian-American physicist Reginald Aubrey Fessenden (1866–1932) devised a method for having the radio waves rise and fall in intensity ("amplitude modulation") in such a fashion as to mimic the rise and fall of sound waves. Sound could be converted into an electric current that varied with the sound-wave variation and this electric current was used to produce the properly modulated radio waves. The radio waves could then be reconverted first to a varying electric current and then to sound duplicating the original. Voice and music could thus be transmitted by radio, something Fessenden demonstrated for the first time in 1906.

The ability of radio messages to travel long distances over the curved face of the Earth was puzzling, inasmuch as radio waves traveled in a straight line and should therefore reach no further than the visible horizon, moving off into the upper atmosphere and outer space beyond that.

What apparently happened was that the radio waves were reflected by areas of the upper atmosphere that were rich in electrically charged atom fragments called "ions." In bouncing between Earth and these areas, they succeeded in traveling long distances about the planetary curve.

The existence of such a region of the upper atmosphere (the "ionosphere") was demonstrated in 1902 by the work of such men as the English physicist Oliver Heaviside (1850–1925) and the British-American electrical engineer Arthur Edwin Kennelly (1861–1939), plus the later work of the English physicist Edward Victor Appleton (1892–1965) in 1924.

The fact that radio waves originating on Earth's surface could be reflected by the ionosphere and kept near the surface meant that any radio waves reaching Earth from outer space would be reflected by the ionosphere and kept in outer space. This was another example of the way in which our atmosphere shielded us from radiation outside the visible light range.

However, the efficiency with which the ionosphere reflected radio waves decreased as the wavelength grew smaller. In fact, the microwave region immediately adjacent to the infrared band was too small in wavelength to be reflected at all and it was too long in wavelength to be absorbed by water vapor or carbon dioxide. This meant that any microwaves coming from any of the objects in space could pass through the ionosphere, survive the passage through the atmosphere, and reach Earth's surface.

There were, therefore, two "windows" through which electromagnetic radiation could reach Earth from the sky. One of them was the narrow and very familiar window through which visible light and immediately adjacent sections of ultraviolet and infrared radiations could reach us. The other was a considerably wider window through which microwaves could reach us. The "microwave window" extends from a wavelength of 0.5 centimeters to 3000 centimeters (30 meters), a stretch of over twelve octaves. There are also some narrow windows such as those we mentioned earlier in the infrared section.

The existence of the microwave window remained obscure because (as sometimes happens in science) it fell between two branches of knowledge.

The radio engineers, primarily concerned with the use of radio waves for communication on Earth, were not interested in those wavelengths that could penetrate the ionosphere. Such wavelengths were useless for their purposes and there was no point in working out methods for generating or receiving them. Astronomers, on the other hand, were not very much concerned with earthbound radio technology and were unaware of the behavior of microwaves. When, finally, radio engineering and astronomy met, it was entirely by accident.

It came about because Bell Telephone Laboratories was interested in radio waves. Telephone calls across oceans or from ships could be carried through to their destination by having them travel in part by way of radio waves ("radio telephony") and the laboratories was interested in determining those factors that interfered with the radio waves introducing random noise, or "static." Electrical discharges, such as those accompanying thunderstorms, were one obvious source of interference, but there might be others.

Put in charge of the project was the American radio engineer Karl Guthe Jansky (1905–1950), who had joined Bell in 1928. Jansky built a series of large rectangles of wire which would serve as an "antenna array" that would receive radio waves from one particular direction much more efficiently than from any other. He mounted the whole on a merry-go-round arrangement so that it could be turned to receive radio waves from any direction and detect the directions of high-intensity reception.

In Holmdel, New Jersey, about 48 kilometers (30 miles) south of New York City, Jansky painstakingly tested the environment for interference. He was able to detect distant thunderstorms without trouble, as well as other obvious sources.

There was, however, always present a low and steady hissing sound, something that was quite different from the crackling of the sudden discharges of thunderstorms and that never vanished. By January 1932 Jansky's curiosity concerning this hissing sound reached the point where it became his major absorption.

He began checking different directions to see where, if anywhere, the hissing noise might be strongest. It seemed at first to be strongest in the direction of the sun and Jansky might well have concluded that, after all, as Edison and Lodge had suspected, the sun gave off radio waves as well as ordinary light waves, and that he was receiving a steady influx of these waves, weakened after traveling across 150 million kilometers and thus capable of producing only that low hiss. It would have been an important finding but not a really thundering one.

If the sun had been at or near the peak of the sunspot cycle, that might have been the answer. By a most fortunate stroke, however, Jansky was tracking down this mysterious phenomenon at a time when the sun was at minimum sunspot activity and was delivering comparatively little in the way of radio waves.

As Jansky checked his direction of radio-wave maximum day after day, he found it drifting away from the sun in a steady progression. He had learned enough astronomy in the course of his investigation to realize that the spot of radio-wave maximum was remaining constant relative to the stars and not to the sun. As a result, he discovered something that even the boldest speculators had not guessed — that radio waves from the stars might be arriving on Earth in sufficient concentration to be detected by something as crude as Jansky's antenna array.

The sound Jansky heard could now be called a "cosmic hiss" and it was coming from a spot in the Milky Way. It was, in fact, coming from the very spot Shapley had pinpointed as the center of the Galaxy only fourteen years before. Jansky reported his findings in the December 1932 issue of the *Proceedings of the Institute of Radio Engineers* and that represents the moment of birth of what is now called "radio astronomy." Jansky's crude device might as well be considered the first "radio telescope."

Yet Jansky's revolutionary discovery of galactic radio noise was not followed up by professional astronomers. They were caught up in the revolutionary findings of the Hooker reflectors and in the plans for other large optical telescopes and shrugged off the microwave finding.

But neither was Jansky's finding entirely ignored. The notion of radio messages from the stars caught the popular fancy, and the newspapers made a fuss over it. The noise was even amplified and sent out over Earthly radios so that people could hear the stellar broadcast. At least one first-rank astronomer, Fred Lawrence Whipple, considered the nature of the radio signals and speculated seriously on them.

Through the lean years that followed Jansky's finding, one *amateur* astronomer carried the load of radio astronomy all by himself. This was the American radio engineer Grote Reber.

Fascinated by the reports of Jansky's work, Reber decided to build a better receiver. He recognized the fact that the radio waves from outer space would be in excessively small quantities and he realized that he would surely need a larger and more elaborate antenna array to receive the weak radiations in any detail beyond the bland and steady hiss that Jansky had received.

As an alternative, he might use a relatively simple antenna but gather radio waves over a large area and focus them on that antenna, similar to the system used in optical telescopes dealing with light waves. Reber moved in that direction and decided to build a paraboloid "dish" for the purpose, something that would be the analogue of the great mirrors of the reflecting telescopes.

It was a great project to be undertaken by an amateur, without help, and in a field in which there were no precedents to follow, but Reber had some advantages working in his favor.

The precision with which a reflecting device need be made paraboloid declines with increasing wavelength. Whereas an optical mirror must be polished and polished to a perfect curve within a millionth of an inch or so, a paraboloid radio receiver, dealing with waves a million times as long as light waves, could vary from the ideal by an inch or so without harm.

Then, too, microwaves are far less affected by atmospheric turbulence and temperature differences than light waves are. Nor are there as many microwave sources in the Earthly environment as there are light sources. For these reasons, the paraboloid reflector need not be enclosed in a tube. The dish could be left bare and that was a great simplification in construction.

It was quite possible, then, for Reber to build a useful paraboloid reflector 9 meters (31 feet) in diameter in his backyard in Wheaton, Illinois, about 65 kilometers (40 miles) west of Chicago. It was only partially mobile. It pointed straight up and could be turned north and south, but not east and west, so that it could detect a radio-wave-radiating object in the sky only as it crossed the north-south meridian passing through the zenith.

On the other hand, microwaves pierce clouds, fog, and mist as light waves do not. Moreover, the sun does not produce microwaves in such quantity as to blank out all else when it is in the sky as it does light. As a result, Reber could use his dish day and night and in all weather. (Reber's dish was the first radio telescope that looked vaguely like an optical one — at least like a telescope mirror.)

There is a serious disadvantage involving the matter of "resolution" in radio astronomy. Resolution involves the exact location of a radiating source in the sky and the ability to distinguish between two closely placed radiation sources, seeing them as two and not as one. The ability to achieve a particular resolution with a receiving instrument of a particular device becomes worse as the wavelength of the radiation being received becomes longer.

Jansky had, for instance, detected radio waves with a wavelength of 15 meters. This is some 30 million times as long as the wavelengths of visible light. At such a radio wavelength, to achieve the same resolution as the human eye could, using visible light, would require a dish receiving radio waves that was 100 kilometers (60 miles) across.

Reber judged, quite correctly, that Jansky, who hadn't been looking for radio waves from space, had not designed his instrument to receive the wavelengths that arrived from space in greatest concentration. Reber felt that the proper wavelengths to look for were considerably shorter than those Jansky detected. He himself concentrated on receiving wavelengths down to as little as 60 centimeters, only one twenty-fifth the length of the waves Jansky had received.

This, combined with the paraboloid shape of his receiver, meant that Reber could expect to detect much fainter sources of radio waves than Jansky could and with far better resolution. Since even the 60-centimeter waves were still a million times longer than visible light waves, that "far better" resolution still wasn't much. Reber's 9-meter (31-foot) reflector fell far short of the kind of resolution the unaided eye could handle using visible light. Two radio sources, separated by less than 12° (twenty-four times the width of the full moon), were picked up as a single source by Reber's dish. He could see the "radio sky" much as someone looking through frosted glass could see the visible sky.

But it was enough; it was a beginning. Reber began to make observations at the start of 1938, experimenting with a variety of receivers and detectors placed at the focus of his paraboloid. In April 1939 he finally began to detect radio waves from cosmic sources.

All along the course of the Milky Way, he detected rises in radio-wave concentration. He found "radio sources" in Cassiopeia, Cygnus, and Taurus but could not attribute them to any particular object. Resolution was too poor.

Painstakingly, though, doing what he could with what he had, Reber prepared the first "radio map" of the sky, using a wavelength of 190 centimeters for the purpose. It was a map that was not to be bettered for fifteen years.

Reber published his results in 1940 and in 1942, and they were noted, but nothing could be done about it then. World War II was on and the attention of scientists was elsewhere.

Radar

Although no systematic work, other than Reber's, was done on radio astronomy during World War II, the conflict had a positive effect on the new field. It was through the needs of that war that microwaves came into important use here on Earth for the first time.

We see by detecting light waves reflected from the objects we are looking at. Light waves are ideal for the purpose because they move so quickly that in the time it takes them to strike an object and be reflected to our eyes, that object has no time to change position perceptibly. Light waves travel in straight lines, generally, so that the object is, in fact, where it seems to be. (There are cases where light waves curve in passing through atmospheric layers at different temperatures and we then see "mirages," that is, apparent objects that are not where we think we see them.) Finally, light waves are so tiny that they make it possible to see things with great resolution, even down to the level of bacteria (if we make use of a microscope).

The great disadvantage of light is that it will not penetrate clouds, mist, or fog. Then, too, in the absence of the sun, at night, light is not present in any great quantity. We can supply artificial light for ourselves at night, but that is usually only of local value.

If we make use of electromagnetic radiation sufficiently longer than those of visible light, it becomes possible to penetrate clouds, mist, and fog without trouble. However, resolution declines as the wavelength increases. In addition, the longer the waves, the greater their tendency to bend around objects of ordinary size, so that they no longer can be considered as necessarily moving in a straight line — nor will they be reflected by the objects they move around.

The thing to do is to choose those wavelengths that are barely long enough to penetrate the clouds yet short enough to give sufficiently good resolution to detect objects of reasonable size. Microwaves, for instance, might be produced in narrow beams to penetrate night, clouds, or fog and bounce off distant airplanes, for instance.

This was an important matter in the 1930s when it seemed that war might come, a war in which the airplane would be a crucial weapon. The United States, Great Britain, France, and Germany all worked on devices for handling microwaves in such a way that an incoming wave of bomber planes might be detected as long as possible before they actually arrived.

Each nation achieved a measure of success in this. In the United States the technique was referred to as "radio detection and ranging." The "radio" refers to the fact that microwaves can be considered ultrashort radio waves. By "ranging" is meant the determination of distance, something that can be obtained from the length of time it takes a beam of microwaves (traveling at the known speed of light) to go from the transmitter to the object being detected and then, after reflection, back to the receiver. Eventually, the expression was reduced to its initial letters and became "radar" and it is by that name that the technique is now universally known.

Of the nations involved in radar research, Great Britain made the most significant advances. The Scottish physicist Robert Watson-Watt patented devices that made it possible to follow a moving airplane by means of radar as early as 1935.

What was needed, however, was the production of a strong pulse of microwaves so that comparatively distant, small, or fast-moving objects could still reflect enough for easy detection. In visible-light terms, what was needed was a searchlight strong enough to illuminate the terrain.

In early 1940 scientists at the University of Birmingham in Great Britain worked out a device in which magnetic and electric fields could manipulate speeding electrons in such a fashion as to transfer energy from those electrons to radiation. The size of the device was chosen so as to make sure that the wavelengths of the radiation were in the microwave range.

This device, called a "magnetron," made it possible, for the first time, to send out powerful beams of microwaves. It was the microwave searchlight needed to illuminate the sky and show the moving planes in it.

The invention of the magnetron came just in time, with a few paltry months to spare, to save Great Britain and, perhaps, the whole free world, from the assault of Hitler. In September 1940 the full fury of the German air force fell upon London. Hitler, unaware of the new efficiency of radar, preferred to attack the city rather than the radar stations.

While one cannot discount the heroic fight of the outnumbered Royal Air Force of Great Britain (concerning whom Churchill said, "Never in the field of human conflict was so much owed by so many to so few"), the fact remains that without radar pinpointing the precess of the German planes, the R.A.F. would not have been victorious.

As it happened, the efforts of the British scientists to protect their nation against enemy assault meant the development of just those devices that would serve to receive, with the utmost delicacy, those wavelengths that were reaching men not only from man's own magnetrons but from cosmic sources many light-years away. The lack of instruments, a lack that had made radio astronomy impractical before World War II, was corrected, and after World War II, it was another story.

Indeed, even during World War II, there were accidental discoveries in radio astronomy. In February 1942 the British found their radar being interfered with. They were receiving microwaves at times when there were no planes in the sky to account for echoes, and they viewed this with great seriousness. If the Germans had discovered methods of jamming the radar reception, enemy planes could come in under cover of a crowd of microwaves from everywhere so that the British could not tell the real thing from the false.

The British assigned J. Stanley Hey to determine the source of the interference and, as it turned out, it wasn't hard. Now that devices had been developed for detecting tiny quantities of microwaves arriving from particular directions (essential to radar) it was easy to note that the interfering microwaves were coming from the sun. This was the first time that microwaves from any specific visible object in space were detected, so that the sun became the first definite radio source.

Hey did not publish this finding till after the war because of the natural tendency to consider everything secret that was even vaguely concerned with military matters. A few months later, in June 1942, the American physicist George Clark Southworth used radar equipment in a deliberate attempt to detect radio waves from the sun and succeeded. His results were kept secret, too.

In September 1943, however, Grote Reber discovered radio waves from the sun and since he had nothing to do with the military, it never occurred to him to suppress the information. So much for secrecy.

Hey's discovery meant more than merely finding microwaves issuing from the sun. That could easily have been anticipated. What he found was that the microwaves were apparently associated with a huge solar flare, and here an important difference showed up between solar light waves and solar microwaves.

The light waves originating from the sun did so as a result of the overwhelming energies generated in the solar interior. Some processes increased or decreased the light-wave production locally, but these effects were so small in comparison with the total light-energy radiated by the sun that there was only the smallest overall effect. In general, the sun delivers light energy at a constant rate, has done so, presumably, over a period of billions of years in the past and will continue to do so, in all likelihood, over another period of billions of years into the future.

The microwave energy delivered by the sun is tiny in comparison to the light energy but is associated with visible disturbances on the surface of the sun and varies by substantial amounts. By concentrating on this part of the electromagnetic spectrum, comparatively small events on the sun (in terms of visible light) stand out in sharp relief. The association of microwave bursts with flares was thus the first clear indication that the study of microwaves might yield information difficult to obtain in the optical range.

The Planetary Echoes

As soon as World War II was over, it became possible to use the newly developed radar techniques for astronomical purposes. The same microwaves that could be produced, bounced off airplanes, and detected on their return might be used to detect objects in space. Man could reach out to touch the heavenly bodies, with a beam of radiation at least, if not with anything corporeal.

In 1945 Hey found, for instance, that microwave beams could be reflected from meteors. Passing meteors left a wake of ions which would reflect the microwaves as though it were a wire in the sky. Hey used three microwave beams situated miles apart, so that from the timing of the different echo returns, the position of the meteor trails could be determined. The most interesting part of this observation was that, for the first time in the history of astronomy, meteor trails could be detected as easily by day as by night.

Meteor trails, however, are to be observed in Earth's atmosphere and these are not, strictly speaking, astronomical objects. The birth of "radar astronomy" really came in 1946 when a Hungarian physicist, Zoltan Lajos Bay, sent out a beam of microwaves to the moon and detected the return echo. Almost simultaneously, and independently, two Americans working for the U.S. Army Signal Corps did the same with more powerful equipment, obtaining more clear-cut echos.

The microwave echoes brought with them several kinds of information. From the time lapse between the emission of the original beam and the detection of the echo, one could determine the distance of the moon. From the manner in which the wavelength of the echo was lengthened or shortened, one could tell whether the part of the moon struck was receding from us or approaching us — and from this one could work out the rate of rotation of the moon.

Then, too, if the moon were perfectly smooth, the beam would be returned unscattered and would be returned in our direction only from the center of the visible face. From the fact that the beam is scattered and that certain quantities are sent back in our direction from off-center positions, estimates could be made as to the general roughness of the lunar surface.

In the case of the moon, none of this is very important. The moon is close enough so that optical studies can be made in great detail and we don't have to rely on microwave echoes. Nevertheless, the techniques developed by touching the moon with microwaves could be used for other more distant targets with greater effect. Then, too, the public was interested by this glamorous achievement of bouncing microwaves off the moon, and that made it easier to gain support for more difficult tasks of a similar nature.

The more distant a body is, the fainter the echo, and the faintness is strongly dependent on distance. If object B is twice as far as object A, the echo from B is only one-sixteenth as strong as that from A, all things being equal.

Then, too, the smaller the body the fainter the echo, but distance is usually more important than size in this respect. The sun, which is by far the largest body in the solar system, and which is large enough to present the same apparent size of target as the moon, is so distant (400 times the distance of the moon) that microwave echoes from its surface are received at less than a hundred-thousandth the intensity of those of the moon.

Nevertheless, radio astronomers * perfected their techniques until the time came when they could detect microwave echoes carrying as little power as a thousandth of a millionth of a millionth of a millionth of a watt, and measure the time lapse of return with an accuracy of a millionth of 1 percent.

It was not till 1959, thirteen years after the first moon echoes were received, that the sun was successfully used as a microwave target.

---

* Although most of the work has been done with microwaves, the force of Jansky's original discovery with what were considered radio waves causes us to speak of *radio* astronomy. Since microwaves can be considered part of the radio region of the electromagnetic spectrum, this is not a serious misnomer.

A team of workers at Stanford University under the astronomer Von Russell Eshleman managed to receive the echoes.

Aside from the accomplishment of the task, little was gained, since the sun's own microwave emissions confused matters and limited the information to be obtained from the echo. It was rather like trying to investigate the nature of a fire by shining the light of a flashlight upon it.

The next most logical target was Venus which, except for the moon, is the nearest sizable object to the Earth. At its closest, Venus is only 100 times as far from us as the moon is, and only a quarter as far as the sun is. It is, of course, much smaller than the sun and microwave echoes from Venus would reasonably be expected to be only about a fiftieth as strong as those from the sun.

Venus became the target for numerous radar astronomers and in the year 1961 no fewer than five teams (three in the United States, one in Great Britain, and one in the Soviet Union) all reported success. The best results were obtained by the Millstone Radar Observatory of the Massachusetts Institute of Technology.

The microwave echoes from Venus were the first to supply significant new information that could not have been obtained otherwise at the time. For one thing, the distance of Venus could be determined with high accuracy in this way — with higher accuracy, in fact, than could be determined by parallax methods using optical telescopes.

The most accurate earlier measurement of the distances of the solar system had come in 1931 at the time of a particularly close approach of the asteroid Eros. It came within 25 million kilometers (16 million miles) of the earth, a distance less than that of any larger body. This made its parallax particularly large and easy to measure. Because Eros was so small as to be no more than a dot of light, even in telescopes, changes in its position were more easily measured than would have been the case if it were a globe covering a perceptible area of the field of vision, as the planets were.

A long detailed program was set up to observe Eros. Fourteen observatories in nine countries took part. Seven months were spent on the project and nearly 3000 photographs were taken. The position of Eros was determined on each one of them, and then there followed ten years of calculations supervised by the English astronomer Harold Spencer-Jones (1890–1960). From the parallax of Eros, its distance at a particular time could be calculated and from that the distance of every other planetary body at any particular time. Most fundamentally, the average distance of the sun from the Earth (the "astronomical unit") could be determined. As a result of the microwave echoes from Venus, however, the dimensions of the solar system, including the astronomical unit, could be determined at once with an accuracy outweighing the major effort of a quarter century earlier.

In this way, radio astronomy, even in its infancy, showed that it could outdo, at a stroke, an optical achievement built up after three centuries of refinement.

The microwave reflection could do more.

Venus is covered by an unbroken and optically impenetrable layer of clouds covering its entire surface. For this reason, the image of the planet, which has been studied by telescope since Galileo's time, is absolutely featureless and yields us almost no information. Even in the early 1960s, less was known of Venus than of distant Neptune.

Microwave echoes have changed that. To microwaves, Venus's cloud layer is no obstacle. In 1965 microwave echoes, bouncing in scattered fashion from the hidden solid surface of the planet, yielded data indicating the presence of mountain ranges. We can now produce very rough radar maps of Venus.

In 1962 moreover, microwave echoes from Venus could be analyzed with sufficient delicacy (by Richard M. Goldstein and Roland L. Carpenter in Goldstone Lake, California) to yield information on the planet's rotation.

Until then it had been suspected that Venus's rotation had been slowed by the sun's gravitational effect until the planet rotated in the same time as it revolved about the sun. (This follows the behavior of the moon, which rotates in the same time it revolves about the Earth.) If Venus is in a gravitational lock, its period of rotation is 225 days, which is the length of its year.

The 1962 studies, however, showed Venus's rotation period to be longer than its year and later and more refined studies showed the period to be 243.1 days. What's more, its rotation was retrograde. Instead of rotating from west to east as Earth and Mars do, it rotates from east to west. Another way of looking at it is to say that Venus's axis had tipped upside-down so that its north pole is roughly where Earth's south pole would be and vice versa.

This is an example of radio astronomy not merely improving on optical astronomy but achieving something that was impossible for optical astronomy at the time, and, in doing so, arriving at a completely unexpected result.

A result, equally startling, was obtained in connection with the planet Mercury. It is smaller than Venus and is farther from us so that obtaining microwave echoes from Mercury requires the ability to detect radiation a hundredth as strong as that to be expected from Venus. Nevertheless, it was in June 1962 that a team of Soviet scientists succeeded in detecting a microwave echo from Mercury.

By 1965 Gordon H. Pettengill and Rolf B. Dyce, working at Arecibo, Puerto Rico, could analyze echoes from Mercury with enough delicacy to calculate its period of rotation.

Mercury does not have a cloud layer as Venus does. In fact, Mercury has virtually no atmosphere and one sees its bare solid surface as in the case of the moon. It is so distant and so close to the sun, usually, that the word "sees" must be taken with some reservation. In 1889, however, Schiaparelli had studied what surface markings he could make out and had decided that the planet rotated on its axis in eighty-eight days. This is the same as its period of revolution about the sun and that was accepted as natural in view of the sun's tidal effect upon the small planet.

The microwave echoes, however, showed that the rotational period, which had been accepted as eighty-eight days without question for eighty years, was actually just under fifty-nine days. As it turned out, this was just two thirds of its period of revolution around the sun and this, too, could be explained by tidal effects.

In the case of Venus, there is no way of checking the radar-reflecting finding optically, but one can at least try in the case of Mercury. With the new data driving them, astronomers studied Mercury carefully and found that optical observations did indeed support the new figure.

Radar echoes have also been obtained from Mars and from Jupiter. Richard Goldstein has detected echoes from nearby asteroids and from distant Saturn (the most distant target yet achieved). Curiously, Saturn's rings reflect microwaves with astonishing efficiency, reflecting about 60 percent of what a silver sphere would reflect. This compares with the corresponding figures of 8 percent for Mars, 5 percent for the moon, and 1.5 percent for Venus.

11. Radio Astronomy

Radio Telescopes

The ability to receive microwave echoes with the precision and delicacy required by radar astronomy depended on the development of improved radio telescopes. Grote Reber's dish was the prototype of bigger ones to come. A dish some 75 meters (250 feet) across and built into a natural cavity in the landscape was used to send signals to the moon and to receive the echoes.

The largest yet was constructed over a natural valley near the town of Arecibo in Puerto Rico. There, in November 1963, a dish 305 meters (1000 feet) across was put into action. It had an area of 73,000 square meters (18.5 acres).

The Arecibo dish was made of a loosely woven wire-mesh surface and could detect microwaves with lengths down to 50 centimeters (20 inches). In late 1972, efforts were begun to improve it by resurfacing it with 38,774 aluminum panels that would make it possible to receive and reflect microwaves with lengths as small as 7 centimeters (2.8 inches).

As an indication of the forethought required in matters other than astronomy itself, each aluminum panel is perforated with small holes. This allows 44 percent of the sunlight to pass through and support the vegetation beneath. Without that, erosion of bare soil would eventually endanger the underpinnings of the dish.

The improvements were completed in November 1974.

The microwaves received by a dish are reflected toward a receiver placed at its focus and the delicacy and efficiency of the receiver has also advanced considerably since Grote Reber's original investigations.

In this respect, a turning point came with the development of a technique which Einstein had discussed, from theoretical considerations, as long before as 1917. Einstein pointed out that a particular molecule could absorb a photon of some characteristic energy size. It could release that energy if it were struck by a photon of that same energy size. The molecule would release the energy as a photon and this, together with the striking photon, the two exactly equal in energy would move off in the same direction.

If there were a number of high-energy molecules, the two photons would eventually strike two other such molecules producing two more photons. All four could strike four molecules, producing four more photons and so on. In this way, a single photon moving into an energy-high substance could produce a whole flood of photons all of the same size and all moving in the same direction.

In 1953 the American physicist Charles Hard Townes put this into practice, using molecules of gaseous ammonia that had been raised to higher energies. These molecules happened to react to photons in the energy range of microwaves. A very weak beam of microwaves entering the ammonia would stimulate the emission of more microwaves of the same energy and there would thus emerge a greatly amplified beam.

Townes called the process "microwave amplification by stimulated emission of radiation," a term which was abbreviated to the initial letters. These were run together and the device was called a "maser" in consequence.

This same system was soon found to work in solid systems as well as in ammonia. The Dutch-American physicist Nicolaas Bloembergen devised a solid maser which could be steadily pumped to a higher energy state by the use of an electric current or by light, even as it was being made to lose its energy through maser action. It was a "continuous maser."

Such a maser can be used to receive the feeble microwave beams focused upon it by one or more reflecting units of a radio telescope and then to emit them again with no change except amplification.

The combination of increased size and delicate reception made the radio telescope enormously more useful than might have been foreseen in the 1940s. Even the best radio telescope cannot "see" the sky as an optical telescope can, however.

Light photons are so energetic that they can be detected in small quantities in different parts of a receiver (whether an eye or a photographic plate) so that sizable areas can be recorded at once, with differences in light intensity making a general picture of the kind we are used to.

Microwave photons are much feebler, and a radio telescope must obtain the microwaves from a single region of the sky and convert this into a tiny electric current with a voltage that varies according to the intensity of the microwave beam. The receiver must scan a region of the sky point by point and the voltage must be plotted for the different points. In the end, a series of wavy lines is obtained, representing parts of the sky with similar intensities. You can have concentric closed curves working toward a center of maximum voltage.

It is as though you had to look at one point of the sky at a time, measuring the light intensity at that point, then at another point and another, and then plot the whole thing. It would take a much longer time than ordinary seeing but in the end you would get the same picture you would get in the usual fashion, provided nothing moved in the interval.

One disadvantage of a large dish is that it is quite likely to be immovable. The 305-meter (1000-foot) spherical receiver at Arecibo, for instance, is fixed in position and points straight upward. The receiver, however, is suspended on a cable far above the dish (at the center of the circular segment represented by the dish) and is designed in such a way as to correct for spherical aberration. It is movable and by appropriate change in position, it can receive waves that originate anywhere up to 20° from the zenith in any direction.

Since the Earth rotates, various portions of the sky come within range of the Arecibo dish, and in the end it can focus about some 40 percent of the sky and follow any particular radio source for a period of time. Anything that remains more than 20° north or south of zenith is beyond the reach of the dish at any time during the day or night.

There is a dish that is 91 meters (300 feet) across at the National Radio Astronomy Observatory at Green Bank, West Virginia, which is partly mobile in the same way that Reber's dish was. The Green Bank dish can move north and south but not east or west. This means that any spot in the sky could be picked up at some time during the twenty-four-hour day as it passed over the meridian, but it could then be studied for only a very short time.

Naturally, it would be convenient to have a dish that could be moved in any direction so that it was as versatile in this respect as an optical telescope. This particularly enticed the English astronomer Alfred Charles Bernard Lovell, who, in 1951, became the first professor of radio astronomy at Manchester University.

He supervised the building of a 76-meter (250-foot) paraboloid dish at Jodrell Bank Experimental Station, about fifteen miles south of Manchester. It was an epic effort in construction that took six years, with the turret rack of a battleship being used to move the receiver. The dish was finally completed in 1957. In 1971 it was renovated to achieve efficient reception in the 21-centimeter (8.3-inch) wavelength, which proved particularly important.

The Jodrell Bank dish was not surpassed till 1971, when a fully steerable dish, 100 meters (328) feet across, was constructed about fifty miles west of Bonn, Germany. The largest one in the southern hemisphere is a 64-meter (210-foot) steerable dish at Parkes, Australia.

Of course, not all radio telescopes need be dishes. They can be made up of antenna arrays and may be the descendants of Karl Jansky's original receiver rather than of Grote Reber's original dish. These arrays may be fixed or they may be mounted on rails for partial mobility. The individual antennas can be adjustable too.

One kind of array has two lines of antennas, crossing at right angles. A large array of this kind was first designed and used by an Australian radio astronomer, B. Mills, and it is therefore called a "Mills Cross."

The original Mills Cross contained 600 antenna elements arranged along two arms each 450 meters (1500 feet) long. The whole was mounted over a horizontal layer of chicken wire, which served to reflect microwaves and give the antenna a second chance at them.

The resolving power of a Mills Cross is equal to that of a dish equal in diameter to the length of an arm, and naturally the Mills Cross is far easier to construct and far cheaper than a dish of that size would be. However, the disadvantage is that the Mills Cross, lacking the concentrating effect of a dish, cannot detect weak micro-wave emissions that the dish would pick up easily. Then, too, a Mills Cross array can't track a source and it can only work at the particular wavelength for which it was designed.

The largest Mills Cross now in use is at Molonglo, Australia, and has arms 1600 meters (1 mile) long. Each antenna is a cylindrical parabolic reflector that can be turned north and south.

The largest antenna array of any kind now in use is at Chuguyev, near the Ukrainian city of Kharkov. Its main arm is over 3000 meters (nearly 2 miles) long and it covers an area of 15,000 square meters (37 acres), just twice that of the Arecibo dish.

Even the largest radio telescopes, whether dishes or antenna ar-rays, are not very good at resolution if they are regarded as single structures in themselves. They can't be, considering the size of the wavelengths they deal with. Even the largest instruments dealing with the shortest wavelengths cannot resolve two sources that are less than 1 minute of arc apart. This is not much better than the eye can do using visible light.

It is possible, however, to use two different radio telescopes (the two not necessarily being of the same type) as radio interferometers. Each of the two, separated by a considerable distance, can be con-nected electronically and can take measurements of the same radio source. The two measurements come at slightly different angles, and by working with the interference of the two separate sets of wavelengths, a resolution can be obtained which would be equal to that of a single radio telescope stretching across the entire distance separating the two components.

Astronomers had to be prepared to separate the component radio telescopes by a considerable distance. When Michelson had used the interferometer principle to measure the diameter of the stars by light waves, he used two mirrors separated by 6 meters (20 feet). When dealing with the much longer microwaves, however, separa-tions must be correspondingly greater.

In 1964 twin dishes were put into use at the Owens Valley Radio Observatory of the California Institute of Technology. Each is 27 meters (90 feet) in diameter and they are mounted on heavy rails so that they can be moved to varying distances from each other, with the maximum separation some 50 meters (1600 feet).

Interferometry is now being used among many radio telescopes. In western New Mexico, an array of twenty-seven dishes, each 26 meters (85 feet) in diameter, is being arranged in the shape of a Y across an area 42 kilometers (26 miles) in diameter. All will be electronically linked and movable on railroad tracks so that distances and arrangements can be modified. This telescope should be in full operation in 1981 and it is hoped that it will yield resolutions in the microwave range as good as that of the Hale telescope in the optical range.

But that, too, isn't the limit. Separate radio telescopes need not be directly connected electrically. Two telescopes can take independent tape recordings of a particular source at a particular time and the two can then be compared, with the effect of interferometry. That means that the base line separating two telescopes can be any length that the size of the Earth makes possible.

"Long base-line interferometry" was first used by Australian and British radio astronomers. Using radio telescopes 100 kilometers (60 miles) apart, resolutions of better than 1 second of arc could be obtained, and radio telescopes began to outdo optical telescopes as far as resolution is concerned.

Longer base lines still were used. The two dishes at Owens Valley can be combined with another pair at Green Bank and a base line of 3200 kilometers (2000 miles) will exist. Nowadays, radio telescopes are used in cooperation across oceans as well as continents and the whole planet is now, in effect, a single telescope.

Using microwaves with a length of 3.5 centimeters, a resolution as small as 0.0003 seconds of arc has been obtained; something that far exceeds anything the best optical telescope could do.

It is astonishing that the same type of observation that seemed basically and hopelessly fuzzy in Grote Reber's time should, a mere thirty years later, become the sharpest method for observing the universe (within its range of wavelengths, to be sure).

Radio Sources

Radio telescopes can, of course, do more, far more, than merely detect microwave beams produced by man and reflected by the planets.

The planets can be sources of microwave radiation of their own.

Every object which is at a temperature above absolute zero ($-273.1°$ C.) — and that means *every* object — radiates photons of all kinds. The average energy of the photons emitted increases with temperature and the wavelength of peak radiation decreases.

We are most aware of this in the case of any body hot enough to deliver appreciable quantities of photons in the visible-light wavelengths. Objects not hot enough to glow visibly can still radiate quantities of infrared radiation as our own bodies do or if too cool even to produce much of that will nevertheless radiate microwaves and longer radio waves. In fact, from the distribution of such purely "thermal radiation," the temperature of nonglowing bodies can be determined.

The American physicist Robert Henry Dicke first detected thermal radiation in the microwave region from the moon in 1946, and in the years that followed thermal radiation was detected from other planets.

One surprise came in connection with Venus. On May 2, 1956, astronomers at the Naval Research Laboratory in Washington, D.C., detected microwave radiation from Venus and found, to their surprise, that its nature corresponded to temperatures far above the boiling point of water.

This was considerably higher than would have been expected if Venus were an airless ball at its distance from the sun. It has a thick atmosphere, however, and it had already been speculated that if this atmosphere happened to be heavy in carbon dioxide and water vapor, this would act as a heat trap. It would allow the high-energy visible-light photons to penetrate the atmosphere and reach Venus's surface but would not allow the lower-energy infrared photons from Venus's surface to penetrate back into space. In this way, heat would be retained by the atmosphere and the temperature would climb just as it does in a greenhouse where the glass allows sunlight in but not infrared radiation out. Venus would thus be the victim of a runaway "greenhouse effect."

Not all radiation is simply the result of temperature effects. In early 1955, two American astronomers, Kenneth Linn Franklin and Bernard F. Burke, using a Mills Cross, discovered a particular pattern of microwaves, whose source they could not determine. Jupiter happened to be in that part of the sky, and it was suggested as the source. Franklin, skeptical, plotted the position of Jupiter during the time the microwaves had been recorded and found that Jupiter's changing position coincided exactly with the path of the radiation.

The radiation from Jupiter could not possibly have a thermal origin, since the planet would have to be at enormous temperatures to release such a flood of radiation at the necessary wavelength. From almost the beginning, it was suspected that Jupiter had an ionosphere, as the Earth had, and charged particles moving through Jupiter's magnetic field could produce such radiation.

The most intriguing aspect of radio astronomy involved the stretches of the universe beyond the solar system. That had come, in fact, at the very beginning, for Jansky had detected radiation from the galactic center, and Reber had plotted the intensity of radiation from various parts of the sky to make his radio map and detected various peaks of emission in the Milky Way.

In 1944 and 1945 Hey, using more powerful equipment than had been available to Reber, undertook to map the radio sky again and found one spot in the constellation Cygnus that was a strong source of microwave radiation. Eventually this was called "Cygnus A."

There was nothing visible in the area optically that might be Cygnus A, but Hey felt certain that some particular object, very small in apparent area, was responsible, and that it was not just generalized radiation from a large patch of the Milky Way. His reason for this was that the microwave source fluctuated, as though it were "twinkling." This would be expected in the behavior of a very thin beam of microwaves passing through the ionosphere but not of a diffuse beam.

Over the next decade and a half, a major effort on the part of the radio astronomers was to improve the resolution of their instruments so that the radio sources could be pinpointed to smaller and smaller regions of the sky and, therefore, be more easily associated with some object that was visible optically.

In 1948 the Australian astronomers John G. Bolton and G. J. Stanley set up a radio interferometer that zeroed in on Cygnus A and boxed it into an area of the sky not more than 8 minutes of arc in diameter (about a quarter the apparent width of the moon). They felt justified in calling the source a "radio star" and for a while that term was used rather indiscriminately for objects of this sort. It turned out to be a misnomer, and the more neutral "radio source" is preferable.

Similar interferometers, set up in Cambridge, England, in 1950, by Martin Ryle and others, quickly located fifty radio sources in the northern hemisphere while Australian astronomers located an equal number in the southern hemisphere.

The first identification of a radio source with an optically visible object was of something in the constellation Taurus. There the radio source "Taurus A" was found to be the Crab nebula, an irregular patch of expanding gas that is all that remains easily visible of a supernova that blazed in Earth's sky in 1054.

The number of radio sources expanded rapidly and before the end of the 1950s, the Cambridge group had produced a third listing of radio sources (3C) containing 450 items. In another decade, the radio sources could be numbered by the thousands and the original calm assumption that long-wave radiation was a minor phenomenon lay in ruins. If we exclude the sun itself, there is more energy reaching us from the universe in the form of infrared and microwave radiation than of visible light.

The radio sources are distributed rather evenly over the entire sky. This meant they could not be concentrated in our galaxy, for then most of them would be found in the Milky Way. The search was on, therefore, for extragalactic radio sources. Taurus A was a failure in this respect, for the Crab nebula is not only in the Galaxy, but in our own section of it. What about Cygnus A, however?

In 1951 the British astronomer F. G. Smith, using a radio interferometer of high resolving power, had boxed Cygnus A into a square 1 minute of arc on the side, and the problem was to find something in that tiny area that could conceivably be a powerful source of microwave radiation.

Here we have the interplay of radio telescopes and optical telescopes. The radio telescope pins down the source and the optical telescope translates that source into something visible to the eye. Baade, making use of the Hale reflector, probed the square within which Cygnus A was located and detected an oddly shaped galaxy there.

It seemed, in fact, to be two galaxies passing through one another. If that were so, it could be argued that turbulence produced in the gas and dust of each would produce enormous quantities of micro-wave emission. Cygnus A, therefore, turned out to be a "radio galaxy," emitting microwaves with an intensity at least a million times that of the average galaxy.

The search was on for "peculiar galaxies," any galaxy that looked distorted or had some oddness to it. Any of these located within an area labeled as a radio source might prove to be a radio galaxy. By 1961 about 100 radio sources were pinned down to specific galaxies.

Actually, there were too many radio galaxies, and these were too energetic for easy explanation. It seemed highly unlikely that there were so many cases of colliding galaxies, or, if there were, that so much energy was produced by mere turbulence.

Eventually, ratio interferometers were designed and built that had such fine resolution as to pinpoint radio sources *within* the galaxies in question. They were found to be in the dust-free centers, or in two spots symmetrically placed on either side of the center. It began to seem that what was happening was somewhere in the center of the galaxies and that it was something explosive that could force the actual source to either side.

In 1961 the American astronomer Clarence Roger Lynds was try-ing to pin down the radio source 3C231 (the two-hundred-thirty-first listed in the third Cambridge catalogue). Within the area marked out by the radio telescope were a group of galaxies in which M81 was the most prominent, and which had been supposed to be the source. Lynds, however, as he sharpened the radio view, zeroed in, not on M81, but on a smaller neighboring galaxy, M82.

The American astronomer Allan Rex Sandage promptly subjected M82 to careful photographing through the Hale reflector and that galaxy was clearly and visibly undergoing a vast explosion. A three-hour exposure, using a special red filter that let through chiefly the light associated with hot hydrogen, revealed jets of hydrogen up to 1000 light-years long, bursting out of the galactic nucleus. (Careful studies of "Sagittarius A," a radio source at the center of our own galaxy, indicates there may have been a catastrophic explosion there, too, at some time in the past.)

Through radio telescopy, then, astronomical catastrophes on a new and hitherto unprecedented scale came into the human vision. What's more, the microwave emissions associated with these galactic explosions were so immense that they could be detected at distances beyond that from which even the Hale reflector could expect to receive optical signals. Indeed, the relatively primitive radio telescopes of the early 1950s could have detected Cygnus A if it were fifteen times as far away as it is. It was clear, then, that the radio telescope would enlarge our knowledge of the universe both in the type of phenomena that could be detected and in terms of sheer distance.

According to Hubble's analysis of the recession of the galaxies, it turns out that any object about 12.5 billion light-years from us would be receding from us at the speed of light. From such an object no energy could reach us as the Doppler effect would reduce all radiation to infinite wavelength. A distance of 12.5 billion light-years would therefore represent the limit of the observable universe.

The Hale reflector could just barely detect the light of galaxies that were somewhere between 1 and 2 billion light-years away, but radio telescopes could, almost from the beginning, do better than that. This implied the possibility of helping to determine some very basic questions about the universe.

In the 1940s astronomical opinion had come to accept the notion of a big bang origin of the universe, a term originated by the Russian-American astronomer George Gamow (1904–1968). This supposed that the universe, a number of billions of years ago, had its matter compressed into a relatively small object which exploded and that the receding galaxies and the expanding universe were a consequence of that explosion.

By the big bang theory, the universe was quite different long ago from the way it is now and the galaxies were spaced much more closely together and were all younger than they are now.

In 1948, however, the English astronomer Fred Hoyle and two Austrian-born colleagues, Hermann Bondi and Thomas Gold, suggested an alternative explanation. The expansion was an eternal phenomenon and new matter formed continuously and very slowly, though still in sufficient quantity to form new galaxies, as the old ones moved apart. The net result of this "continuous creation" theory would be that, on the whole, the galaxies would always be the same distance apart and there would always be young galaxies as well as old ones. Therefore, the universe would be the same in its overall appearance at all times.

There seemed a chance that radio telescopes might offer a way of choosing between these two theories. It takes time for light to travel. A galaxy a hundred million light-years away is seen as it was a hundred million years ago; one that is a billion light-years away is seen as it was a billion light-years ago. One need only study very distant galaxies and see if they are closer together than they are now, as the big bang theory would predict, or no closer together at any time, as the continuous-creation theory would predict.

The very distant galaxies that can be seen in the Hale reflector are still not sufficiently far away to make the difference in average separation large enough to measure clearly — but what about the distant radio sources? If they are farther away than even the most distant optically visible galaxies, they must also date farther back in time.

In the mid-1950s Ryle analyzed the manner in which the number of radio sources increased as they grew fainter. They should increase more rapidly with distance according to the big-bang theory than according to the continuous-creation theory. It seemed to Ryle that the manner of their increase did indeed jibe more with big bang than with continuous-creation, but the data was very borderline and those supporting continuous-creation were not convinced.

Something more was needed.

Quasars

For the most part, radio sources were associated with everything but ordinary stars, despite the fact that they were originally called radio stars.

The first ordinary star known to send us microwaves was the sun itself. The quantity of microwaves received from it, however, was so small that if the sun were at stellar distances its microwave radiation would be undetectable. It would follow that radio astronomers might not expect to detect microwaves from ordinary stars.

But not all stars are ordinary.

In 1958 Lovell's group at Cambridge picked up microwave emission from a faint red dwarf, UV Ceti, which was only 8.6 light-years away and whose peculiarity had been discovered no more than ten years before by the Dutch-American astronomer Willem Jacob Luyten. This star, the first other than the sun to prove a radio source, apparently produces flares no larger than those of the sun but much larger proportionately to its own shrunken body, and it is these flares that produce the bursts of microwaves. Other such "flare stars" have since been discovered but all are fairly close to us. Farther away, such red dwarfs would not be discernible to either optical or radio instruments.

Might there be extraordinary stars that would produce enough microwave energy to be detectable over fairly large distances? Some of the radio sources had been pinned down to very small areas within which there were no galaxies to be seen. Unless the source was a galaxy too far off to be detected optically, the source might be a star.

In 1960 Sandage, using the Hale reflector, studied the region within which radio source 3C48 had been pinpointed. Within that region, nothing at all was to be seen except a single 16th-magnitude star that had never been thought of as anything but a perfectly ordinary star of the Milky Way galaxy.

Now that attention was concentrated on it, however, it seemed to be not entirely ordinary. There was a tiny wisp of nebulosity associated with it. Was the small nebular wisp a sign of some unusual behavior or property that accounted for its large microwave emission?

Another small radio source was 3C273 and the Australian astronomer Cyril Hazard noted that it was so located that the moon could sometimes pass before it. The moon had been used previously to help in making precise locations, and Hazard proposed to use it again. In 1962 he trained a 64-meter (210-foot) radio telescope on the spot just before the moon passed by and noted the exact position of the lunar edge when the microwaves were cut off.

He found that 3C273 was actually a double source, the two being separated by 19 seconds of arc and each source being 10 seconds of arc in diameter. The only object that seemed to be located in the right place was a 13th-magnitude star which, like 3C48, seemed to have a small nebulosity associated with it. Indeed, the second radio source was in the nebulosity.

Two other stars associated with radio sources, 3C196 and 3C286, were also located at about this time. All four objects were stars in appearance but all had strange properties. They were each rich in ultraviolet radiation, and each had a peculiar spectrum containing unidentified lines.

In 1964 a physicist at Princeton, Hong-Yee Chiu, suggested it was unsafe to call the objects stars. He felt they should be called "quasi-stellar sources." This means no more than "star-resembling sources" and that seemed to be as far as one should go. The phrase "quasi-stellar" was quickly shortened to "quasar."

The spectra of the quasars remained the prime puzzle, for the lines possessed patterns that had never been seen in any other object. In 1963 it occurred to the Dutch-American astronomer Maarten Schmidt that four of the lines in the spectrum of 3C273, the brightest of the quasars, resembled what might be expected of hydrogen, except that hydrogen lines never had that distribution in that part of the spectrum.

Could the lines have been shifted from a part of the spectrum in which the pattern would indeed occur commonly? If so, they would have had to be shifted so far that it would mean that 3C273 was receding from us at the velocity of over 40,000 kilometers (25,000 miles) per second. That seemed unbelievable, but if it were true, other lines fell into place and could be accounted for.

Schmidt, together with the American astronomer Jesse Leonard Greenstein, turned to other quasar spectra and found that, in each case, sense could be made out of the lines if a huge red-shift were supposed.

Such enormous red-shifts meant that, according to Hubble's picture of an expanding universe, the quasars were very distant from us. Even the closest, 3C273, was over a billion light-years away, and the others were much farther.

The quasars, if their enormous red-shifts are accepted as indicating enormous speed of recession and consequently great distance, were the farthest objects known and perhaps the farthest objects that could be known. Other quasars have been found by the dozens, new records for distance being established now and then.

In 1971 a quasar was detected and given the designation oH471. In 1973 its spectrum was recorded and its red-shift proved to be so great that its distance was placed at 12 billion light-years. This is very nearly the limit of observation, for it had to be receding from us at nearly the speed of light. Newspaper headlines therefore reported the finding in terms of "Astronomers see the end of the universe."

But what must the quasars be in order to be visible at such huge distances? They must be at least a hundred times as luminous as galaxies such as our own and yet they must be much smaller than galaxies. What can pack so much energy into so small a volume?

Back in 1943 Carl K. Seyfert, while still a graduate student in astronomy, detected a peculiar galaxy, which has since been recognized as one of a group now called "Seyfert galaxies." They may possibly make up 1 percent of all known galaxies though actually only a dozen examples are known.

In most respects, Seyfert galaxies are normal and have only moderate red-shifts. The nuclei, however are very compact, very bright, and seem unusually hot and active — rather quasarlike, in fact. Perhaps quasars are very large Seyfert galaxies that are located so far from us that only the bright centers (and bits of nebulosity in the nearest) can be seen. What can be the source of all that compact energy, either in the Seyfert centers or in the quasars? That is a question that still goes unanswered.

When the quasars were first found to have enormous red-shifts, it was argued that this completed the argument Ryle had advanced in connection with radio sources increasing in density with distance. It was held that the distant reaches of the universe were markedly different from our own neighborhood, that the universe was different when it was younger, and that the big bang theory of creation was correct and not the continuous-creation theory.

Not all astronomers, however, agree that the red-shifts of the quasars imply that they are at great distances. Other explanations of the red-shifts have been advanced — that the quasars are objects that have exploded out of galaxies comparatively near to us or that they are objects so massive that they have produced a gravitational red-shift. Even if they *are* at great distances, it can be argued that their distribution is fairly even after all and can be made to fit the theory that the universe has not changed with time.

In 1964 the American physicist Robert Henry Dicke pointed out that radio telescopes, reaching out so many billions of light-years, were also reaching out billions of years into the past—so many billions of years that they might actually detect the big bang taking place.

We would then be seeing the big bang at such a distance and consequently the source would be receding from us so rapidly that the energetic photons liberated would not be seen in their true light. There would be a gigantic red-shift that would move them into the microwave region. Moreover, since we would see the big bang if we looked far out into space (meaning far into the past) in any direction, the microwaves ought to be coming from all parts of the sky indiscriminately, as a feeble background radiation.

The search for the background radiation began at once, and in 1965 A. A. Penzias and R. W. Wilson of Bell Telephone Laboratories, using a delicate "radiometer" designed by Dicke in 1945, reported that after all microwave emission was accounted for, there was still a faint general background of radiation, of exactly the type to be expected of the big bang. (As it turned out, this radiation had been detected before but had not been recognized for what it was. It even accounts for some of the "snow" on television screens.)

The presence of the background radiation is the strongest evidence yet in favor of the big bang theory, and is considered by many to be conclusive. It means that radio telescopy has reached out not only to the end of the universe, in space, but to the beginning of the universe, in time, as well.

Dust Clouds and Pulsars

If radio telescopy can tell us surprising things about the most distant reaches of the universe in space and time, it can tell us equally surprising things about matters close by.

Optically, we see the bright stars that make up our own galaxy, but there is other matter as well. There are not only planets that may be circling other stars as they do our own, but there are also vast clouds of dust and gas that spread between the stars. Some of these clouds are visible as glowing nebulae, lit by the stars they enclose. Some are visible as dark clouds obscuring the stars behind them.

Some of the elements of the thin dust and gas between the stars can be identified by their absorption of specific wavelengths of starlight. As long ago as 1904 the German astronomer Johannes Franz Hartmann (1865–1936) had detected the absorption line of calcium in starlight passing through the clouds.

Not very much, however, can be done in this fashion and astronomers soon reached an apparent limit.

This is not surprising. Since the 1930s they have been convinced that most of the material in the interstellar clouds, as much as 95 percent even, is cold hydrogen. Such hydrogen does not emit, obscure, or absorb visible light and it might as well not be there as far as optical telescopes and spectroscopes are concerned.

But what about microwaves?

In 1944 a Dutch astronomer, Hendrik Christoffel van de Hulst, was hiding from the German armies that had occupied his land during World War II. He lacked an observatory or instruments and was forced to confine his work to pen-and-paper theoretical calculations.

He considered the behavior of the single proton and the single electron that made up the cold hydrogen atom. Their magnetic fields might line up in the same way or in opposite ways, and there is a slight energy difference between the two line-ups. Hydrogen atoms might occasionally absorb energy and move into the higher-energy line-up and then later emit that energy again.

The energy produced would be very small and would be represented by a microwave photon with a length of 21 centimeters (8.3 inches). The emission for any given hydrogen atom would take place only very rarely — once in 11 million years — but considering the vast quantity of hydrogen atoms present in outer space, there should be a continuous drizzle of this 21-centimeter (8.3-inch) microwave beam.

Once the war was over, this wavelength was searched for, and in 1951 two men working independently, the Swiss-American Felix Bloch and the American Edward Mills Purcell, located it. Clouds of cold hydrogen could now be followed, here and there, in the skies above us, and the concentrations of hydrogen in our galaxy could be mapped.

From these maps, it was clear that the hydrogen formed a series of spirals about the nucleus of our galaxy. Since it seemed certain that the hydrogen was associated with starry concentrations, this represented conclusive observational proof that our own Milky Way galaxy was indeed a spiral galaxy, with our own solar system in one of the spiral arms. This had been taken for granted earlier, to be sure, and the tracing of lines of hot hydrogen clouds and of very bright stars which tend to form in dusty areas had, by 1951, made a spiral structure seem probable, but it was the microwave studies that produced the final bit of evidence.

Hydrogen is not the only cold substance that can be detected by radio astronomy in the vast distances between the stars. Every different atom or atom combination radiates or absorbs different wavelengths in the microwave region producing a virtual "fingerprint" by which each can be recognized conclusively. In a few cases, an optical "fingerprint" can be produced. In 1937, for instance, spectra obtained with the Hooker telescope had revealed the presence of carbon-hydrogen (CH) and carbon-nitrogen (CN) combinations in the interstellar gas clouds.

On the whole, though, astronomers did not expect to find much in the clouds. The atoms, they felt, were spread so widely apart that the kind of collisions required to produce atom combinations would be too rare to produce them in detectable quantity, except where carbon, nitrogen, and oxygen were concerned. These were the only atoms capable of making combinations that were present in reasonable quantity, in among the overwhelming presence of hydrogen.

The presence of CH and CN was understandable, therefore, and the presence of the microwave absorption lines confirmed in 1963 what the optical astronomers had found a quarter century earlier. An oxygen-hydrogen combination (OH, "hydroxyl") ought also to exist, perhaps, though it had not been found optically. It would radiate or absorb microwaves in four characteristic wavelengths and in 1963 two of these wavelengths were located by radio astronomers at M.I.T.

There seemed not much hope that one could go beyond that. The chances of the kind of collisions that could produce combinations of more than two atoms seemed impossibly small, yet in 1968 observers at the University of California, including Townes, the inventor of the maser, located microwave emissions from interstellar space that were characteristic of molecules of water and of ammonia.

The water molecule is a three-atom combination (H_2O) and the ammonia molecule is a four-atom combination (NH_3). Thus was born the study of "astrochemistry."

In 1969 a four-atom combination, involving the carbon atom, was discovered. This was formaldehyde (H_2CO). Molecules made up of five, six, and seven atoms (all including carbon) were then discovered and by the early 1970s over two dozen different molecular combinations had been detected.

How these may have been formed is still a puzzle but one thing seems clear. The compounds found in outer space seem to be those which are en route to the carbon-containing chemicals characteristic of life. Chemists on Earth have speculated on how the life chemicals might have arisen from simpler substances and have wondered how much they might trust their conclusions, considering that they could never go back in time to check. Now they see that even in the utterly hostile environment of outer space, carbon-containing compounds begin to form. Thus, radio astronomy comes to the aid of biological speculations on earth.

The presence of fairly complicated molecules in interstellar dust clouds was odd enough, but there was odder still for radio astronomers to discover.

Some radio sources twinkle as a result of the influence of the Earth's ionosphere on the microwave beam. It was as the result of such twinkling that Bolton felt Cygnus A to be a small source by which the concept of the radio star had originated.

Attempts were made to study such scintillations and to study variations in microwave emissions from quasars. In the process of doing so, there came some indication, in 1964, that there might be a more rapid fluctuation of some radio sources, a fluctuation that could not be blamed on the ionosphere. It occurred at moderately long wavelengths that till then were being neglected by radio astronomers, and it occurred too rapidly for the instruments then available to study in detail.

The English astronomer Anthony Hewish devised a large array of 2048 antennas spread out over an area of 18,000 square meters (4.5 acres). It was designed to be able to detect rapid fluctuation at wavelengths in the meter range.

In July 1967 the new radio telescope was set to scanning the heavens and, within a month, a young graduate student, Jocelyn Bell, reported receiving bursts of microwaves from a place midway between the stars Vega and Altair — very rapid bursts, too. Hewish had expected rapid fluctuations but not that rapid. Each burst of microwaves lasted only one twentieth of a second and they came at intervals of one and one-third seconds. Indeed, they came with remarkable regularity. They came every 1.33730109 seconds.

Hewish felt that what was being observed was a kind of "pulsating star" and this became shortened to "pulsar." He located three others before he announced his discovery in February 1968. Since then additional pulsars have been found by the dozens. Two thirds of them are found along the narrow band of the Milky Way, an indication that, unlike quasars, they are part of our own galaxy.

All the pulsars are very regular in their behavior, but the period varies from pulsar to pulsar. One has a period as long as 3.7 seconds. On November 18, 1968, astronomers at Arecibo detected a pulsar in the Crab nebula, which had a period of only 0.033089 second. It was delivering microwave bursts thirty times a second and is the shortest-period pulsar known.

Naturally, the question arose as to what could produce such short flashes with such fantastic regularity. It had to be some massive body (to account for all the energy) which was engaging in some very regular periodic motion. It had to be revolving about another body, or rotating about its axis, or pulsing in and out in a period of anywhere from a few hundredths of a second to a few seconds.

No object known to astronomers could move with such a short period. Even white dwarfs, the smallest stars known, could not rotate, revolve, or pulsate rapidly enough.

Could there be something smaller than a white dwarf but just as massive? If we could imagine all the subatomic particles of the smashed atoms that make up a white dwarf, collapsing closer and closer together, the star would get smaller and smaller and its gravitational field would become more and more intense. Eventually the gravitational field, acting upon its own substance, would become so strong that electrons would be pulled into protons, forming neutrons. The entire star would become a mass of neutrons in contact.

As long before as 1934, the existence of such "neutron stars" had been suggested by Baade and by the Swiss astronomer Fritz Zwicky

(1898–1974). The properties were later worked out in some detail by the American physicist J Robert Oppenheimer (1904–1967).

If the sun were to collapse to form a neutron star, its entire mass would be concentrated into a tiny ball perhaps no more than 15 kilometers (9 miles) across. Thomas Gold suggested that a pulsar might be a rotating neutron star, small enough to rotate in four seconds or less. Electrons would be held so tightly by the neutron star's enormous gravity that they would escape only at the magnetic poles, producing microwaves as they did so.

The neutron star would therefore be something like a hose that was spraying microwaves in a sweep as it turned. Each time it turned past us, we'd receive a pulse of microwaves, very briefly.

Gold suggested that if this were so, then the neutron star had to be losing energy and, therefore, slowing its period of rotation. Of those known, the Crab nebula pulsar is the shortest-period and, by this line of reasoning, the youngest. If it was formed at the time of the great supernova of 1054, as seems almost certain, it is a little over 900 years old. When its pulses were studied closely, it was found to be slowing up as Gold had predicted. The period increased by 36.48 billionths of a second each day. Similar slow-ups were noted for other pulsars as well.

Could such neutron stars be observed optically? Should not the electrons emerging from the neutron star produce bursts of visible light as well as microwaves? Keen attention was focused on the Crab nebula, and in January 1969 it was noted that the light of a dim star within the nebula *did* flash on and off in precise time with the microwave pulses. This was the first optical pulsar discovered, the first visible neutron star.

12. Beyond Earth

Particles

Visible light and microwaves are the two sections of the electromagnetic spectrum that pass through the atmosphere and reach the surface of the earth. Each presented mankind with enormous quantities of information about the universe. Is there anything else that reaches the surface of the earth from outer space?

The answer is yes. For one thing, there are gravitational influences reaching our planet. Albert Einstein, in his General Theory of Relativity, published in 1916, had shown that gravitation could also make itself felt as waves, but these waves were not among those which, like light and microwaves, were part of the electromagnetic spectrum. Just as electromagnetic radiation can be viewed as having the aspect of particles, in which form they could be called photons, so gravitational waves can also be spoken of as "gravitons."

The gravitational effects we experience most strongly are from the sun and the moon, and, to a lesser extent, from the planets. It seemed unlikely that any gravitons coming from the more distant reaches of the universe could be detected. Gravitons energetic enough to be detected would have to arise from huge masses engaged in some form of rapid periodic motion, and even the pulsars didn't seem energetic enough to do the job.

Nevertheless, the American physicist Joseph Weber set about trying to detect them. He made use of large aluminum cylinders about 1.5 meters (5 feet) long and 0.6 meters (2 feet) wide. Each weighed some 3100 kilometers (3.5 tons) and each was suspended by a steel wire in a vacuum chamber.

Under the influence of a gravitational wave that could be longer than the Earth itself, the cylinders would be very slightly distorted. Use was made of crystals which set up an electrical potential when distorted and the setup was so designed as to record motions as small as a hundredth the width of a proton (which is itself only a hundred-thousandth the width of an atom).

Weber made use of two of these cylinders, 960 kilometers (600 miles) apart, one in Baltimore and one in Chicago. Since a single gravitational wave from the distant stars would sweep over both of them, only a distortion affecting both of them within half a second of each other would count.

Using a "gravity telescope" of this kind, Weber began to report the detection of gravitons in 1969. He observed enough to suspect that violent events must be taking place in the galactic center, events so violent as to be difficult of explanation. Others, however, have not been able to repeat Weber's work and the matter remains in doubt.

To photons and gravitons, both massless particles, we can add a third, the "neutrino," and also a fourth which is a twin of the neutrino but its opposite in some ways and which is called an "antineutrino." Antineutrinos are usually produced when electrons are produced; neutrinos when the electrons' opposite twin, positrons, are produced. Electrons and positrons carry an electric charge and are easily detected even though they are only $1/1800$ as massive as even the least massive atom. Neutrinos and antineutrinos are lighter still, having zero mass, and, worse yet, have no electric charge at all. What's more, unlike photons (which are also without mass and electric charge), neutrinos and antineutrinos don't interact with the particles making up matter. Neutrinos and antineutrinos go through matter just about as easily as they travel through a vacuum and so they are almost impossible to detect.

The existence of the neutrino and antineutrino was first suggested in 1931 by the Austrian physicist Wolfgang Pauli (1900–1958) on purely theoretical grounds. For a quarter century that existence remained just that — purely theoretical.

Once nuclear reactors became common, however, things were different. By Pauli's theory, such reactors ought to release floods of antineutrinos. One out of many trillions of them might react with a proton.

In 1956, therefore, two American physicists, Clyde Lorrain

Cowan, Jr., and Frederick Reines, set up a device designed to detect the consequences of just such a reaction and no other. In this way they finally succeeded in spotting antineutrinos and finally proving their existence beyond a doubt.

This had astronomical implications at once. The sun (and other stars as well, naturally), in the course of the nuclear reactions that proceed in its central region, produces enormous numbers of neutrinos. Energetic photons are also produced in vast quantities, but photons react readily with matter and are constantly being absorbed and reemitted. It takes photons enormous lengths of time to reach the surface and be radiated into space, and by then they have undergone so many changes that they tell us little about events in the solar interior.

Neutrinos, on the other hand, which scarcely react with matter, pass through the sun's substance as though there is nothing there. Moving at the speed of light, they reach the sun's surface in three seconds. If they are moving in the right direction, they reach Earth in a little over eight minutes and then, of course, pass right through it by the trillions. Occasionally, though, one might be blocked and detected, and from the energies and numbers of those recorded, some information might be gained concerning what is going on in the center of the sun, from which place the neutrinos have come directly.

One method of detecting even very few neutrinos was suggested by the Italian physicist Bruno Pontecorvo. He pointed out that if a variety of chlorine atoms called chlorine-37 absorbs a neutrino into its nucleus it becomes argon-37, a completely different type of substance.

Chlorine itself is a gas and can be concentrated into considerable density only by large pressures or by liquefying it at low temperatures. One way of getting a great many chlorine-37 atoms into one place at normal pressure and temperature is to fill a large tank with tetrachloroethylene, a common dry-cleaning liquid. If this is exposed to a beam of neutrinos from the sun, very tiny quantities of argon-37 accumulate. This can be flushed out by bubbling helium or ordinary argon through the fluid. The argon-37, swept out in this manner, is radioactive and so can be detected.

If this tank of tetrachloroethylene (a "neutrino telescope") is placed deep in a mine, the layers of rock above prevent anything from outer space reaching the tank except for neutrinos. Reines placed such a tank in a South African gold mine two miles deep in the Earth — so that we have the seeming paradox of a telescope hidden under two miles of rock so that it can see the center of the sun. In 1965, after observations lasting nine months, Reines reported the observation of seven neutrinos.

In 1968 the American physicist Raymond R. Davis placed a still more elaborate neutrino trap in a deep mine in Lead, South Dakota. It was a tank 15 meters (48 feet) long and 6 meters (20 feet) wide, containing 380,000 liters (100,000 gallons) of tetrachloroethylene.

Solar neutrinos were indeed detected, but in less than half the quantities that were to be expected if the events in the solar center are as astronomers think they are. Either something is wrong with the telescope or astronomical thinking concerning the solar center needs to be revised.

In addition to massless particles — photons, gravitons, neutrinos, and antineutrinos — mankind has become aware of massive particles from outer space, too. It came about because as the twentieth century opened, physicists were studying the radiations of uranium and similar metals. They discovered that radiations, which were more penetrating than light, included gamma rays, the most energetic and shortest-wave photons known.

Such radiation could be detected by an "electroscope" which consists of two thin sheets of gold leaf attached to a rod. The sheets of gold leaf are enclosed in a box designed to protect them from disturbing air currents, but the rod emerges from the upper end of the box. If the end of the rod is electrically charged, the two sheets of gold leaf gain the same charge and repel each other. They move stiffly apart in a V shape.

If penetrating radiation gets through the box into the air inside, it knocks electrons out of the atoms with which it collides, forming electrically charged ions. The ions remove the charge from the gold leaf and the two sheets collapse toward each other. The rate at which they approach each other is a measure of the quantity of radiation in the vicinity.

It was discovered, though, that the gold leaf collapsed very slowly, even when there was no known radioactive substance in the vicinity, and even though it was surrounded by thick material that ought to keep out such radiation.

The best guess was that there were present radiation sources in the soil that released very energetic radiation in very small quantities. In 1911 the Austrian physicist Victor Franz Hess (1883–1964) undertook to prove this by removing the electroscope from the surface of the Earth altogether. He took one with him into a balloon that lifted to a height of 500 meters (1600 feet) above the surface. He felt that the radiation from the soil would be blocked off by a few hundred meters of air and that the leaves of the electroscope would now stay apart.

He proved to be wrong! They collapsed more quickly when they were high in the air. The radiation, whatever it was, came not from the soil but from outer space. The American physicist Robert Andrews Millikan (1868–1953) suggested, in 1925, that this radiation be called "cosmic rays" because it reached us from the cosmos.

Millikan thought they were a new and still more energetic variety of photon, but the American physicist Arthur Holly Compton (1892–1962) showed in the early 1930s that the radiation was curved out of its path by Earth's magnetic field and that therefore it must consist of electrically charged particles.

Eventually it was shown that cosmic-ray particles were speeding atomic nuclei that carried a positive electric charge. The most common atom in space is hydrogen, so that most of the particles were hydrogen nuclei, or simple protons, but complex combinations of protons and neutrons (the nuclei of heavier atoms) were also found in small quantities.

"Counters" had been devised which reacted whenever a single subatomic particle entered, closing an electric circuit to produce a click and producing a track of some sort to indicate the path followed by the particle. The German physicist Walther Bothe (1891–1957) suggested that the penetrating property of cosmic rays could be taken advantage of by having a number of counters in a straight line. Other particles would never be energetic enough to pass through all, but cosmic rays could do so. Therefore any time all the counters reacted, a cosmic-ray particle had entered. Such "coincidence counters" could naturally be oriented in different directions and would from a "cosmic-ray telescope."

236

Cosmic-ray particles, possessing electric charge, are for that reason affected by electromagnetic fields. They are constantly curving (even if only slightly) out of the straight line in response to these fields and by the time they reach us, after having traversed uncounted light-years of space, the direction from which they come is no indication at all of where they originated.

It is not surprising, then, that though astronomers could pinpoint photon sources with great accuracy, they had little hope of doing the same for cosmic-ray sources in the sky. There was only one exception to this:

The huge flare of February 28, 1942, which brought about Hey's discovery of the sun's microwave emissions, was also followed by an increase in the intensity of the cosmic-ray level detected on Earth. This happened in the case of other solar flares, notably one on November 19, 1949, and it was not long before it was quite clear that the sun was a cosmic-ray source. People could talk of "solar cosmic rays" and of "galactic cosmic rays."

Apparently the sun is constantly emitting streams of its substance, mostly protons (hydrogen nuclei), in all directions, as a result of the highly energetic processes that proceed in its uppermost layers. Astronomers can virtually see this happening in the form of "prominences" which send huge gouts of incandescent material upward from the sun's surface and in the streamers of the sun's corona, which is its outer atmosphere.

The corona may also be viewed as growing thinner and thinner the farther from the sun but persisting, detectably, as a thin stream of protons moving outward at speeds up to 400 kilometers (250 miles) per second. There had been suggestions to this effect as early as 1896 by a Norwegian physicist, Olaf Kristian Birkeland (1867–1917), and the gathering evidence supported it firmly. In 1958 the American physicist Eugene Norman Parker called this outward stream of protons the "solar wind."

The more energetic the processes on the solar surface, the more energetic the protons added to the solar wind by those processes. A large solar flare can add a stream of protons so energetic that they fall into the cosmic-ray range. The best the sun can do, however, is to produce only "soft cosmic rays," protons with energies near the lower limits of the cosmic-ray range.

The more energetic galactic cosmic rays must originate from stars where more energetic processes are going on than are found in the sun — from exploding stars such as novas and supernovas, or from the more mysterious violences recently discovered in the universe, such as exploding galaxies and quasars. On the other hand, the protons of galactic cosmic rays may start with low energies and be accelerated by the magnetic fields they pass through, becoming only gradually high-energy.

Either way, there remains a chance that cosmic rays, even though the routes they follow are complex, can yield information about the distant reaches of the universe and about the cataclysmic processes of dying stars, information that perhaps might be reached in no other way.

Balloons and Rockets

Such photons as reach the surface of the Earth are relatively unchanged as a result of their trip through the atmosphere. Cosmic-ray particles, however, collide with atmospheric atoms and molecules and what reaches the surface is not at all what exists in the high reaches of the upper atmosphere.

It was with respect to cosmic-ray research, then, that scientists first made serious attempts to move off the Earth's solid surface altogether.

In a way this was a continuation of the drive that had led Lowell to the clear desert air of Arizona and Hale to the mountains of southern California. That had been an attempt to get the thickest, dirtiest, and most weather-ridden parts of the atmosphere beyond or below one — yet the best one can do in this respect is not much if one must stand on the surface. Even the highest mountain observatories manage to get above only about 40 percent of the atmosphere.

The most practical method of getting off the surface of the Earth in the early decades of the twentieth century was to use balloons. Indeed, it had been from a balloon that Hess had first discovered cosmic rays.

The first balloons capable of carrying men off the surface of the Earth were constructed in 1782 by the French brothers Joseph Michel Montgolfier (1740–1810) and Jacques Etienne Montgolfier (1745–1799). They used hot air as the lifting agency. Larger balloons, using hydrogen for lift, could, within decades, carry men kilometers above the surface of the Earth, although the lowering temperature and the increasing thinness of the air with height made the higher flights more and more dangerous to men in open gondolas.

The real chance of using balloons for astronomy came with the development of sealed aluminum gondolas, within which men could keep air at comfortable pressures and temperatures regardless of height, and with the use of helium as a lifting agent instead of the dangerously inflammable hydrogen. The developer of such balloons was the Swiss physicist Auguste Piccard (1884–1962), who made his first flight in 1931 and attained a height of nearly 16 kilometers (10 miles), almost twice the height of the highest mountain peak on Earth. By the 1970s, heights in excess of 40 kilometers (25 miles) had been attained.

Balloons with sealed gondolas reach the stratosphere. Some 99.9 percent of the atmosphere is below them. From the vantage point of such a high-flying balloon, one is nearly in outer space. The sky is so dark that the solar corona can be seen and, even with the sun in the sky, so can some of the brighter stars.

In the stratosphere there is virtually no water vapor between the balloon and the sky, and spectra can be taken through the entire range of infrared radiation between the visible light and microwave "windows" of radiation that reaches Earth's surface.

Thus, the American physicist John Donovan Strong used a specially designed Schmidt telescope which he took up in a balloon in order to measure the infrared absorption in the upper reaches of Venus's atmosphere. The highest point he reached was 26 kilometers (16 miles) on October 28,1964, and from that height the evidence was definite. There was indeed water vapor in the clouds of Venus.

Similar spectra obtained of the reflected light of Mars by the German-American astronomer Martin Schwarzschild indicated the presence of very small quantities of water vapor on Mars, while on the other hand infrared spectra of red giant stars showed them cool enough to possess water molecules in their atmospheres, too.

Naturally, the sun was a prime target for balloon astronomy. In September 1957, from a balloon reaching 25 kilometers (15 miles) above Earth's surface, a telescope and camera working by remote control took pictures of the sun's surface sharper than any ever made previously.

The telescope was 2.5 meters (8 feet) long and had a 30-centimeter (12-inch) paraboloid mirror of quartz. It was guided by light-sensitive devices that could move it to face the sun and hold it so steadily. Exposures were made at the rate of one per second and after the photography was complete, a parachute attached to the instruments was released from the balloon and they were retrieved safely.

In order to allow for change of shape of the mirror as a result of temperature change, the film was kept moving forward and backward. Most of the photographs were out of focus therefore, but about one out of twenty would just happen to catch the shifting mirror focus and be perfectly sharp. Thousands of pictures were taken and, after two flights, ten perfect photos had been made.

In March 1970 a balloon-borne telescope, a 91-centimeter (36-inch) reflector, took photographs of the planet Uranus that were so clear they showed the gradual decrease in luminosity toward its edges ("limb-darkening"). Its equatorial bulge could be measured with a new degree of accuracy, too.

Yet even the best balloons have their limits. Though they opened the infrared region of the spectrum to astronomers, they could not do more. The ultraviolet radiation of the sun and other stars is stopped at atmospheric heights greater than astronomers had expected and above those which even the best balloons could reach prior to the 1960s. Photons beyond the microwave region could not be received, nor could the solar wind be studied. For full information, astronomers had to get their instruments (if not themselves) beyond the atmosphere altogether — truly beyond Earth.

The one way by which an Earthly object can leave the atmosphere altogether is by making use of Newton's Third Law of Motion. If part of an object's mass is fired out in one direction, the rest of the object moves in the other. This is demonstrated by the kind of rockets used in Independence Day displays, and the principle works better in a vacuum than it does in the atmosphere. Naturally, to reach beyond the atmosphere, a rocket would have to carry not only fuel but oxygen for the fuel to burn in.

Rockets were first invented by the Chinese in the 1200s. In 1801 a British artillery expert, William Congreve (1772–1828), having learned about rockets in India, put them to military use. Some were used against the United States in the War of 1812, notably at the bombardment of Fort McHenry in 1814, and it was this that inspired Francis Scott Key to speak of "the rocket's red glare" when he wrote "The Star-Spangled Banner" to commemorate that bombardment.

Rocket weapons faded out in the face of improvements in conventional artillery, but about the beginning of the twentieth century two men independently conceived a new and finer use of rockets — that of exploring the upper atmosphere and outer space.

The first was a Russian physicist, Konstantin Eduardovich Tsiolkovsky (1857–1935). In 1898 he wrote a long article in which he described a spaceship that would be powered by a rocket exhaust, and in 1903 he began a series of articles for an aviation magazine in which he went into the theory of rocketry quite thoroughly.

Where Tsiolkovsky was content to theorize, the American physicist Robert Hutchings Goddard (1882–1945) chose to experiment. He had grown interested in rocketry as a teen-ager and in 1914 had already obtained two patents involving apparatus. In 1919 he published a small book entitled *The Method of Reaching Extreme Altitudes*.

In 1923 he began to work with a new idea in rocketry (one that Tsiolkovsky had recommended), the use of engines that combined liquid fuel, such as gasoline, with liquid oxygen. Much more power could be developed in this way than by using gunpowder.

In 1926 he was ready to launch his first liquid-fuel rocket from a farm in Auburn, Massachusetts. It was about 1.2 meters (4 feet) long, 15 centimeters (6 inches) in diameter, and was held in a frame like a child's jungle gym. When fired it rose 56 meters (184 feet) high in the air and reached a speed of 95 kilometers (60 miles) an hour.

Goddard managed to get a few thousand dollars from the Smithsonian Institution and in July 1929 sent up a larger rocket near Worcester, Massachusetts. It went faster and higher than the first. More important, it carried a barometer and a thermometer, along with a small camera to photograph their readings. This was the first instrument-carrying rocket.

He then shifted the scene of his activities to New Mexico (partly because his Massachusetts neighbors objected to his noisy experiments) and in the early 1930s finally fired rockets that reached speeds faster than sound and that rose 2.5 kilometers (1.5 miles) into the air.

Meanwhile, a society devoted to rocket experiments was founded in Germany. Among its members were the rocket enthusiasts Willy Ley (1906–1969) and Wernher von Braun, both of whom were eventually to come to the United States.

Once Adolf Hitler came to power in Germany in 1933, he seized upon rocketry and turned it once again to war use. In 1936 a secret experimental station was built at Peenemünde, on the Baltic seacoast of Germany. There, by 1938, rockets capable of flying a distance of 18 kilometers (11 miles) were built. In a few years, they became good enough to be able to carry loads of explosives across the English Channel and in 1944 Wernher von Braun's group put these "missiles" into action. They were the famous V-2 rockets. (The V stood for "vergeltung," meaning "vengeance.")

Goddard lived just long enough to see this awful triumph of the rocket. He died on August 10, 1945.

The V-2 weapons interested Germany's adversaries, the United States and the Soviet Union. Immediately after Germany's defeat, both the victorious nations made efforts to capture Germany's rocket experts. The United States got most of them, including Wernher von Braun. (Willy Ley had left Germany long before — when Hitler came to power.)

Soon after the war, captured V-2 missiles were used by the United States to carry instruments into the upper atmosphere in a project that was under the leadership of the American physicist James Alfred Van Allen. One of them reached a height of 184 kilometers (114 miles), nearly five times as high as any balloon could reach. In 1949 the United States put a small American rocket on top of a V-2. When the V-2 reached its maximum height, the small rocket took off and, with little interference from the thin air about it, added its velocity to that of the V-2 first stage and reached a height of 385 kilometers (240 miles.) Man-made objects were finally reaching points where the atmosphere was no longer appreciable.

Another way of reaching great heights was to send a balloon as high into the atmosphere as possible and then to launch a small rocket from it. In 1952 a number of such "rockoons" were launched by a team under Van Allen.

Rockets, whether launched from the ground or from balloons, offered astronomers their first chance of studying the entire solar spectrum, particularly the short-wave range in the ultraviolet and beyond. The first such measurement was made from a height of 80 kilometers (50 miles) by way of a V-2 rocket launched by the United States in 1946. Measurements of the spectrum were made down to 0.22 micrometer. Since then the solar spectrum has been photographed in detail well into the x-ray region.

What's more, x-rays were detected from the sun's corona. This confirmed coronal temperatures in the million-degree range, something the Swedish physicist Bengt Edlen had first maintained in 1940. That, in turn, made the notion of a solar wind more credible.

In 1956 instruments rocketed above the atmosphere detected ultraviolet radiation from the stars for the first time — notably from Spica, the brightest star in the constellation Virgo.

Two rockoons, launched in 1953 near Newfoundland, detected surprisingly high levels of radiation at heights over 48 kilometers (30 miles). At the time this was attributed to faulty instruments and was ignored, but in a few more years astronomers would be having a change of heart on the matter.

Yet however high such rockets might reach, they remained in the upper atmosphere and beyond for only short periods of time and, on the whole, only fugitive bits of information were brought back. Considering the effort expended in rocketry that was not enough. What was needed was a rocket that could get out in space and stay there.

This was not at all impossible. Newton had established the theory three centuries before. If a rocket can be sent away from Earth in such a way as to attain a speed of at least 8 kilometers (5 miles) per second, and if it can be guided in such a way as to speed along beyond the atmosphere in a direction more or less parallel to Earth's surface, it would move into orbit. It would circle the Earth for an indefinite period as an "artificial satellite."

To establish such an artificial satellite seemed a feasible project for the 1950s.

Satellites and Probes

Both the Soviet Union and the United States did their best to design rockets that would place a satellite in orbit in the course of the International Geophysical Year, which was to run from July 1, 1957, to December 31, 1958.

The Soviet Union attained this end first and *Sputnik I* (Sputnik is the Russian word for "satellite") was placed in orbit on October 4, 1957, only a few weeks after the centennial of Tsiolkovsky's birth.

Sputnik I was designed to do no more than carry a transmitter that would send out a regular signal. Lovell's steerable radio telescope was completed just in time to pick up those signals and to play a major role in following subsequent satellites.

Once it became possible to orbit a satellite, the next step was to make one large enough to carry any of a wide variety of instruments that could make measurements, convert them into coded radio pulses, and send them to Earth for decoding. Such "telemetering" ("measuring at a distance") had first been used in connection with balloons, in 1925, by a Russian physicist, Pyotr A. Moltchanoff.

On November 3, 1957, the Soviet Union sent up a second satellite, *Sputnik II,* which contained a live dog. It was the first time a living organism was placed in orbit. By telemetry, the dog's heartbeat could be followed and when the batteries of the satellite ran down after a hundred hours, the dog was put painlessly to death by a mechanism controlled from Earth.

The United States launched its first orbiting satellite, *Explorer I,* on January 31, 1958, under the guidance of Von Braun. It was smaller than the Soviet satellites, but Van Allen had been working for a long time on techniques of "miniaturization" in which instruments were made as small as possible and were packed as efficiently as possible. American satellites could therefore pick up surprising amounts of information for their size.

Many of the early satellites were used for purely Earthly purposes — for mapping Earth and its resources, for studying its cloud cover and weather, for serving as communication relays from one part of the planet to the other, for determining the exact shape of the planet, and so on.

Astronomic discoveries beyond Earth's atmosphere had their

beginning with the United States' first satellite. *Explorer I* had an orbit elliptical enough to bring it as close as 350 kilometers (217 miles) above Earth's surface at one end of its orbit and out to 1860 kilometers (1155 miles) at the other. It carried devices to record cosmic rays and the radiation of other electrically charged particles at these varying distances.

Up to a height of 800 kilometers (500 miles) the radiation count per minute was about as expected, increasing slowly with height. Above that mark, however, the radiation-count dropped suddenly, sometimes all the way to zero. *Explorer III,* launched on March 26, 1958, sent back similar information, and so did the Soviet satellite, *Sputnik III,* launched on May 15, 1958.

Van Allen did not believe it possible for the radiation count to drop to zero. Recalling anomalously high readings attained by rockoons, he wondered if instead it rose so high that the instruments were "blinded."

When *Explorer IV* was sent up on July 26, 1958, it carried special counters designed to handle heavy loads. One of them, for instance, was shielded with a thin layer of lead to keep out most of the radiation. This time the counters told another story. *Explorer IV,* reaching a height of 2200 kilometers (1370 miles), sent down counts which, allowing for the shielding, disclosed that radiation intensity was far higher than scientists had imagined.

The first important astronomical discovery made through rocketry, then, was that belts of electrically charged particles surrounded the Earth. These were fed by the solar wind and by cosmic rays, and followed the lines of magnetic force generated by the Earth's magnetism.

The radiation belts were not distributed symmetrically about the Earth, later satellite studies showed. The solar wind pushed these radiation belts toward Earth's surface before parting to either side. There was a sharp boundary, therefore, between the radiation belts and the space outside. On the side away from the sun, the radiation belts bulged away from the Earth, being dragged out by the solar wind into a long affair shaped like a comet tail.

The radiation belts were at first called the "Van Allen belts" but later came to be called the "magnetosphere." The boundary of the magnetosphere, with the solar wind beyond, is the "magnetopause."

Once rockets were placed in orbit, it did not take much more push to lift them away from Earth altogether, never to return. The speed required by a satellite to go into orbit about Earth was a minimum of 8 kilometers (5 miles) per second, while that for breaking away from the Earth forever and going into an independent orbit about the sun as an "artificial planet" was 11 kilometers (7 miles) per second.

Such artificial planets had their use just by existing. By measuring the competing gravitation effects on them of Earth and sun, the scale of the solar system could be measured at least as accurately as by radar reflection from Venus.

Even more important, though, it was possible to make such an object, in the course of its orbit about the sun, move near some astronomical body and send back information concerning it. Such an object would be a "probe."

The first artificial planet was launched on January 2, 1959, by the Soviet Union. It was a "lunar probe" since it was designed to pass near the moon. *Luna 1* passed within 6000 kilometers (3700 miles) of the moon's surface. On September 12, 1959, *Luna 2* was launched and, three days later, actually struck the moon, becoming the first man-made object ever to land on any world other than the Earth.

Neither *Luna 1* nor *Luna 2* indicated any sign of a magnetosphere about the moon nor any sign of a magnetic field. This was no surprise, however, since Earth's magnetic field is thought to originate from eddies in its liquid iron core, set into motion of Earth's rotation, and the moon has too low a density to have much of a liquid iron core, if any.

On October 4, 1959, the Soviet Union launched *Luna 3* and it passed behind the moon, taking photographs as it did so. This was an electrifying feat since the moon revolves about the earth in such a way as to show us, always, the same side. The far side of the moon had never been seen by human eyes prior to that time. Nor could it ever be seen by human eyes from Earth's surface under any circumstances.

It is conceivable that the magnetosphere might have been deduced from observations taken from Earth's surface, but the details of the moon's far side could not have been. The feat of *Luna 3* represents the first extension of man's knowledge for which rocketry was an indispensable technique.

Luna 3's map of the far side of the moon was very primitive and sketchy, but other rockets followed. On March 31, 1966, the Soviet Union sent up *Luna 10*, which eventually took up an orbit about the moon, the first man-made object to be in orbit about any astronomical object other than the Earth. The United States followed with *Lunar Orbiter 1*, launched on August 10, 1966. Such moon-orbiting probes succeeded in mapping the entire lunar surface with precision.

It was clear, for instance, that the "maria," the large, relatively smooth areas that cover much of the side of the moon facing us, are almost altogether absent from the far side. The reason for this difference between the two lunar hemispheres is, as yet, uncertain.

The next steps were soft landings on the moon, soft enough to keep instruments in working order, so that photographs of the moon could be taken from its surface and sent back to Earth and so that information concerning the chemistry of the lunar surface could be transmitted as well. The first probes to make a beginning at this were *Luna 9*, launched by the Soviet Union on January 3, 1966, and *Surveyor I*, launched by the United States on May 30, 1966.

Other probes went farther afield. The first great planetary probe was *Mariner II*, launched by the United States on August 27, 1962. It traveled 290 million kilometers (180 million miles) in 109 days to make its rendezvous with Venus on December 14, 1962. It passed within 34,000 kilometers (21,000 miles) of the surface of the planet.

Mariner II, testing the properties of the space in the neighborhood of Venus, found that Venus did not have a magnetosphere. Since it was approximately Earth's size and density, it should certainly have a liquid iron core, but its slow rate of rotation was apparently insufficient to set up the necessary eddies in the liquid iron.

More important still, *Mariner II* recorded microwave radiation from Venus and confirmed the earlier indication of Earthbound microwave receivers that the planet was very hot, with a surface temperature of 450° C. (800° F.).

Further confirmation of this was received from several Soviet probes that, beginning in 1967, actually landed on the surface of Venus and sent back information concerning an atmosphere some ninety times as thick as ours and almost entirely carbon dioxide.

Still more spectacular results were obtained from a series of Mars probes. The first of these was *Mariner IV*, launched on November 28, 1964. After a 228-day journey, the probe passed Mars on July 14, 1965, at a distance of about 10,000 kilometers (6100 miles) above its surface.

Mars, like the moon, was too small to have much of a melted iron core, for it had no magnetosphere, despite a rotation rapid enough to set up eddies in the core if it had existed. Its atmosphere turned out to be thinner than astronomers had thought and was only 1 percent as dense as our own.

Most important of all was the fact that twenty-one pictures were taken of the Martian surface at close range and were sent back to Earth. What they showed were craters, like those on the moon, something few had suspected.

Other Mars probes followed. Between July 28 and August 5, 1968, *Mariner 6* and *Mariner 7*, approaching to within 3500 kilometers (2180 miles) of the Martian surface, sent back over 200 photographs, and the canals of Schiaparelli and Lowell vanished forever. There were no signs of them. The anticanal astronomers were correct and what had seemed to be canals could only have been fortuitous lines of craters, with imagination filling in the detail.

In November 1971 *Mariner 9* went into orbit around Mars and was the first man-made object ever to orbit about a planet other than Earth. It ranged in distance from 1650 to 17,000 kilometers (1025 to 10,610 miles) above the surface, and it produced a virtually complete map of Mars. It showed that though Mars was heavily cratered on one hemisphere, the other showed signs of active geologic processes.

A small bright spot that earlier astronomers had named Nix Olympica (Snows of Olympus) turned out to be the largest-known volcano in the solar system. It was at least 15 kilometers (9.5 miles) high, 500 kilometers (310 miles) across at the base, and had a main crater that was 65 kilometers (40 miles) in diameter. It was thirty times greater in volume than the largest Earth volcano.

In addition, there was a huge canyon cutting across Mars for as long as the United States is wide and four times as deep as the Grand Canyon.

Then, too, the small Martian satellites were photographed — the first space-probe photographs of any satellites other than our moon.

Both Phobos and Deimos proved irregular in shape, pitted with craters, and their appearance, all told, was remarkably like a pair of potatoes. Phobos is 25 kilometers (15 miles) long and 20 kilometers (12 miles) wide, while Deimos is about half that in length and in width.

Since then, successful probes have been sent out to two other planets.

On March 29, 1974, *Mariner 10* passed within 35,000 kilometers (21,700 miles) of Mercury's surface and sent back photographs of a world as heavily cratered as the moon. Surprisingly, it turned out that Mercury had a weak magnetic field. Since its rotation is too slow to set up eddies in what is undoubtedly an iron core (it is a dense world) there is the possibility that because of its small size the core is solid and is a weak permanent magnet.

Meanwhile, on December 3, 1973, *Pioneer 10* passed within 135,000 kilometers (85,000 miles) of the cloud layers of Jupiter, taking measurements of an enormous magnetosphere, which, if it were only visible to the eye, would cover a portion of the sky, as seen from Earth, as large in appearance as the moon.

From the data sent back to Earth, it would seem that Jupiter is a very hot ball of hydrogen in which the hot gas turns, under huge pressures, to even hotter liquid some 10,000 kilometers (6100 miles) below the cloud layer.

A second probe, *Pioneer 11,* passed Jupiter's surface at a distance only one-third that of *Pioneer 10* a year later, skimmed over the polar region, and then headed outward for a rendezvous with Saturn.

The two Jupiter probes took some photographs of the large satellites of Jupiter. Io and Europa, the two inner ones, are moonlike in density. Io, the innermost, is enveloped in a thin layer of sodium vapor and may possibly be covered with a dry coating of salt. The outer ones, Ganymede and Callisto, are low enough in density to be icy in structure, perhaps, and a photograph of Callisto, seems to show a polar ice cap.

Both *Pioneer 10* and *Pioneer 11* will eventually leave the solar system, the first man-made objects to do so. Each carries a 6 x 9 inch gold-covered aluminum slab on which is etched a message that is obscure by ordinary standards, but which may make sense to any members of an advanced civilization that recovers it from space (a most unlikely eventuality, of course).

X-Rays and Black Holes

Useful probes are confined to the solar system — at least for the foreseeable future. Even if probes could be aimed to some of the nearby stars, the length of time it would take them to reach their destination, and the extreme unlikelihood of being able to receive decipherable measurements from such distances, make such stellar probes impractical.

Nevertheless, satellites can be used to receive information from the distant stars. In particular, those portions of the electromagnetic spectrum that cannot be received on Earth's surface because of the blanketing air can be received by satellite.

The first true space observatory, OSO (Orbiting Solar Observatory), was launched on March 7, 1962. It carried no telescope but during seventy-seven days of almost perfect operation it transmitted nearly 1000 hours of data on solar radiation and related phenomena.

Succeeding satellites of the sort were more sophisticated. OSO-IV, launched on October 18, 1967, carried some 115 kilograms (250 pounds) of instruments in a circular orbit 550 kilometers (350 miles) above Earth's surface. It carried an ultraviolet spectroheliograph and x-ray detectors. Its instruments could be aimed at the sun, automatically, with an accuracy of within 1 minute of arc. OSO-VI could manage an accuracy of within 0.5 minute of arc.

OSO-VII, launched on September 29, 1971, carried a coronagraph into orbit and took the first photographs of rapidly moving structures in the sun's corona. It also detected cool regions in the corona over the sun's poles and recorded gamma-ray emissions in solar flares.

Satellites of a more general nature belong to the OAO (Orbiting Astronomical Observatory) group. OAO-II, placed in orbit in December 1968, carried eleven telescopes with mirrors ranging in diameter from 40 centimeters (16 inches) to 20 centimeters (8 inches).

It was placed in circular orbit about 770 kilometers (480 miles) above Earth's surface. It carried through a systematic sampling of the ultraviolet output of 50,000 stars and found that in 1 percent of the stars it observed, ultraviolet radiation was six to forty times as intense as expected.

Beyond the ultraviolet, *Explorer XI,* launched April 27, 1961, had carried a detector that recorded twenty-two gamma-ray photons, the first such energetic photons to be observed from space. The gamma rays were not detected directly. Occasionally, a gamma ray forms an electron-positron pair and these charged particles can be picked up along with the flash of light that accompanies the formation. The device, long and cylindrical, can be thought of as a "gamma-ray telescope."

The most interesting information, however, came in connection with the detection of x-rays.

Once x-rays were found to be emitted by the sun, it occurred to the Italian physicist Bruno Rossi that solar x-rays might be reflected from the moon. A rocket was sent up on June 18, 1962, carrying instruments ("x-ray telescopes," they might be called) designed to record x-rays. These were picked up — not from the moon but from the direction of the galactic center. In October 1962 two weaker sources were discovered in other parts of the sky.

The next year rockets were sent up by a group under the leadership of the American astronomer Herbert Friedman in order to scan the entire sky for regions showing x-ray activity. Many such regions were found and a new branch of the science, "x-ray astronomy," came into existence.

On December 12, 1970, *Explorer 42* was sent up with two x-ray detectors aboard. Since it was launched from Kenya, Africa, it was named "Uhuru," a Swahili word meaning "freedom." For three years it scanned the entire sky and located more than 100 x-ray sources. Some of them were quasars, some pulsars, some supernova remnants, some distant galaxies. The strongest sources were concentrated in the Milky Way and were in our own galaxy.

The nature of the x-ray sources is of interest, of course, since only extremely energetic processes could produce x-rays, especially in such quantities as to make the radiation detectable at stellar distances.

One possible source would be a star condensed beyond the point of detection in the ordinary way.

Compact stars, like white dwarfs, in which gravitational implosion broke down the structure of atoms, had been known for half a century. The pulsars, which were still more compact stars in which all the subatomic particles were turned to neutrons and were drawn into contact, had just been discovered.

By theoretical reasoning, it could be shown that a particularly massive star could implode with such gravitational force as to break down the neutrons themselves. When that happens, there remains nothing further to impede the implosion and the diameter of the object approaches zero while its density approaches the infinite.

The surface gravity becomes so great that nothing material can escape and the object can only add more matter and grow in mass. Whether slowly or quickly, depending on how much matter there is in the vicinity, it must continue to grow. It is a gravitational "hole" into which any quantity of matter can fall, even ultimately the entire universe, but from which nothing can emerge.

Furthermore, not even photons can escape so that the object cannot possibly appear as anything but a lightless, nonluminous "black hole."

But how can a black hole be discovered if it emits neither matter nor radiation? The answer is that it does emit gravitons. It exerts a gravitational effect and can be detected in that manner.

If a black hole is near another star, for instance, matter from the star will, little by little, be sucked into the black hole. The matter will spiral in and some of the energy it gains under the gravitational pull is emitted as electromagnetic radiation. From points within 200 kilometers (125 miles) of the black-hole center, energy is released in the form of x-rays. It is possible, therefore, that an x-ray source *may* be a black hole.

The most likely case is that of Cyg X-1, a strong x-ray source in the constellation Cygnus (the Swan). In the vicinity of the x-ray source, a visible star (known as HDE-226868) has been spotted. It is many times as massive as the sun and yet it is circling the x-ray source. From the star's orbit, it can be deduced that the x-ray source is an even more massive object.

Ordinarily, such a large star would appear quite bright, but this one can't be seen at all. Combining this invisibility with the face of copious x-ray emission, astronomers now strongly suspect that Cyg X-1 is a black hole about which an ordinary star is circling.

In a way this is the most important discovery yet made by rocketry, since the existence of black holes makes it necessary for astronomers to rethink their theories as to the beginning and end of the universe.

Will the universe end as a black hole, or as a group of black holes? If so, how did the universe begin? Surely the original cosmic egg which exploded on the occasion of the big bang could only have been a black hole, and, if so, how could it explode? Or is the universe still a black hole, if it is taken in its entirety?

And what really happens to matter in a black hole? Does it squeeze through into a big bang at the other end? Or a little bang if the black hole is a small one? Does every black hole, large or small, become a "white hole" at some other point, possibly far distant in space — or even time? Is a quasar such a white hole?

It's a whole new ball game in some ways.

13. Man in Space

Footsteps on the Moon

With rockets carrying instruments into orbit, it was an inevitable thought that they might carry human beings as well. Manned flights to the moon had been dreamed of since ancient times, and they were a staple ingredient in the stories that had appeared in science fiction magazines since the 1920s.

On April 12, 1961, Yuri Alexeyevich Gagarin, in the Soviet vessel *Vostok 1,* became the first man to orbit the Earth. He made a single orbit in 108 minutes and was brought safely back to Earth. (When he died seven years later, a few weeks after his thirty-fourth birthday, it was nonspatially, in an air crash.) Later that same year, on August 6, Gherman Stepanovich Titov, in *Vostok 2,* circled the Earth for seventeen orbits.

The first American to go into orbit was John Herschel Glenn, Jr., who was launched on February 20, 1962, and circled the Earth three times before returning safely.

The feat was repeated frequently by men of both nations and the flights lasted longer and grew more elaborate.

In May 1963 the American astronaut L. Gordon Cooper, Jr., set an endurance record by remaining in orbit for nearly thirty-five hours and circling the Earth twenty-two and a half times. This was surpassed the next month when the Soviet cosmonaut Valery Bykovsky remained in space for eighty-one orbits, totaling 119 hours in space. At the same time the Soviets placed Valentina Tereshkova in orbit, and she was the first (and so far still the only) woman in space.

In October 1964 the Soviets placed *Voshkod I* in orbit, with three men on board. It spent sixteen orbits in space and was the first multiply manned space shot. On March 18, 1965, *Voshkod 2* was placed in orbit with two men on board. One of them, Alexei Leonov, left the spaceship and spent ten minutes in open space, encased in a spacesuit and attached to the ship by a tether. It was the first "space walk."

That same year, the United States launched three two-man spaceships of the Gemini series, whose orbits could be adjusted in space and which could be maneuvered from within. This was the first time any vessels in orbit were successfully maneuvered. In June 1965 Edward White, one of the astronauts on *Gemini 4,* became the first American to walk in space. He remained outside his ship for twenty-one minutes.

On August 21, 1965, *Gemini 5* was launched with L. Gordon Cooper and Charles Conrad aboard. Cooper was the first man to be placed in orbit twice. *Gemini 7,* launched on December 4, 1965, orbited Earth 220 times and remained in space for two weeks. It was clear that human beings could remain in space, without harm, for the length of time it would take to reach the moon and return.

On March 16, 1966, *Gemini 8,* with Neil A. Armstrong and David R. Scott aboard, succeeded in docking, or joining, with an unmanned vessel. This was the first docking in space, a maneuver that was essential to a manned landing on the moon, since the plan was to have a three-man vessel placed in orbit about the moon, and then have part of it, with two men aboard, separate, land on the moon, and dock again on returning, while the remainder with one man stayed in orbit in the interim.

For the first six years of the man-in-space program, there had been no deaths. In 1967 came the inevitable strokes of ill fortune. In January three American astronauts, Virgil I. Grissom, Edward H. White II, and Roger Chaffee, died on the ground in a fire that broke out in their space capsule during routine tests.

Later that year, on April 23, the Soviet cosmonaut Vladimir M. Komarov died when the parachutes of *Soyuz 1* fouled on reentry. Komarov was the first man to die in the course of a space flight. Since then, however, three other Soviet cosmonauts have died in the course of landing their three-man vessel.

The accidents forced a delay in manned programs in both nations. The United States had been about to begin the Apollo program, a series of three-man launchings that were planned to bring men to the moon. The first of these flights was delayed for a year and a half while the vessels were redesigned to provide additional safety against fire.

It was not until October 11, 1968, that *Apollo 7*, the first flight of the new series, was launched. *Apollo 8,* launched on December 21, 1968, flew to the moon and went into orbit around it before returning to Earth. *Apollo 10,* launched on May 18, 1969, did the same, maneuvering down to within 15 kilometers (9 miles) of the lunar surface in the process.

Finally, on July 16, 1969, *Apollo 11* was launched, with Neil A. Armstrong, Edwin E. Aldrin, Jr., and Michael Collins on board. On July 20, while Collins piloted the main part of the vessel in orbit, Armstrong and Aldrin took a small lunar lander down to the moon, where Armstrong became the first, and Aldrin the second, human being to set foot on any world other than the Earth.

Three hundred and sixty years after Galileo, with his first telescope, had shown the moon to be a world with mountains, craters, and smooth areas that looked like seas — there were human footsteps on that world.

Five other trips, on *Apollos 12, 14, 15, 16,* and *17,* were successfully carried through. Each mission performed more elaborate experiments and observations than the one before, and all of it was seen in clear television view from Earth. People on Earth could see men driving a powered vehicle on the moon. (Only one vessel aimed at the moon did not make it. An accident in flight aborted the mission of *Apollo 13,* but the ship and its crew were brought safely back to Earth.)

Before the Apollo program was brought to its end, twelve Americans had walked on the surface of the moon.

To astronomers, the great accomplishment of the flights to the moon was the bringing back of rocks from the lunar surface. It was the first extraterrestrial material ever to reach Earth, with the exception of meteorites.

The lunar rocks seemed to show that the moon was virtually free of water and of organic material and was, therefore, a world utterly without life.

This had been suspected, in essence, by astronomers, since the

1600s, when it had become apparent that the moon had neither an atmosphere nor free water — but there had been some hope for the kind of traces of air and water that might have made possible very primitive life at the bacterial level, if nothing more. Those hopes were dashed.

In addition, the lunar rocks were different from those of Earth in that they were less rich in those elements which were relatively volatile — that is, the compounds of which would vaporize when subjected to considerable heat. That, together with the presence of glassy fragments on the lunar surface (something rare on Earth), made it seem that the moon had been subjected to periods of great heat, the effects of which the Earth had somehow escaped.

Since both Earth and moon occupy virtually the same position in space, it seemed obvious that if one were subjected to periods of great heat, so had the other. It might be that Earth's atmosphere and ocean protected its solid surface from the heat to which the moon's solid surface had been nakedly exposed — or else that the Earth and moon were not always in the same place.

The moon is extraordinarily large in terms of Earth's size and extraordinarily distant from Earth. No other satellite in the solar system is even close to being as large or as distant in comparison to the planet it circles.

This gives rise to the attractive speculation that the moon is not a natural satellite of the Earth but was once an independent planet that had been captured by the Earth's gravitational field. The moon's original orbit might have been markedly elliptical and might have carried it closer to the sun by a good bit than the Earth ever gets. That may be the reason for its scorched surface.

The Large Space Telescope

Despite the victorious landings on the moon, the future of manned flight seems sharply limited. There are few other practical targets.

The moon landings were deceptively simple. The moon can be reached in three days and it remains always within 400,000 kilometers (250,000 miles) of Earth.

The next closest large body is Venus, which, on occasion, may be as close as 40,000,000 kilometers (25,000,000 miles) to Earth but which also recedes to distances six times as great when it is on the other side of the sun from us. Furthermore, all of it is extraordinarily hot at all times and it seems unlikely that human beings will be able to approach its surface in the foreseeable future.

Mercury is, at times, as close to us as 80,000,000 kilometers (50,000,000 miles) and has a night side which would offer a haven from the sun for the duration of four weeks. A flight that would carry men to Mercury, which is at a distance from the sun only one third of what it is from Earth, with the consequent increase in radiational dangers, is not something that possesses many attractions, however.

It would seem, then, that our search for additional targets would carry us outward, away from the sun. There we have Mars, which is, at times, as close as 57,000,000 kilometers (35,000,000 miles) to Earth. It is less distant than Mercury and far more pleasant as an object of manned exploration than Venus is.

To reach Mars, however, would require a round trip of over a year, in place of the week that suffices for the moon. For flights to targets beyond Mars, voyages of several years and even of decades would be required.

If we restrict ourselves to the Earth-moon system, there are advances yet to be dreamed of. A permanent colony might someday be established on the moon, or its materials may be used to build a completely artificial home (or homes) for human beings in nearby space. It might be that human beings will finally occupy more than one world.

If so, the colonists on the moon, or on some artificial space structure, accustomed to low gravity, used to an engineered environment rather than a natural one, inured to living under enclosed conditions, might be able to undertake the long voyages that would be required to explore the outer solar system and, eventually, perhaps the nearer stars as well.

But that is a long-term dream. When it comes, astronomy may be revolutionized, but in what directions can astronomy advance now, short of a time of long space voyages?

On Earth's surface, optical telescopy has reached its limit. The Hale telescope and the 600-centimeter (236-inch) telescope being built in the Soviet Union are astronomical dinosaurs, and it is unlikely that anyone will ever attempt larger mirrors still. The rapidly increasing engineering difficulties and expense put it out of the question.

The next step, indeed, is to take advantage of the electronic techniques developed since the construction of the Hale telescope and make use of smaller telescopes in cooperating groups.

A Multiple-Mirror Telescope (MMT) is now being developed by the Smithsonian Astrophysical Observatory and the University of Arizona. It will use six relatively small mirrors, each 183 centimeters (72 inches) across, arranged to produce precise superimposition of their images. The overall light-gathering effect will be that of a single mirror with a diameter of 450 centimeters (176 inches) and its resolution will be that of a single mirror of 600 centimeters (237 inches).

The mirrors are mounted on an openwork steel frame 8 meters (26 feet) high and 7 meters (23 feet) across. Individual mirrors will be able to have their positions adjusted for perfect focus. The whole will be set in a revolving building constructed on a concrete slab that rests on bedrock. The building can revolve for 270° in either direction.

The MMT will be installed on Mount Hopkins in the Santa Rita Mountains south of Tucson, Arizona, at an elevation of 2640 meters (8650 feet) and it should be completed by the summer of 1976. If it works as well as its designers hope, it will match the Hale telescope in effectiveness. It will be more flexible, for if anything occurs to one of the six units, it will affect the entire device only marginally and it can be withdrawn for repairs without stopping the observational program. Furthermore, additional units can be added that will enhance light-gathering power and resolution still further.

Nevertheless, regardless of how well the MMT does, it will still be blanketed by the air. It will still be blind to the short-wavelength regions beyond the near ultraviolet, to much of the infrared region, and to the long-wave radio region. It will be subjected to the obscuration of weather and to the various interferences inseparable from the presence of air.

On Earth's surface, radio telescopes have about reached their limit as well, since already they use the full diameter of the Earth as a base line so that further advances in resolution do not seem possible.

There would seem no question, then, but that with mankind's new capacities in rocketry, the next step forward is telescopy in outer space. Here the emphasis on radio telescopy is limited. The solar wind acts as a kind of thin atmosphere and interferes with microwave reception, particularly in the longer wavelengths. Only wavelengths less than ten centimeters would offer much chance of improved resolution if cooperating radio telescopes were placed on space stations or even on the moon.

For an optical telescope in space, the solar wind would present little interference. An optical telescope in space would perceive the full electromagnetic spectrum. There would be no interference from scattered light by the atmosphere or by gravitational distortion of the telescope components.

The Hale reflector can detect features on the moon that are about 900 meters (3000 feet) across. The same telescope above the atmosphere, with none of the interferences of the trembling air, would detect objects only 30 meters (100 feet) across. And while astronomers no longer need to depend on telescopes to study the moon long distance, the same improvement brought about simply by the absence of air would extend to every other object in the sky.

There have been telescopes placed in orbit, to be sure, but they have been relatively small and have had to do their work automatically. The need for automatic operation has greatly complicated the engineering and has meant that the telescopes are relatively short-lived and can be put to only limited use.

There have also been manned telescopes in space. Between May 1973 and February 1974, three-man crews have operated the equipment on board the space station Skylab on three separate occasions. The operation was for a one-month period the first time, then a two-month period, and finally a three-month period. For six months altogether, telescopic observations of great interest were made of such objects as the solar corona and Comet Kahoutek.

The usefulness of having men on board the Skylab was enormous. They were able to correct some of the mishaps that befell the space station, to make repairs, and they were, of course, far more flexible in their approach to the problems of investigation than any mechanical devices could have been in the present state of the engineering art.

The telescopes available on the Skylab, however, were small ones. Something bigger and better is needed.

As long ago as 1962 it was suggested that a reflecting telescope with a mirror as large in diameter as 305 centimeters (120 inches) could be put into orbit.

Since such an orbiting telescope would be unaffected by gravitational pull, it need be much less massive than a similar telescope on Earth's surface. The 305-centimeter (120-inch) reflector at Lick Observatory weighs some 130,000 kilograms (145 tons) but the projected Large Space Telescope would weigh only 11,000 kilograms (12 tons). Its lesser mass and its freedom from gravitational pull would allow it to respond to automatic control with unprecedented precision.

Such a telescope is indeed being planned under a program of the National Aeronautics and Space Administration (NASA). It would have a tube 12.5 meters (41 feet) long and, if government support is maintained, could be in orbit in 1981.

It would do its work automatically but would be visited occasionally by successive crews brought into orbit and back by space shuttle. The periodic appearance of astronomers would allow for the replacement of components, the carrying-through of repairs, the organization of new procedures, and so on. Allowing for human care would decrease the necessity for making the automation of the telescope foolproof and would therefore greatly decrease the expense while increasing the versatility of the instrument.

It is planned to orbit the Large Space Telescope at heights of between 650 and 1000 kilometers (400 and 600 miles) above Earth's surface. At lower heights, the thin wisps of the upper atmosphere would bring it down before too many years; at greater heights the magnetosphere would interfere. Within those limits and with adequate care, the Large Space Telescope should remain in efficient working order for at least ten years, and possibly considerably longer.

In orbit, the Large Space Telescope, working much nearer the limits set by the nature of light itself (thanks to the absence of gravitational and atmospheric distortions) should be able to detect objects one-hundredth as bright as those visible to the larger Hale reflector on Earth's surface. It would produce clear images of less than 0.1

second of arc in diameter and record objects of the 29th magnitude. Thus man would be able to see ten times as far into the universe.

Since it would have the entire electromagnetic spectrum open to it, it could study the ultraviolet and infrared regions with a precision and detail never possible before. It would be able to work at all times, since bad weather would never interfere and since even the near presence of the sun would not prevent observations of the stars.

It is, of course, impossible to predict exactly what the Large Space Telescope might discover — just as it was impossible to predict in advance that Galileo's telescope would detect four satellites about Jupiter, or that Rosse's Leviathan would discover spiral galaxies, or that radio telescopes would discover quasars and pulsars.

We can be pretty sure, though, that the Large Space Telescope will, for instance, be able to resolve the stars in the inner regions of the globular clusters and that this will make it possible to learn much more about stellar evolution than we now know.

By observing the very faint galaxies, too — galaxies a billion and more light-years away in space and therefore a billion and more years away in time — the Large Space Telescope may make it possible for us to gain the information we need to choose among the various theories about the universe that now exercise the minds of astronomers.

The information it gathers may tell us at last, unequivocally, whether the universe will expand forever, or whether the expansion is slowing and will be followed by a contracting phase and eventually a new expansion in a grand and eternal oscillation.

It may help us learn more about the violent events of the universe, about quasars, about exploding galaxies, about the gravitational implosions that produce black holes.

It may in this way tell us how the universe began and how it will end. We may even, in our studies, learn what comes after the end and whether there will be a new beginning — and what came before the beginning and whether there was an earlier end.

And if the Large Space Telescope makes it possible for the mind of man to stretch to the very beginning and end of space and time, what a glorious culmination that will be for the succession of events that began when primitive human beings first lifted their wondering and unaided eyes to the glories of the heavens.

INDEX

Index